THE AIR PILOT'S MANUAL

Volume 5

Instrument Flying
Radio Navigation Aids
Instrument Procedures
Night Flying
IMC Rating
Night Rating

Trevor Thom

graphics by
Robert Johnson

Airlife

England

Nothing in this manual supersedes any legislation, rules, regulations or procedures contained in any operational document issued by Her Majesty's Stationery Office, the Civil Aviation Authority, the manufacturers of aircraft, engines and systems, or by the operators of aircraft throughout the world.

Airlife Publishing Ltd.

101 Longden Road, Shrewsbury SY3 9EB, Shropshire, England.

Printed in England by Livesey Ltd., Shrewsbury, England.

THE AIR PILOT'S MANUAL Vol. 5

CONTENTS

PERSONAL PROGRESS TABLE	
Theory	Exercises
Section 1>	

EDITORIAL TEAM

Trevor Thom
A Boeing 757 and 767 Training Captain with a European airline, Trevor has also flown the Airbus A320, Boeing 727, McDonnell Douglas DC-9 and Fokker F-27 airliners. He has been active in the International Federation of Airline Pilots' Association (IFALPA), based in London, and served as IFALPA representative to the Society of Automotive Engineers (SAE) S7 Flight-Deck Design Committee, a body which makes recommendations to the aviation industry, especially the manufacturers. Prior to his airline career Trevor worked as a Lecturer in Mathematics and Physics, and as an Aviation Ground Instructor and a Flying Instructor. He is a double degree graduate from the University of Melbourne and also holds a Diploma of Education.

Robert Johnson
An experienced aviator, Bob prepared the illustrations and diagrams, cover design, and the final sub-edit and layout of the manuals for printing. His aviation experience includes flying a Cessna Citation II-SP executive jet, a DC-3 (Dakota) and light aircraft as Chief Pilot for an international University, based in Switzerland, and seven years on Fokker Friendship, Lockheed Electra and McDonnell Douglas DC-9 airliners. Prior to this he was an Air Taxi Pilot and also gained technical experience as a Draughtsman on Airborne Mineral Survey work in Australia.

Peter Godwin
Chief Flying Instructor at Bonus Aviation, Cranfield, Peter has amassed over 10,000 instructional flying hours. As a member of the CAA Panel of Examiners, he is an Instrument Rating and Type Rating Examiner and currently instructs for the Basic Commercial Pilot's Licence and Instrument Rating. Previously he was CFI at Leavesden Flight Centre and London School of Flying, Elstree and Denham.

John Fenton
A Flying Instructor since 1970, John is former joint proprietor and assistant CFI of Yorkshire Flying Services at Leeds/Bradford. He is a PPL Examiner and was awarded the Bronze Medal from the Royal Aero Club for his achievements and contributions to air rallying. John has made considerable contributions to the field of flying instruction in the UK and pioneered the use of audio tapes for training.

Edward Pape
Director of MSF Aviation, Manchester and Portugal, and a former Chief Flying Instructor of the Lancashire Aero Club, Ed has amassed over 5000 instructional flying hours and is dedicated to Private Pilot training.

Graeme Carne
A part-time Flying Instructor, Graeme currently flies the Shorts 360 on Regional Airline operations, based in Blackpool. Prior to this he flew the Beechcraft King Air 200 as a Corporate Pilot.

ACKNOWLEDGEMENTS

We greatly appreciate the input that has been made by the following:

The Civil Aviation Authority, British Airways/Aerad, Capt. Horace Galop (British Aerospace Flying College, Prestwick), Jeppesen & Co. GmbH, Allied Signal (Bendix/King Radio Corp.), Narco Avionics; Bill Bennett, Bill Constable, Robyn Hind, Rick James, David Langford, Robert Lawson, Ian Suren (ex-ICAO, Montreal), and of course Airtour International and Robert Pooley Ltd.

INTRODUCTION

Air travel becomes much more reliable when aeroplane operations are not restricted by **poor weather** or by **darkness**. This is possible to achieve with a suitably equipped aeroplane and a Pilot skilled in instrument flying.

The *instrument-qualified* Pilot and the *instrument-equipped* aeroplane must be able to cope with restricted visibility – for instance, when flying in cloud, mist, smog, rain or snow, all of which may make the natural horizon and ground features difficult, or even impossible, to see.

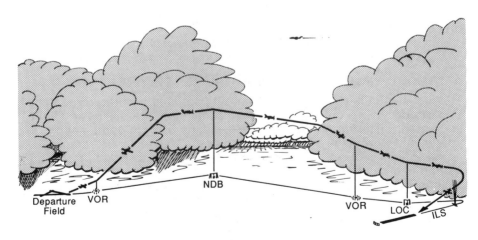

Fig. 1. A Typical Flight on Instruments.

You must learn to trust what you see on the instruments. Man generally uses his **vision** to orientate himself with the surroundings, supported by other bodily senses (such as feel and balance) which can sense gravity. Even with the eyes closed, however, a person can usually manage to sit, stand and walk on steady ground without losing control. This becomes much more difficult on the tray of an accelerating or turning truck, or even in an accelerating lift (elevator).

In an aeroplane, which can accelerate in three dimensions, the task becomes almost impossible – unless he has the use of his eyes. The eyes must gather information from the external ground features, including the horizon, or, in poor visibility, gather substitute information from the instruments. A Pilot's eyes are very important. The starting point in instrument training is using the eyes to derive information from the instruments in the cockpit.

Fig.2. The Eyes, and the Instruments.

ATTITUDE FLYING, AND APPLIED INSTRUMENT FLYING

The first step in becoming an Instrument Pilot is to become competent at **Attitude Flying on the Full Panel** containing the six basic Flight Instruments. The term *Attitude Flying* means using a combination of **power** and aeroplane **attitude** to achieve a desired **performance** in terms of flight path and airspeed. Attitude Flying on Instruments will be taught as an extension of visual flying, with your attention gradually shifting from external visual clues to the instrument indications in the cockpit, until you are able to fly accurately on instruments alone.

Partial (or Limited) Panel attitude instrument flying will be introduced fairly early in your training. For this exercise, the main control instrument, the *Attitude Indicator,* is assumed to have malfunctioned.

The *Direction Indicator,* often powered from the same source as the AI, may also be unavailable. Partial Panel training will probably be practised concurrently with Full Panel training, just so the exercise does not assume an importance out of proportion to its difficulty. You will perform the same basic flight manoeuvres, but on a reduced number of instruments. The Limited Panel exercise will increase your instrument flying competence, as well as your confidence.

Fig.3a. The Full Panel.   *Fig.3b. The Partial Panel.*

Unusual Attitudes should never occur inadvertently! Practice in recovering from them, however, will increase both your confidence and your overall proficiency. This exercise will be practised on a Full Panel, and also on a Limited Panel.

After you have achieved a satisfactory standard in attitude flying, both on a Full Panel and on a Partial Panel, **your instrument flying skills will then be applied** to en route flights using *Radio Navigation Aids* and *Radar.*

Procedural instrument flying (i.e. getting from one place to another) is based mainly on knowing where the aeroplane is in relation to a particular radio ground transmitter *(orientation),* and then accurately *tracking TO* or *FROM* the ground station. **Tracking** is simply *attitude flying,* plus a *wind correction angle* to allow for drift. Typical radio aids used are the *ADF, VOR, DME* and *ILS,* as well as ground-based *Radar.* In many ways, en route navigation is easier using the Radio Navigation Instruments than it is by visual means. It is also more precise.

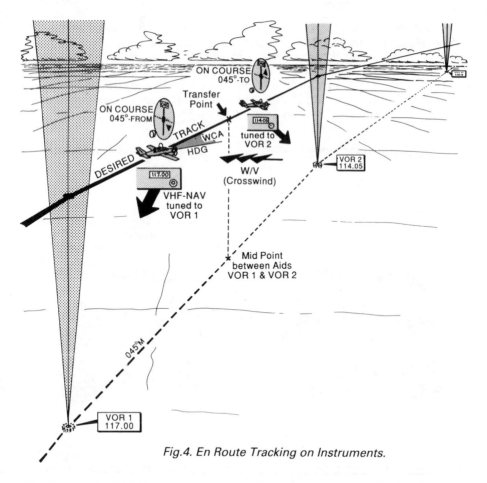

Fig.4. En Route Tracking on Instruments.

Having navigated the aeroplane on instruments to a destination, a visual approach and landing may be made if suitable conditions exist. If, however, **instrument conditions** exist, then an *Instrument Approach* can be made. The option is there to make an Instrument Approach in *visual conditions* also, if desired, but this will probably add some minutes to the overall flight time.

Only *published* Instrument Approach Procedures may be followed, with charts commonly used in the UK available from *Aerad* or *Jeppesen.* An instrument approach usually involves positioning the aeroplane over (or near) a ground station, and then using precise attitude flying to descend along the published flight path at a suitable airspeed.

If visual conditions are encountered on the instrument approach before a predetermined minimum height (or *Decision Height*) is reached, then the aeroplane can be manoeuvred for a landing. If, however, visual conditions are **not** met before Decision Height for the approach, a *Missed Approach* should be carried out. The options are to climb away and manoeuvre for another approach, or to divert elsewhere.

Fig.5. Plan and Profile of a Precision Instrument Approach
(Aerad chart for Luton ILS/DME Rwy 08).

(ix)

THE AEROPLANE, AND THE GROUND TRAINER

The **Simulator** or **Ground Trainer** is an extremely valuable training aid for practising both *Attitude Flying* and *Instrument Procedures.* It allows certain manoeuvres (for instance, climbing turns at 5000 ft) to be practised without having to pre-flight check an actual aeroplane, then taxy out, wait in the queue, take-off and climb for ten minutes. It is not dependent on weather – strong crosswinds on the runway making take-off for aeroplanes impossible will not stop your practice. It allows easy conversation between the Student and Instructor without engine noise or the distraction of radio calls. Time can be 'frozen', whilst the Instructor discusses some fine point before the exercise continues.

Manoeuvres can be repeated without delay and without interruption. Instrument Procedures (such as an ILS approach to busy Manchester International Airport) can be practised repetitively in the Simulator – a situation probably not possible in the aeroplane because of the heavy commercial traffic in the area. Procedures at aerodromes about to be visited in the aeroplane can be practised beforehand – very useful when about to proceed into unfamiliar territory.

The fact that most Ground Trainers do not move, and experience only the one-g gravity force, is not really a disadvantage for instrument training, since one of its aims is to develop the ability to interpret the instruments using your eyes, and to disregard the other senses. The Ground Trainer is also less expensive to operate than an aeroplane. This, and the many other advantages, make it an extremely valuable aid. But, it is still **not** an aeroplane!

Fig.6. The Ground Trainer;   *the Aeroplane.*

Instrument Flying in the aeroplane is the real thing! It is very important psychologically to a Pilot that he feels confident about his instrument flying ability in an actual aeroplane, so **in-flight** training is important. There will be more noise, more distractions, more duties and different bodily feelings in the aeroplane. G-forces resulting from manoeuvring will be experienced, as will turbulence, and these may serve to upset the senses. Despite the differences, however, the Ground Trainer **can** be used very successfully to prepare you for the real thing. And it will save you money. Practise in it often to improve your instrument skills. Time in the real aeroplane can then be used more efficiently.

ATTITUDE INSTRUMENT FLYING

The **performance** of an aeroplane in terms of **flight path** and **airspeed** is determined by a combination of the **power** set and the **attitude** selected. Aeroplane attitude has two aspects – pitch and bank. **Pitch Attitude** is the angle between the longitudinal axis of the aircraft and the horizontal. **Bank Attitude** is the angle between the lateral axis of the aeroplane and the horizontal.

Fig.7a. Pitch Attitude.   Fig.7b. Bank Attitude.

For a given aeroplane weight and configuration, a particular **attitude** combined with a particular **power** setting will always result in a similar **flight path** through the air, be it a straight and level flight path, a climb, a descent or a turn. **Any change of power and/or of attitude will result in a change of flight path and/or airspeed.**

The Pilot selects Pitch Attitude using the elevator. In visual conditions, he refers to the external natural horizon. **At any time** (in cloud, at night, or in visual conditions) he can select a specific Pitch Attitude with reference to the **Attitude Indicator (AI)** on the Instrument Panel. In visual flight, the Pitch Attitude can be estimated from the position of the natural horizon in the windscreen. In instrument flight, Pitch Attitude is selected with reference to the AI, using the position of the *centre dot* of the wing bars relative to the *Artificial* Horizon Line. The centre dot represents the nose of the aeroplane.

The Pilot selects Bank Attitude (i.e. *Bank Angle*) using the ailerons. In visual conditions, he refers to the angle made by the external natural horizon in the windscreen. On instruments, he selects bank angle on the **Attitude Indicator**, either by estimating the angle between the wing bars of the miniature aeroplane and the Artificial Horizon Line, or from the *sky pointer* position on a graduated scale at the top of the AI.

Fig.8a. Low Pitch Attitude,   Fig.8b. Level Pitch Attitude,
     and Wings Level.   and Right Bank.

Most of the Pilot's attention during all flight, irrespective of whether he is flying visually or on instruments, is concerned with achieving and holding a suitable attitude. A very important skill to develop when flying on instruments, therefore, is to **check the Attitude Indicator every few seconds**. Other tasks must, of course, be performed, and there are other instruments to look at as well, but the eyes should always return fairly quickly to the AI.

To achieve the desired **performance** (in terms of flight path and airspeed), the Pilot must not only place the aeroplane in a suitable **attitude** with the flight controls, he must also apply suitable **power** with the throttle. Just because the aeroplane has a high pitch attitude does not mean that it will climb – it requires climb power as well as climb attitude to do this. With less power, it may not climb at all. *Attitude Flying* is the name given to this skill – controlling the aeroplane's flight path and airspeed with changes in attitude and power. The techniques used in attitude flying are the same visually or on instruments.

Pitch Attitude is Not Angle of Attack

The Pitch Attitude is the geometric relationship between the longitudinal axis of the aeroplane and the horizontal. Pitch Attitude refers to the aeroplane's **inclination to the horizontal**, and not to where it is going. The Angle of Attack, however, is the angle between the wing chord and the relative airflow. The Angle of Attack, therefore, is **closely** related to **flight path**. Pitch Attitude and Angle of Attack are different, but they are related in the sense that, if the pitch attitude is raised, then the angle of attack is increased. Conversely, if the pitch attitude is lowered, then the angle of attack is decreased.

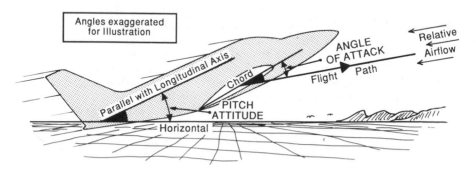

Fig.9. Pitch Attitude and Angle of Attack are NOT the Same.

An Aeroplane Flies the Same, in or out of Cloud

The Principles of Flight do **not** change when an aeroplane enters cloud. The aeroplane will fly the same, and be controlled in the same way. The only difference is that the Pilot loses reference to external visual clues, and must derive substitute information from the Instrument Panel.

Flying visually, the Pilot is *already* deriving a lot of information from the instruments. The exact altitude, for instance, cannot be determined from external features – he **must** look at the Altimeter. Similarly, the precise heading is found on the Direction Indicator or the Magnetic Compass, and not by reference to external features. The precise airspeed can only be determined from the Air Speed Indicator. Also, to set a precise power, he must look (briefly) at the Power Indicator.

Balance, in turns as well as in straight and level flight, is maintained precisely with reference to the Balance Ball, in both visual and instrument flight. The main change, it seems, when switching to instrument flying is to transfer attention from the natural horizon outside the cockpit to the Artificial Horizon Line of the AI in the cockpit.

The IMC-Rated or Instrument-Rated Pilot is no different from other Pilots, except that he has acquired more knowledge, and can derive **more** information from the Instrument Panel. An Altimeter, for instance, can tell you more than just the current **altitude** – it also says something about the *rate* of change of height, and if the selected *Pitch Attitude* is correct for height to be maintained. Similarly, the Direction Indicator can provide Heading information, but it also can tell you if the wings are banked – if the heading is changing and the Balance Ball is centred, then the wings are banked.

The skill of instrument interpretation (deriving all sorts of information from various instruments) will develop quickly during your instrument training. It is not difficult – it just takes practice. The aeroplane will fly the same on instruments, as when you are flying visually, and you will control it in the usual way. The information required to do this is available – **in the cockpit**.

During instrument training, most manoeuvres will be performed first of all in *visual conditions,* where the AI indications can be related to the appearance of the natural horizon in the windscreen. After a satisfactory standard of visual flying is demonstrated, practice will occur in *simulated instrument conditions* – probably achieved by your Instructor restricting your view of the outside world with a screen.

His view will remain unobstructed so that he can act as *Safety Pilot,* keeping a look out for other aircraft, and monitoring the position of the aeroplane. You will concentrate on attitude flying using the instruments, interpreting their indications, and then responding with the controls. You should then be able to cope with **actual** instrument conditions.

A good understanding of each manoeuvre, and the ability to put it into practice in visual conditions, will speed up your instrument training. *The Air Pilot's Manual* Volume 1 contains detailed briefings for each visual manoeuvre, if you happen to be a little rusty.

SCANNING THE INSTRUMENTS

Scanning the instruments with your eyes, interpreting their indications, and applying this information is a **vital** skill to develop if you are to become a good Instrument Pilot.

Power is selected with the throttle, and can be checked (if required) on the Power Indicator. Pitch Attitude and Bank Angle are selected using the control column, with **frequent** reference to the Attitude Indicator. With both correct power and attitude set, the aeroplane will perform as expected. The Attitude Indicator and the Power Indicator, because they are used when controlling the aeroplane, are known as the **control instruments**.

The **actual** performance of the aeroplane, once its power and attitude have been set, can be cross-checked on what are known as the **performance instruments** – the Altimeter for height, the Air Speed Indicator for airspeed, the Direction Indicator for direction, and so on.

A valuable instrument, important in its own right, is the Clock or **Stopwatch**. Time is extremely important in instrument flying. The Stopwatch is used in Holding Patterns (e.g. 1 minute or 2 minute holding patterns), in timed turns (e.g. a 180° change of heading at Rate 1, which is a change of heading at 3°/sec, will take 60 seconds), and it is also used to measure time after passing certain ground beacons during Instrument Approaches (e.g. knowing the Ground Speed of the aeroplane, it is possible to determine the time it will take to travel a further known distance).

Another group of instruments on the panel contains the **Radio Navigation Instruments**, which indicate the position of the aeroplane relative to selected radio navigation facilities. These *radio navaids* will be considered in detail later in your training, but the main ones are:

- the *Automatic Direction Finder* (ADF), which has a needle that points at an NDB ground station;
- the *Distance Measuring Equipment* (DME), which indicates the slant distance in nautical miles to the selected DME ground station; and
- the *VHF Omni Range* (VOR) Cockpit Display, which indicates the aeroplane's position relative to a selected track.

Study Fig.10. opposite.

Scanning is an art that will develop naturally during your training, especially once you know what to look for. The main scan to develop initially is that of the six basic Flight Instruments – concentrating on the AI, and radiating out to the others as required. We have devoted a whole chapter to this subject (coming shortly). Then, as you move on to en route instrument flying, the Radio Navigation Instruments will be introduced.

Fig. 10. A Typical Instrument Panel.

CONTROLLING THE AEROPLANE

During instrument flight, the aeroplane is flown using the normal controls according to the *picture* displayed on the Instrument Panel. From this picture, you will, with practice, know what control movements (elevator, aileron, rudder and throttle) are required to either maintain the picture as it is, or to change it.

When manoeuvring the aeroplane, a suitable **control sequence** to follow (the same as in visual flight) is:

1. **Visualise** the desired new flight path and airspeed.

2. **Select the Attitude and the Power required** to achieve the desired performance by moving the controls, and then *checking* when the aeroplane has achieved the estimated attitude on the AI.

3. **Hold the attitude** on the AI, allowing the aeroplane to settle down into its new performance, and allowing the instruments that experience some lag to catch up.

4. **Make small adjustments** to attitude and power until the actual performance equals the desired performance.

5. **Trim** (which is vital, if you are to achieve accurate and comfortable instrument flight). Heavy loads can be trimmed off earlier in the sequence to assist in control, if desired, but remember that the function of trim is to relieve control loads on the Pilot, and **not** to change aircraft attitude.

| CHANGE | CHECK | HOLD/ADJUST | TRIM |

Fig. 11. Change – Check – Hold – Adjust – Trim.

Some helpful hints to follow.

- Derive the required information from the relevant instrument, e.g. direction from the Direction Indicator, altitude from the Altimeter.

- **Do not be distracted** from a scan of the Flight Instruments for more than a few seconds at a time, even though other duties must be attended to, such as check lists, radio calls and navigational tasks.

- **Relax.** (Easier said than done at the start, but it will come with experience.)

- **Respond to deviations** from the desired flight path and/or airspeed. Use the AI as a *control instrument,* with power as required. For instance, if you are 50 ft low on altitude, then raise the pitch attitude on the AI slightly and climb back up to height. Do not accept steady deviations – it is just as easy to fly at 3000 ft as it is to fly at 2950 ft. A lot of instrument flying is in the mind and, in a sense, it is a test of **character** as well as of *flying ability.* **Be as accurate as you can!**

- **Do not over-control.** Avoid large, fast or jerky control movements, which will probably result in continuous corrections, over-corrections and re-corrections. This can occur if attitude is changed without reference to the AI, or it might be caused by the aeroplane being out-of-trim, or possibly by a Pilot who is fatigued or tense.

SENSORY ILLUSIONS CAN LEAD YOU ASTRAY

Most people live in a *one-g* situation with their feet on the ground. However, some variations to this do occur in everyday life – for instance, when driving a car. Accelerating a car, hard braking, or turning on a flat bend will all produce g-forces on the body different to the 1g of gravity alone. A passenger with his eyes shut could **perhaps** detect this by bodily feel or with his sense of balance.

A right turn on a flat road, for instance, could be detected by the feeling of being thrown to the left – but it might be more difficult to detect if the curve was perfectly banked for the speed. A straight road sloping to the left (and causing the passenger to lean to the left) might give him the **false impression** that the car is turning right, even though it is in fact not turning at all. The *position sensing systems* of the body, using nerves all over the body to transmit messages of feel and pressure to the brain, can be 'fooled' in this and other ways.

Fig.12. Turning Right – or simply Leaning?

The **organs within the inner ear**, used for balance and to detect accelerations, can also be *fooled,* as in a car travelling around a **banked** curve. The sensing system interprets the g-force holding the occupants firmly and comfortably in the seats in a banked turn as a vertical force, which it is not. The inner ear organs also have other limitations, one being that a constant velocity is not detected (another train passing our train – is it moving, or are we?), nor is a very gradual change in velocity. False impressions of motion can also be caused by unusual g-forces – for instance, by rapid head motion, or by lowering the head.

More complicated *illusions* can occur in an aeroplane, which, of course, has the ability to move and accelerate in **three dimensions**. Pulling up into a steep climb, for instance, holds a Pilot tightly in his seat, which is exactly the same feeling as in a steep turn. With his eyes shut, it is difficult to say which manoeuvre it is.

Another example is: decelerating whilst in a turn to the left may give a **false impression** of a turn to the right. Be aware that your senses of balance and bodily feel can lead you astray in an aeroplane, especially with rapidly changing g-forces in manoeuvres such as this. The one sense that can resolve most of these illusions is *sight.* If the car passenger could see out, or if the Pilot had reference to the natural horizon and landmarks, then the confusion would be easily dispelled.

Unfortunately, in instrument flight the Pilot does *not* have reference to ground features, however he can still use his very vital sense of sight to scan the instruments, and obtain substitute information. Therefore, an important instruction to the budding Instrument Pilot is "**Believe your eyes and what the instruments tell you**".

It is good airmanship to avoid any situation in flight or prior to flight that will affect your vision. Whilst in cloud at night, for instance, turn off the strobe light if it is bothering you. It could induce Vertigo, a sense of dizziness or of whirling around, if sufficient of its flashing light is reflected into the cockpit. If flying in dark conditions with electrical storms in the vicinity, turn the cockpit lights up bright to minimise the effects of nearby lightning flashes. If expecting to fly out of cloud tops and into bright sunlight, have your sunglasses handy. Protect your sight!

Whilst sight is the most important sense, and must be protected, also avoid anything that will affect your balance or position sensing systems. Avoid alcohol, drugs (including smoking in the cockpit) and medication. Do not fly when ill or suffering with an upper respiratory infection (e.g. a cold). Do not fly when tired or fatigued. Do not fly with a cabin altitude higher than 10,000 ft AMSL without using oxygen. Avoid sudden head movements, and avoid lowering the head. Looking for a dropped pen on the cockpit floor can have a strange effect on your balance.

Despite all these *don'ts,* there is one very important *do* – do **trust what your eyes tell you from the instruments**.

THE RATING AND ITS PRIVILEGES

Information regarding requirements and privileges of the UK IMC Rating, and also the Night Rating, is included as Appendices to this manual. Detailed information on these ratings and the full Instrument Rating is available in CAA publication CAP 53.

*'Good, clear knowledge
minimises
Flight Training Hours'.*

1

INSTRUMENT FLYING

Intentionally Blank

1

INSTRUMENT SCANNING TECHNIQUE

The *performance* of an aeroplane is determined by the *power* set and the *attitude* selected. In visual flying conditions, the **external natural horizon** is used as a reference when selecting pitch attitude and bank angle. The Power Indicator in the cockpit is only referred to occasionally, for instance when setting a particular power for cruise or for climb.

In instrument conditions, when the natural horizon cannot be seen, pitch attitude and bank angle information is still available to the Pilot in the cockpit from the **Attitude Indicator**. Relatively large pitch attitude changes against the natural horizon are reproduced in miniature on the Attitude Indicator.

In straight and level flight, for instance, the wings of the Index Aeroplane should appear against the artificial horizon line, whilst in a climb they should appear one or two *bar widths* above it.

In a turn, the wing bars of the Index Aeroplane will bank along with the real aeroplane, whilst the artificial horizon line remains horizontal. The centre dot of the Index Aeroplane represents the aeroplane's nose position against the horizon.

Fig.1-1. The Attitude Indicator is the Master Instrument for Pitch Attitude and Bank Angle.

The AI, whilst it shows pitch attitude and bank angle directly, does **not** indicate balance or yaw. Balance information can be obtained simply by moving the eyes from the AI diagonally down to the left to the **Balance Indicator**, to check that the Balance Ball is indeed being centred with rudder pressure. The eyes should then return to the AI.

Fig.1-2. A Simple Scan for Balance.

Directional information can be obtained from the **Direction Indicator** or from the Magnetic Compass. From the AI, the eyes can be moved straight down to the DI to absorb heading information, before returning to the AI. Each eye movement to obtain particular information is very simple, starting at the AI and radiating out to the relevant instrument, before returning again to the AI.

Fig.1-3. A Simple Scan for Direction.

Airspeed information is also very important, and this is easily checked by moving the eyes left from the AI to the **Air Speed Indicator**, before returning them to the AI.

Fig.1-4. A Simple Scan for Airspeed.

The **Altimeter** is the only means of determining the precise altitude of the aeroplane, in visual as well as in instrument conditions. To obtain altitude information, the eyes can move from the AI towards the right where the Altimeter is located, before moving back to the AI.

Fig.1-5. A Simple Scan for Altitude.

The rate of change of altitude, either as a Rate of Climb or a Rate of Descent in feet/minute, can be monitored on the **Vertical Speed Indicator** by moving the eyes from the AI diagonally down to the right to the VSI, before returning them to the AI. The VSI, since it is often used in conjunction with the Altimeter, is located directly beneath it on most instrument panels.

Fig. 1-6. A Simple Scan for Vertical Speed Information.

A turn is entered using the AI to establish bank angle and the Balance Indicator to confirm balance. Additional information on the turning rate is available from the **Turn Coordinator**. The normal rate of turn in instrument flying is 3°/second, known as Rate 1, and this is marked on the Turn Coordinator (or on the older instrument called the Turn Indicator).

Fig. 1-7. A Simple Scan for Turn Rate.

With these **six basic Flight Instruments, plus the Power Indicator**, it is possible to fly the aeroplane very accurately and comfortably without any external visual reference, provided they are scanned efficiently, and the Pilot controls the aeroplane adequately in response to the information that he derives from them.

Control the Aeroplane to achieve the Desired Performance.

The *attitude* selected on the **AI** and the *power* set on the **Power Indicator** determines the *performance* of the aeroplane, hence these two instruments are known as the **control instruments**. The AI is located centrally on the instrument panel directly in front of the Pilot, so that any changes in attitude can be readily seen. Because continual reference to the Power Indicator is not required, it is situated slightly away from the main group of Flight Instruments, easy to scan occasionally, but not in the main field of view.

Fig.1-8. The Control Instruments are used to select Attitude and Power.

The other Flight Instruments are **performance instruments** that display how the aeroplane is performing (as a result of the power and attitude selected) in terms of:

- altitude, on the Altimeter and VSI;
- direction, on the DI and Turn Coordinator; and
- airspeed, on the ASI.

Fig.1-9. Performance is displayed on the Performance Instruments.

THE SELECTIVE RADIAL SCAN

Of the six main Flight Instruments, **the Attitude Indicator is the master instrument**. It will be the one most frequently referred to (at least once every few seconds in most stages of flight). The eyes can be directed selectively towards the other instruments to derive relevant information from them as required, before being returned to the AI. This eye movement radiating out and back to selected instruments is commonly known as the **selective radial scan**.

For instance, when climbing with full power selected, the estimated climb pitch attitude is held on the Attitude Indicator, but with reference to the Air Speed Indicator to confirm that the selected pitch attitude is correct. If the ASI indicates an airspeed that is too low, then lower the pitch attitude on the AI (say by a half bar width or one bar width), allow a few seconds for the airspeed to settle, and then check the ASI again.

The key instrument in *confirming* that the correct attitude has been selected on the AI during the climb is the Air Speed Indicator. Because it determines what pitch attitude changes should be made on the AI during the climb, the **ASI** is the *primary* performance guide to pitch attitude in the climb.

*Fig.1-10. The ASI is the Primary Instrument in the Climb
to confirm Correct Pitch Attitude.*

Approaching the desired cruise altitude, however, more attention should be paid to the Altimeter to ensure that, as pitch attitude is lowered on the AI, the aeroplane levels off right on the desired altitude. Once cruising, any minor deviations from altitude detected on the Altimeter can be corrected with small changes in pitch attitude. Because now it is the Altimeter which determines what pitch attitude changes on the AI are required to maintain level flight, the **Altimeter** is the *primary* performance guide to pitch attitude in the cruise.

*Fig.1-11. The Altimeter is the Primary Instrument in the Cruise
to Confirm Correct Pitch Attitude.*

If climb power is still set after the aeroplane has been levelled-off at cruise altitude, the aeroplane will accelerate, shown by an increasing airspeed on the ASI. At the desired speed, the power should be reduced to a suitable value.

Whilst it is usual simply to set cruise power and then accept the resulting airspeed, it is possible to achieve a precise airspeed by adjusting the power. Because the ASI indications will then determine what power changes should be made during level flight, the **Air Speed Indicator** is the *primary* performance guide to power requirements in the cruise.

Fig.1-12. The ASI is the Primary Instrument in the Cruise to confirm Correct Power.

Heading is maintained with reference to the DI, any deviations being corrected with gentle coordinated turns. Because the indications on the DI will determine what minor corrections to bank angle should be made on the AI during straight flight, the Direction Indicator is the *primary* performance guide to zero bank angle in maintaining a constant heading.

Fig.1-13. The Direction Indicator is the Primary Instrument in Straight Flight to Confirm Wings Level.

THE 'BASIC T' SCAN

A basic scan suitable for straight and level flight (where altitude, direction and airspeed need to be monitored) is centred on the AI, and radiates out and back, following the *Basic T* pattern on the panel, to the relevant performance instrument:

- the DI to confirm heading (and correct with small turns on the AI);
- the Altimeter to confirm altitude (and correct with pitch changes on the AI);
- the ASI to confirm airspeed (and, if desired, correct with power changes).

Fig.1-14. The 'Basic T' Scan in Cruise Flight.

If cruise power is set and then left alone with the resulting airspeed being accepted (as is often the case in a normal cruise), then scanning the ASI need not be as frequent, and the scan can concentrate on the AI, DI and Altimeter. Also, once established and well-trimmed on the cruise, the aeroplane will tend to hold height because of its longitudinal stability, making it less essential to scan the Altimeter continually compared to when the aeroplane is out of trim. The aeroplane may not be as stable laterally as it is longitudinally, however, and so **the DI should be scanned quite frequently** to ensure that heading is maintained.

Visual Pilots are used to scanning the Altimeter regularly, since it is the only means of accurately holding height, but they may not be used to scanning the DI quite so frequently as is necessary in instrument conditions. This skill will have to be developed.

What about the other Flight Instruments?

In smooth air, the **VSI** will show a *trend* away from cruising altitude often before it is apparent on the Altimeter, and can be used to indicate that a minor pitch attitude correction is required if altitude is to be maintained. The VSI provides *supporting* pitch information to that provided by the Altimeter, although it is of less value in turbulence, which causes the VSI needle to fluctuate.

If the wings are held level on the AI, and heading is being maintained on the DI, then it is almost certain that the aeroplane is in balance with the **Balance Ball** centred. Normally, the Balance Indicator does not have to be scanned as frequently as some of the other instruments, but it should be referred to occasionally, especially if heading is changing whilst the wings are level, or if the seat of your pants tells you that the aeroplane is skidding or slipping.

The **Turn Coordinator** will show a wings-level indication during straight flight, and provides *supporting* information regarding bank to that provided by the DI during straight flight.

USE A LOGICAL SCAN FOR EACH MANOEUVRE

Starting with your eyes focused on the AI, scan the performance instruments that provide the information required. Certain information will be obtained from different instruments depending upon the manoeuvre. Primary pitch information (to confirm whether or not the pitch attitude selected on the AI is correct) is obtained from the Altimeter during cruise flight, but from the ASI during climbs and descents. There is no need to memorise particular scan patterns, since they will develop naturally as your training progresses.

Do not allow the radial scan to break down. **Avoid fixation** on any one instrument, since this will certainly cause a breakdown in the radial scan and result in deviations from the desired flight path and/or airspeed. Fixation on the DI, for instance, can lead to heading being maintained perfectly, but in the meantime altitude and airspeed may go out of control – tendencies which would have been detected (and corrected for) if the Altimeter, VSI and ASI had been scanned. **Keep the eyes moving, and continually return to the AI.**

Occasionally, the eyes will have to be directed away from the main Flight Instruments for a short period, for instance when checking the Power Indicator during or following a power change, or when periodically checking the oil temperature and pressure instruments, the ammeter, or the suction gauge, or when referring to Instrument Approach Charts, filling in the Flight Log, or tuning radios. Do not neglect the radial scan for more than a few seconds at a time, even though other necessary tasks have to be performed.

Avoid omission of any relevant instrument. For instance, after rolling out of a turn, check the DI to ensure that the desired heading is being achieved and maintained. The wings might be level and the aeroplane flying straight, but on the wrong heading.

Use available resources. For instance, with correct power set and the correct attitude selected on the AI, it is possible to hold altitude at least approximately using only the AI and the Power Indicator but, if precision is required, then the Altimeter *must* be included in the scan as the primary reference for Altitude. Furthermore, do not forget that *supporting* instruments can provide additional information to back-up primary instruments. For instance, altitude is indicated directly on the Altimeter, but any *tendency* to depart from that altitude may first be indicated on the VSI (especially in smooth air), which makes it a very valuable *supporting* instrument to the Altimeter.

Fig.1-15. A Suitable Scan During Straight and Level Flight.

2

THE INSTRUMENTS

THE ATTITUDE INDICATOR

The Attitude Indicator is the only instrument that gives a **direct** and immediate picture of pitch attitude and bank angle. Its main features are an **artificial horizon line** that remains horizontal as the aeroplane banks and pitches about it, and an **Index Aeroplane** that is fixed to the case of the instrument and moves with the aeroplane. The AI is the **Master Instrument** in the cockpit, providing a clear visual representation of the aeroplane's movement in two planes (pitching and rolling). However, since the AI does not have any 'landmarks' on its artificial horizon line, it does **not** provide any information in the yawing plane.

Fig.2-1. Typical Attitude Indicators.

Pitch attitude is indicated on the AI by the relative positions of the Index Aeroplane and the artificial horizon line. Ideally, they will be perfectly aligned when the aeroplane is in the level attitude, with the central dot in the wing bars directly over the horizon line. When the aeroplane is pitched up into the climbing attitude, the Index Aeroplane moves with it and appears above the horizon line. This is achieved within the instrument, not by the Index Aeroplane moving up, but by the horizon line moving down. Conversely, when the aeroplane is pitched down into the descent attitude, the horizon line will appear above the Index Aeroplane.

Small horizontal lines marked above and below the artificial horizon line indicate the number of degrees of pitch up or pitch down but, generally, there is no need to use these. Most Pilots alter pitch in terms of **bar width**, one bar width being the thickness of the wing bar and the central dot on the Index Aeroplane (or of the horizon line, if it is thicker). The central dot is easier to use when setting pitch attitude against the horizon line during a banked turn, since the wing bars will, of course, be at an angle to the horizon.

Bank Attitude is displayed both by the **bank pointer** against degree markings at the top of the AI, and by the **angle** between the wing bar of the Index Aeroplane and the artificial horizon line. Some instruments have converging lines on the earth part of the background to enhance the picture and assist in estimating the bank angle. Bank pointer displays vary in design, but are easy to interpret.

How It Works

The basis of the AI is a self-erecting gyroscope with a vertical spin axis. It may be driven either electrically or by an airflow induced over vanes on the edge of the gyroscope by suction. The gyroscope is connected to the artificial horizon line and, when spinning fast enough and with the spin axis stabilised vertically, holds it horizontal. Because the spin axis is vertical and the gyroscope spins in the horizontal plane, the AI cannot provide a reference in the yawing plane, but only in pitch and roll.

Fig.2-2. The AI provides Pitch and Bank Information Only.

If the spin axis of the gyroscope moves off the vertical for some reason, the AI's internal *self-erecting* mechanism, which senses gravity, will realign it at a rate of approximately 3°/minute. The AI should work perfectly in steady 1g conditions, when the artificial horizon line should be exactly horizontal.

Faults

The Attitude Indicator, even though it is an exceptionally good instrument, is not perfect. Its power source can fail, and it does have some small gyroscopic precession errors induced during rapid speed changes and in turns (but they are generally small and easily coped with). Any tendency to follow a slightly incorrect artificial horizon bar will be detected by scanning the other instruments, and corrective action can be taken to maintain height and/or direction.

If the power source fails, then the AI may become unusable. An electrically-driven AI should then show a red warning flag, but the vacuum-driven AI may just gradually run down and give a false indication without a warning flag. For this reason, the Suction Gauge should be periodically checked for a vacuum of approximately 4.5"Hg (especially since the DI may also be vacuum-driven).

Any acceleration (such as a rapid speed change or a turn) will exert additional g-forces on the aeroplane. Everything within it, including the Pilot and the AI's self-erecting mechanism, will sense a false 'gravity' force, which may cause the gyroscope's spin axis to move off the vertical briefly, resulting in a slightly incorrect artificial horizon line.

During a rapid acceleration, the horizon line will move down and, if the Pilot follows it, the aeroplane will have a lower pitch attitude than desired. Conversely, during a deceleration, the horizon line will move up, causing a false pitch down indication, i.e. the AI will display a greater pitch down attitude than the aeroplane actually has. The Pilot will detect these small pitch errors in his scan of the vertical performance instruments, and either maintain height in level flight using the Altimeter and VSI, or maintain airspeed in a climb or descent using the ASI.

Skids, sideslips and turns exert additional forces that may cause the artificial horizon line to move off the horizontal briefly, resulting in a small error in bank display. The Pilot will detect this in his scan of the other instruments, and can maintain heading and wings level with reference to the DI in straight flight, or maintain a particular turn rate during a heading change with reference to the Turn Coordinator. The small bank error in the AI will be greatest following a turn of 180° (possibly up to 5° of bank error), and will cancel itself out at the completion of 360°.

These precession errors correct themselves fairly quickly and can, in general, be disregarded in light aircraft, which do not have high rates of acceleration and deceleration. A good scan will ensure that errors in the AI will not affect the accuracy of instrument flying, with height, heading or airspeed (as the case may be) held with reference to the other instruments.

Some types of AI have a gyroscope which will topple when the aeroplane is in extreme attitudes well beyond normal flight attitudes (typically in excess of 60° of pitch and 100° of roll). This will temporarily render the AI useless. Some gyroscopes can be caged, and then uncaged once the aeroplane is back in straight and level flight.

Some newer types of AI, however, can tolerate any aircraft attitude (360° of pitch and/or roll) without the gyroscope toppling. If the self-erecting mechanism is unable to cope with large errors, then this may also make the AI unusable. If, however, the AI becomes unusable for any reason, accurate instrument flight is still attainable, although more difficult using the other instruments. The chapter on *The Limited Panel* discusses this in detail.

Pre-Flight Checks of the AI

After engine start-up, and allowing the AI gyroscope time to stabilise (which may take several minutes), the AI should be checked for serviceability. There should be no electrical warning flag visible for an electrically-driven gyroscope, or adequate suction should be indicated for a vacuum-driven gyroscope. The artificial horizon line should appear horizontal, and the Index Aeroplane should be checked to ensure that it is aligned with the artificial horizon line when the aeroplane is on level ground.

Whilst taxying to the take-off position, the AI can be observed as the aeroplane makes right and left turns (which will be in the yawing plane only), to check that the artificial horizon bar does not move appreciably. Significant bank or pitch errors could indicate something wrong within the gyroscopic system. (Whilst not recommended, the AI pitch error caused by rapid deceleration can be demonstrated during a straight taxi by applying the brakes, which will cause a false pitch down indication as the horizon bar moves up.)

THE POWER INDICATOR(S)

Different types of engines and propellers require different types of power instruments. For this reason, the Power Indicator in the cockpit will be referred to as just that, whereas in a specific aeroplane it may be the *Tachometer,* in another the *Manifold Pressure Gauge,* and in another (a jet) the *EPR Gauge.*

In an aeroplane fitted with a *fixed-pitch propeller* (i.e. most basic trainers), the power instrument is a **Tachometer**, which measures engine rpm. Moving the throttle forward increases power by increasing engine rpm, displayed by the Tachometer needle moving clockwise.

More advanced aeroplanes have a *Constant Speed Unit* (CSU) propeller whose rpm can be set to a constant value with a pitch lever or pitch knob placed beside the throttle. With rpm set, a power increase made by advancing the throttle is shown in the cockpit as an increase in Manifold Pressure (MP) on the **Manifold Pressure Gauge**, which is now the main power indicator.

A power increase on a *jet engine* made by advancing the throttle may be shown on an **Engine Pressure Ratio** (EPR) gauge, which may be the main power indicator to the Jet Pilot. There are a variety of instruments that can perform this function.

From the point of view of instrument flying, it does not matter what sort of aeroplane is being flown and what sort of power instruments it has, but what does matter is that the Pilot has a power indicator in the cockpit that he will refer to when power changes are being made. For this reason, we will use a **non-specific** type of indicator in the illustrations, mainly to show power increases or decreases. Endorsement training on the aeroplane that you are flying will include knowledge of its particular power indicators and engine/propeller controls.

Fig.2-3. Typical Power Indicators.

THE DIRECTION INDICATOR

Although it does not automatically sense magnetic heading, **the Direction Indicator can indicate magnetic heading once it has been aligned with the Magnetic Compass.** The DI will be either electrically-driven or vacuum-driven, and its power source in many aeroplanes is the same as that for the AI.

The modern DI cockpit display is a vertical compass rose of 360° that can rotate around a model aeroplane fixed in the centre of the dial with its nose pointing up. Typically, the rose is labelled every 30° with a number or letter, with large markings every 10° and smaller markings every intermediate 5°. The compass rose can be rotated using a slaving knob until the direction determined from the Magnetic Compass appears at the top of the dial. As heading changes, the compass rose rotates until the new heading is at the top of the dial, either under a fixed marker or at the nose of the model aeroplane.

There may be further *fixed* markings relative to the nose of the aeroplane at the 45°, 90° and 180° positions. The reciprocal to the heading can be read off the bottom of the dial. The abeam bearings can be read off the 90° markings. Mental arithmetic calculations are not necessary. To turn left 45°, for instance, simply note the direction at the 45° left marking, and perform a banked turn to the left until it appears at the top of the dial. The modern DI is an easy instrument to interpret because, in a left turn, for instance, the model aeroplane appears to move left relative to the compass rose. (In actual fact, it is the compass rose that rotates to the right.)

Fig.2-4. Typical Modern DIs.

The DI is a non-magnetic instrument. It contains a gyroscope with a lateral horizontal spin axis, which provides the DI card with short-term directional stability. The gyro-stabilised DI is not subject to the problems which the Magnetic Compass experiences as a result of magnetic dip (i.e. turning and acceleration errors), nor does it oscillate in rough air. It is a much easier instrument to use than the Compass in the short term, especially in turns and in turbulence, although the Magnetic Compass still remains as the long term reference.

Older Directional Gyros do not have a compass rose, but rather a circular strip card that can rotate, with heading shown under a lubber line. In fact, it is not the card that rotates; it is the aeroplane changing heading that moves around the card, similar to the Magnetic Compass. It is a more difficult presentation to interpret than the modern DI, since only 30° either side of heading are shown and, if the aeroplane turns left, the lubber line moves to the right relative to the card. For instance, in the situation shown below, to take up a heading of 110°M from a heading of 120°, the aeroplane should turn left.

Fig.2-5. An Older Directional Gyro.

Faults

The DI will gradually drift off direction due to internal mechanical reasons (e.g. friction and gimbal effect), and also because of *apparent drift* resulting from the earth's rotation. As the earth rotates about its axis at 15°/hour, the direction in space from a point on the earth's surface to North continually changes. This effect increases towards the poles, and is zero on the equator. The aeroplane can compound this effect as it flies across the face of the earth. Realigning the DI periodically with the Magnetic Compass solves the problem.

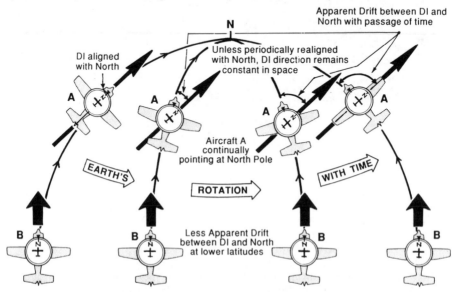

Fig.2-6. The DI will gradually drift off Direction.

Older DIs have internal limits that may cause them to lose their direction-holding ability if bank angle or pitch attitude exceeds 55°. Newer types will not topple, however, even in extreme attitudes.

For several reasons, therefore, the DI must be periodically realigned with the Magnetic Compass, which is unaffected by the rotation of the earth and always points, at least within a few degrees, towards Magnetic North during steady straight flight. Remember that a small correction may have to be made to the Magnetic Compass to allow for Deviation due to extraneous magnetic fields in the aeroplane. The correction required is found on the Deviation Card displayed in the aeroplane. If not allowed for, the Deviation error of the Compass will be carried through onto the DI.

The DI should be checked at least every 15 minutes, and reset to the correct heading with reference to the Magnetic Compass (and Deviation Card) during steady straight flight. For the DI to be acceptable in normal operations, this correction should not exceed 3° in 15 minutes.

Complete failure of the DI makes life a little more difficult for the Instrument Pilot, since he must scan right across to the Magnetic Compass (with its turning and acceleration errors) for heading information. Since the AI and DI often share the same power source, loss of one may mean the loss of the other, a situation considered under *Flying on a Limited Panel.*

Pre-Flight Checks of the DI

After start-up, the electrical or vacuum power source should be checked to ensure that the gyroscope will get up to speed. Once up to speed, the DI should be aligned with the Magnetic Compass using the slaving knob. The DI can then help in orientation on the ground – for instance, in which direction will the take-off be.

Whilst taxying, the DI should be checked for correct functioning: "turning right, heading increases – turning left, heading decreases".

At the holding point, just prior to take-off, the DI should again be checked against the Magnetic Compass (but not whilst turning or accelerating), and it can be used to verify that the correct runway is about to be used.

THE ALTIMETER

The Altimeter is an aneroid barometer that measures *static pressure* and relates it to height in the atmosphere. The lower the pressure, the greater the height. It is a vital instrument if altitude is to be accurately maintained. It is also vital in determining height above the aerodrome during an instrument approach to land in cloud or poor visibility. An aeroplane, unlike a car, must be navigated in three dimensions. The Altimeter is the most important instrument for *vertical navigation.*

The Altimeter relates the static pressure at the aeroplane to a height in the International Standard Atmosphere (ISA), a theoretical 'average' atmosphere which acts as a measuring stick. The main purpose of the ISA is to calibrate Altimeters but, unfortunately for Altimeters, the real atmosphere can differ significantly from the Standard Atmosphere.

Fig.2-7. The Altimeter is a Pressure Sensitive Instrument.

Since pressure varies from place to place, and from time to time, the Altimeter has a small subscale that allows a Pilot to select the pressure level from which height will be measured. Subscale settings that will be used in a typical flight are:

• Aerodrome QNH for circuit operations, to provide altitude (height AMSL);
• Aerodrome QFE for circuit operations, to provide height Above Aerodrome Level;
• Regional QNH for en route cruise at or below the Transition Altitude (usually 3000 ft AMSL in the UK, and higher in places);
• Standard Pressure 1013.2 mb for cruising at Flight Levels above the Transition Altitude.

The only place a Pilot can really check the accuracy of an Altimeter is on the aerodrome. With aerodrome QFE set in the subscale, the Altimeter should read zero. (Conversely, on the ground with the Altimeter reading zero, the current QFE should appear in the subscale.) With Aerodrome QNH set in the subscale, the Altimeter should read Aerodrome Elevation (or vice versa). Accuracy should be within +/− 50 ft (i.e. +/− 2 mb approximately, since 1 mb is equivalent to 30 ft in height). If the aerodrome is *not* on reasonably flat ground, then allow for the fact that Aerodrome Elevation is measured at the highest point on an operating runway, which may be at a slightly different height AMSL to an aeroplane elsewhere on the aerodrome.

*Fig.2-8. The Altimeter measures Height
above the Pressure Level set in the Subscale.*

How the Altimeter Works

The Altimeter contains a sealed, but expandable, capsule that is surrounded by the current static pressure. As the aeroplane climbs and static pressure decreases, the sealed capsule is able to expand. Through a linkage, it drives a pointer around the Altimeter scale to indicate height above the pressure level already selected in the subscale. There may be a short lag in time, however, before any actual changes in height are actually registered on the Altimeter.

Different Altimeter Presentations

A Pilot **must** interpret the Altimeter reading correctly since it provides absolutely vital information. Lives have been lost in the past because of Pilots (even Professional Pilots) misreading the Altimeter by 10,000 ft. Learn how to read them accurately right at the start!

The most easily understood Altimeter presentation is a simple digital readout of height, supported by a single pointer indicating 100s of feet.

It will make one complete revolution of the dial for every 1000 ft gain or loss of altitude. The digital readout displays the actual altitude. The pointer does not indicate the complete altitude, but only the last three digits of it (e.g. at 15,200 ft it would indicate 200). It is very useful to an Instrument Pilot, however, because it gives a better picture of any tendency to depart from a height than does a set of changing digits. Trends of 20 or 50 ft either side of the precise altitude are more easily spotted on the pointer and corrected with an attitude change on the AI.

Fig.2-9. The Digital Altimeter, plus Pointer.

The more **common Altimeter** presentation has three pointers of varying shapes and sizes:

- The long thick pointer measures 100s of feet. It will move once around the dial for each 1000 ft change in altitude. If it is on 7, then that means 7 x 100 = 700 ft.

- The short fat pointer measures 1000s of feet. It will move once around the dial for a change of 10,000 ft. If it is on 4 (or just past it), then that means 4,000 ft. To reinforce to a Pilot that the aeroplane is below 10,000 ft, a striped sector remains visible, gradually becoming smaller as 10,000 ft is approached.

- The pointer with a stubby base and a long fine pointer measures 10,000s of feet. If it is on 1 (or just past it), then that means 10,000 ft. This pointer is particularly easy to misread.

Fig.2-10. The 100s Pointer; the 1,000s Pointer; the 10,000 Pointer.

Pre-Flight Checks

During the walk-around, the Pilot should check that the static vent is clear (since a blocked static vent will affect the Altimeter, the VSI and the ASI). The altimeter subscale can be set to QFE (when the Altimeter should read approximately zero), or to QNH (when it should read Aerodrome Elevation).

Density Error

The Altimeter is calibrated to read the height above the pressure level selected in the subscale as if the characteristics of the real atmosphere (temperature, pressure, density) were identical to the International Standard Atmosphere. They rarely are, which means that the Altimeter reading will not match the True Altitude precisely.

A string dropped to sea level would be a different length to the Altimeter's Indicated Altitude. Usually, this is not significant, since all aeroplanes in the one area will have their Altimeters affected identically, and so vertical separation will not be degraded. Aeroplanes are always cruised on Indicated Altitude (i.e. what appears on the Altimeter), and not on True Altitude.

Whilst density error is of little significance in normal operations, an interesting point may occur later in your training on Precision Instrument Approaches. In very warm air, the density will be less than standard. Climbing a true 1000 feet, the Altimeter will sense less than 1000 ft difference in density in the thinner air, i.e. the Altimeter will under-read. The aeroplane is actually at 3100 ft, but the Altimeter only indicates 3000 ft. In air colder than ISA, the reverse is the case: the Altimeter will indicate higher than the aeroplane actually is.

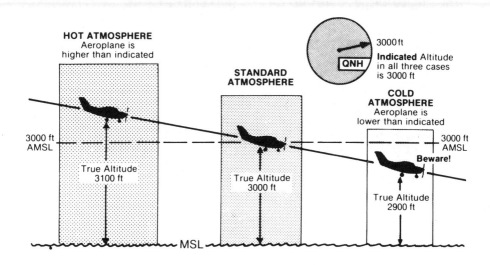

Fig.2-11. Indicated Altitude may not be True Altitude.

A Pilot carrying out an instrument approach to a runway by following an ILS glide slope will check height as he passes the Outer Marker (either AMSL on QNH, or AAL on QFE). He might notice a small difference between the Indicated Altitude on the Altimeter compared to the height published on the Instrument Approach Charts. The actual height is fixed but, even if the aeroplane is exactly on slope, the Altimeter reading may be a little different to the published value. In warm air, it will read a little lower; in cold air, it will read a little higher.

Fig.2-12. A Typical ILS Approach Profile.

THE VERTICAL SPEED INDICATOR

The VSI provides a readout of the **rate of change of altitude**. If the aeroplane climbs steadily through 250 ft in 30 seconds, then the VSI should read 500 ft/min. Its dial is usually marked in 100s of feet either side of a zero marking, with 500 ft/min UP or DOWN clearly labelled.

The VSI, as well as being useful in climbs and descents, is a very useful instrument when trying to achieve precise *level* flight. In smooth air, it will show any **trend** to move away from an altitude very quickly. It will respond faster to an altitude change than the Altimeter, and allow a pitch attitude correction to be made on the AI before the Altimeter has hardly registered any change in height. In rough air, however, the VSI pointer fluctuates, making it a less valuable instrument.

With large and sudden attitude changes, the VSI may briefly show a reversed reading because of disturbed airflow near the static vent, with some lag before a steady Rate of Climb or Descent is indicated. In such a case, allow the indication to settle before using its information.

The main value of the VSI is the support it gives to the Altimeter when maintaining height, and the Rate of Climb or Descent it displays during climbs and descents.

How the VSI Works

The VSI has an expandable capsule connected to the static line so that it contains the actual static pressure. The VSI instrument case containing the capsule is also connected to the static line, but through a metered leak. As the aeroplane changes altitude, the static pressure within the capsule changes immediately, but the metered leak causes the pressure change surrounding the capsule to be more gradual.

On a climb, the pressure in the capsule changes instantaneously to the now lower static pressure. The case that surrounds the capsule, however, contains the original higher pressure which takes some time to change. The effect is to compress the capsule, driving a pointer around the dial to indicate a Rate of Climb.

Fig.2-13. The VSI compares Static Pressure in the Capsule with Delayed Static Pressure in the Case.

The changed pressure gradually leaks into the instrument case. If the aeroplane continues to climb, the pressure within the instrument case never quite catches up with the external static pressure within the capsule, and so the VSI continues to indicate a Rate of Climb. Once the aeroplane levels off, however, the two pressures do gradually equalise, and the VSI reads zero.

The VSI is good as a *trend* instrument ("Am I going up? Or am I going down?"), as well as a *rate* instrument ("How fast am I going up or down?"). Whereas the trend is obvious almost immediately in smooth air, the precise rate will take a few seconds to settle down.

Pre-Flight Checks

Like all static pressure instruments, the VSI requires a static vent and line that is not blocked. The VSI should also indicate approximately zero whilst the aeroplane is on the ground (and not climbing). Indication errors may exist in some VSIs, in which case allowances will have to be made for this in flight. For instance, if it indicates 100 ft/min UP whilst on the ground, then this may have to be the "zero" position in flight, checked of course against the Altimeter when cruising.

THE TURN COORDINATOR, AND THE TURN INDICATOR

The Turn Coordinator is an advanced modification of an earlier instrument, the Turn Indicator. They are both *rate gyroscopes,* where the rotating mass has freedom to move about two of its three axes and is designed to show movement of the aircraft about the third axis. The gyroscope in the Turn Indicator or Turn Coordinator will not topple in extreme attitudes, making for a very reliable instrument. It may be driven electrically or by suction.

Fig.2-14a. The Turn Coordinator.

Fig.2-14b. The Turn Indicator.

The **Turn Indicator** has a lateral horizontal spin axis (with a vertical spinning gyro) attached to a gimbal. The gimbal axis is fixed and aligned with the aeroplane's longitudinal axis. The Turn Indicator is designed to show motion about the *normal axis,* i.e. the *rate of turn* in the yawing plane.

Fig.2-15. The Turn Indicator.

28

Any turning motion of the aircraft is mechanically transmitted to the spin axis, and exerts a force on the spinning mass of the gyroscope. In the illustration below, the force exerted on the gyro by a left turn is translated 90° by the gyroscopic precession effect, causing the gyro and its spin axis to tilt. This tilting is opposed by a spring – the greater the turning force, the greater the tilt. The tilt is transmitted to a pointer which moves on the Turn Indicator Dial, usually calibrated to show Rate 1 turns left or right. Some instruments, however, have their dials calibrated to turns other than Rate 1, a point which must be established before relying on the instrument.

The **Turn Coordinator** is a very clever development of the same principle. The gimbal axis is angled up at about 30° to the aeroplane's longitudinal axis, which makes the gyro sensitive not only to *turning* about the normal axis, but also to *banking* about the longitudinal axis. Since a turn is commenced by banking the aeroplane, the Turn Coordinator will react to roll, even before the aeroplane actually starts turning.

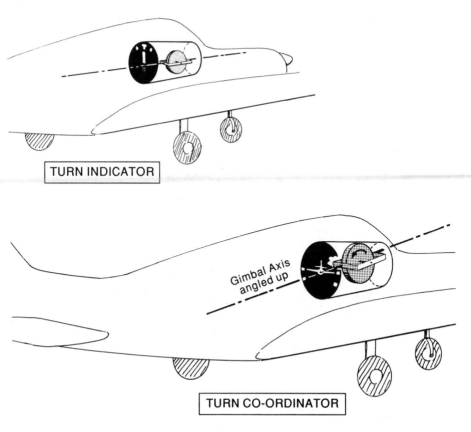

TURN INDICATOR

TURN CO-ORDINATOR

Fig.2-16. The Turn Coordinator Gyro is Angled to make it sensitive to Banking as well as Turning.

The Turn Coordinator presentation is usually a set of wings pivoted in the centre of the instrument, the wings moving to indicate the direction of bank. Calibrations around the edge of the instrument show Rate 1 turns. Note that the wings are pivoted in the centre and so will *not* move up or down to indicate pitch attitude. Many Turn Coordinators are labelled **"No Pitch Information"**. The "2 MIN" label refers to a Rate 1 turn taking 2 minutes to achieve a heading change of 360°.

A significant advantage of the Turn Coordinator is that it can be used quite comfortably to keep the **wings level** in straight flight if the Attitude Indicator has failed. The wings of the Turn Coordinator will react first to *roll,* and then to *yaw.*

Pre-Flight Checks of the Turn Coordinator (and Balance Indicator).

During the taxi, a very simple check is to turn the aircraft and observe the indications: 'Turning Left (on the Turn Coordinator) – Skidding Right' (on the Balance Indicator), followed by 'Turning Right – Skidding Left'.

Any doubts about calibration can be checked with a timed Rate 1 turn in flight.

THE BALANCE INDICATOR

The Balance Indicator is a very simple, and very useful, mechanical device that indicates the *direction of the g-forces,* i.e. the combined effect of the earth's gravity force and any turning force. It has no power source.

The Balance Indicator is usually incorporated into the presentation of the Turn Coordinator (or Turn Indicator). It is simply a small ball, free to move like a pendulum bob, except that it moves in a curved cylinder filled with damping fluid. In straight flight, it should appear at the lowest point in the curved cylinder (like a pendulum bob hanging straight down), and the aeroplane is then said to be *in balance.* If there is any *slip* or *skid,* the ball will move to one side in the same way as a pendulum bob would swing out. Similarly, the Pilot would feel a force pushing him out, usually through *the seat of his pants.* If the ball is out to the right, apply right rudder pressure to centralise it.

Right Rudder
required

Fig.2-17. In Balance;   *in a Right Skid.*

In **a balanced turn**, the Pilot will feel no sideways forces, nor will the Balance Ball, which should remain centralised. Any sideways force (either a *slip* in towards the turn or a *skid* out) will be shown by the Balance Indicator (and felt in the seat of your pants). This can be counteracted with same-side rudder pressure to centralise the ball.

Fig.2-18. Slipping Turn: More Right Rudder Required.

Fig.2-19. A Comfortable and Balanced Turn.

Fig.2-20. Too Much Right Rudder in this Case – A Skidding Turn.

THE MAGNETIC COMPASS

The Magnetic Compass is the *source* of directional information in the cockpit. In steady flight, it aligns itself with Magnetic North so that the aeroplane's Magnetic Heading appears under the Lubber Line. Small errors in this reading due to other known magnetic fields in the aeroplane can be allowed for by the Pilot by using information on the *Deviation Card*.

The Magnetic Compass does, however, experience *dip errors* when the aeroplane is turning (especially through N or S), and when accelerating (especially on E and W). The easiest approach for a Pilot is to align the gyroscopic Direction Indicator (which is *not* subject to these errors) with the Magnetic Compass during steady straight flight periodically, and then use it as a short term guide to magnetic direction, rather than the Compass.

If, however, the DI is unserviceable and the Magnetic Compass has to be used, certain allowances for these dip errors need to be made. They are:

- *Undershoot* the heading when turning through North.
- *Overshoot* the heading when turning through South.
- Expect an *apparent* turn North on the Magnetic Compass when accelerating on East or West.
- Expect an *apparent* turn South on the Magnetic Compass when decelerating on East or West.

NOTE: These allowances apply to dip errors in the Northern Hemisphere. They are greatest towards the North Pole, decrease towards the Equator, and are reversed in the Southern Hemisphere.

Pre-Flight Checks of the Magnetic Compass

The Magnetic Compass should be checked that it is secure, and that the Bowl is full of fluid and without bubbles. Its reading can be checked against a known heading, at least approximately. Ensure that no magnetic materials are stored near it, as these could introduce large errors. During the taxi, the card can be checked for free movement during a turn.

3

STRAIGHT AND LEVEL FLIGHT

Flying **straight** means maintaining a constant heading, which can be achieved by holding the wings level with the ailerons and keeping the aeroplane in balance with the ball centred using rudder pressure.

Flying **level** means maintaining a constant height, which can be achieved by holding the correct pitch attitude for the power set.

Straight and level flying is very important, since most flights contain a cruise segment which, on occasions, may be quite long. Accurate straight and level flying is important for aerodynamic efficiency, fuel efficiency and comfort, and is one sign of a good Pilot.

THE CONTROL INSTRUMENTS

The control instruments for straight and level flight, as for all flight, are:
- the **Attitude** Indicator; and
- the **Power** Indicator.

With reference to these control instruments, the Pilot can use the controls (the control column for pitch and bank attitude, the throttle for power) to select straight and level flight at the desired height and airspeed. The AI gives a **direct and instantaneous picture** of the aeroplane's pitch attitude and bank angle, and the Power Indicator gives a direct reading of power.

Fig.3-1. The Control Instruments.

33

THE PERFORMANCE INSTRUMENTS

The **Vertical Performance** of the aeroplane is indicated to the Pilot primarily on:

- the **Altimeter**;
- the **Vertical Speed Indicator (VSI)**; and, to a lesser extent,
- the **Air Speed Indicator (ASI)**.

Fig.3-2. The Vertical Performance Instruments showing a Gradual Loss of Height.

The Altimeter indicates height directly. The VSI indicates any trend away from that height. The ASI indicates airspeed, but can also provide information indirectly regarding pitch attitude and height. For instance, an increasing airspeed at a constant power setting means a lower pitch attitude and, in straight and level flight, possibly a loss of height.

For the Altimeter reading to be meaningful, the Pilot must have the appropriate pressure setting in the subscale, since this will be the pressure level from which the Altimeter measures height. The subscale is generally set to:

- Regional QNH for en route cruise at or below the Transition Altitude;
- Standard Pressure 1013.2 mb for en route cruise above the Transition Altitude; and
- either Aerodrome QNH or QFE for circuit operations.

Fig.3-3. Set the Altimeter Subscale Correctly.

Horizontal Performance, in directional terms, is indicated to the Pilot primarily on:
- the **Direction Indicator (DI)**; and
- the **Turn Coordinator (TC) and Balance Ball.**

*Fig.3-4. The Directional Performance Instruments
during a Left Turn Towards North.*

The DI gives a direct reading of magnetic direction provided it has been correctly aligned with the Magnetic Compass during steady flight. It also gives an indirect indication of bank (because, if the heading is changing in coordinated flight, then the wings are banked), plus an indirect indication of rate of turn (by comparing the heading change with the time taken).

The Turn Coordinator (or the older style Turn Indicator, also known as the *bat and ball*) indicates the rate of turn. The Balance Ball is important, since coordinated flight is almost always desirable to avoid any sideslip or skid through the air.

Horizontal performance in terms of airspeed is indicated on the Air Speed Indicator.

Fig.3-5. The Full Panel During a Left Turn to Regain Heading 360°M at Altitude 2000 ft and 100 kt.

KEEP THE AEROPLANE IN TRIM

When properly trimmed, the aeroplane should maintain level flight with little or no assistance from the Pilot. If not properly trimmed, level flight is much more difficult to maintain, and the Pilot is likely to become fatigued and tense on the controls. **Instrument flying requires a light touch**, and this is only possible when the aeroplane is well trimmed and the Pilot relaxed.

Remember that trim is used **only** to relieve steady control pressures exerted by the Pilot, and **not** to change aeroplane attitude. Significant trim changes in straight and level flight will generally only be required when the Pilot makes significant changes in airspeed, or changes in configuration, for instance by lowering the flaps.

The natural stability designed into the aeroplane will help it to maintain pitch attitude in rough air as well as smooth air, even though there may be some significant deviations from altitude as a result of turbulence. The Pilot can correct for altitude deviations with smooth elevator control, but should avoid constant re-trimming in turbulence.

STAY RELAXED

A relaxed Pilot with a fast instrument scan and a light touch on the controls will be a good Instrument Pilot.

If at any time you feel tense on the controls, a good *untensing* technique is to first ensure that the aeroplane is in trim and then (provided conditions are not turbulent) release all pressure on the elevator control for just a moment or two. Flex your fingers, before replacing them on the control column. The thumb and first two fingers will be more than sufficient for adequate control; a full hand grip may lead to lack of sensitive control and to further tenseness. **Being in trim is vital!**

DIFFERENT CRUISE SPEEDS REQUIRE DIFFERENT PITCH ATTITUDES

The pitch attitude established on the Attitude Indicator will vary for different cruise speeds. For instance, the pitch attitude required for low speed cruise will be *higher* than that for normal cruise, in order to generate sufficient Lift at the lower speed to balance the Weight. This is summarised in the Lift Formula ($L = C_L.\frac{1}{2}$ Rho $V^2.S$), which tells us that the Lift produced (L) is a function of the angle of attack (C_L) and the indicated airspeed (related to $\frac{1}{2}$ Rho V^2). A high angle of attack at a low airspeed is capable of producing the same Lift as a low angle of attack at a high airspeed.

Fig.3-6. Low Speed Cruise;   High Speed Cruise.

The VSI and the Altimeter will confirm if the pitch attitude selected on the AI is correct to maintain height with that power set. If not, then do something about it. The power required will differ with each airspeed, but more of this later.

Also, compared to when it is light, a heavily-laden aeroplane will require a greater Lift force to support the greater Weight, and so will require a higher angle of attack at a given cruise speed, hence a higher pitch attitude in the cruise. The Pilot may not notice this directly, but reference to the VSI and Altimeter will ensure that the correct pitch attitude is selected no matter what the Weight is. What may be noticeable to the Pilot, however, is the higher power required to maintain airspeed because of the higher Drag.

When establishing straight and level flight, the Pilot uses the **control** instruments, namely the power indicator (throttle) and the AI (control column), to set the expected power and pitch attitude. Fine tuning to accurately hold height, confirmed on the Altimeter and VSI, is achieved by making minor corrections about this pitch attitude with the elevator.

MAINTAINING HEADING

Keeping the wings level and the ball centred will ensure that the desired heading is maintained. The heading can be monitored on the **Direction Indicator**, with any tendency to turn being indicated on the **Turn Coordinator**. The DI is the primary performance instrument used to maintain a constant heading. Remember that it should be realigned periodically with the Magnetic Compass (every 10 or 15 minutes whilst in steady flight).

Fig.3-7a. Keep Wings Level and Ball Centred to Achieve Straight Flight.

Fig.3-7b. Monitor DI and TC for Heading Performance.

If the aeroplane is allowed to drift off heading, then small coordinated turns (bank and rudder) should be made to regain it. With a reasonable scan rate, the Pilot will always have the aeroplane within a few degrees of the desired heading. **Aim for perfection as an Instrument Pilot**, and at least remain within the Heading limits of +/–5°.

As a guide, when correcting for small heading errors, limit the bank angle to the number of degrees to be turned or even less. For instance, a heading change of 5° can be comfortably made with a bank angle of 5° or less. If a significant heading change is required, however, do not exceed the bank required for a Rate 1 turn (at 120 kt this will be approximately 120/10 + 7 = 12 + 7 = 19° bank angle). Approaching the desired heading, level the wings with aileron and balance with rudder pressure to maintain coordinated flight.

Fig.3-8. Making a Slight Turn Right to Regain Heading.

MAINTAINING HEIGHT

Perfectly level flight is almost impossible to achieve in real life. *Level* flight, in practice, actually consists of a series of very small climbs and descents as the aeroplane moves off altitude and is brought back to it again by the Pilot. Once again, aim for perfection, and certainly do not allow the aeroplane to deviate from the desired altitude by more than +/– 100 ft in smooth air; turbulence of course will make this accuracy more difficult to achieve, in which case do the best you can.

The Pilot **controls** straight and level flight by setting the correct pitch attitude on the Attitude Indicator and the correct cruise power on the Power Indicator, and then **monitors** vertical performance on:
- the Altimeter;
- the Vertical Speed Indicator;
  and, to a lesser extent,
- the Air Speed Indicator.

Fig.3-9a. Set Power and Attitude.   *Fig.3-9b. Monitor Vertical Performance.*

The **Altimeter**, with the correct setting in the subscale, is used to ensure that the correct altitude is indeed being flown. It will indicate deviations from this altitude but, **in smooth air, the earliest sign of a tendency to deviate from altitude will be shown not on the Altimeter but on the Vertical Speed Indicator**.

Often, a slight correction to pitch attitude can be made on the AI in response to a **trend** on the VSI before any significant deviation is registered on the Altimeter. A large VSI indication may mean a large pitch attitude correction is required. A VSI reading of 600 ft/min down might suggest an initial pitch correction of one bar width up, whereas a VSI reading of only 150 ft/min might suggest that one half bar width correction is adequate.

Fig.3-10. In Smooth Air, the VSI indicates the Pitch Error
well in advance of the Altimeter.

In rough air, the VSI reading unfortunately will fluctuate considerably, making it of less value to the Pilot. In this situation, the Altimeter becomes the best guide to any tendency to deviate from Altitude.

The **Air Speed Indicator** also provides valuable information regarding level flight. If cruise power is set, and the airspeed gradually increases, then the pitch attitude is too low and the aeroplane will be gradually descending. This will of course be evident on the VSI and Altimeter, and corrective action taken by raising the pitch attitude.

Small Deviations from Altitude

In a stable cruise, a small climb will usually be accompanied by a small loss of airspeed. For a gain in altitude of less than 100 ft, the Pilot need only make a slight adjustment to pitch attitude, say by lowering it a half bar width on the Attitude Indicator, to regain altitude (and airspeed).

Once the aeroplane is at or near altitude, the pitch attitude can be raised slightly to maintain level flight. No power alterations should be required during these small corrections to height. Minor adjustments to altitude using elevator alone can be thought of as gentle *zooms* and *dives*.

*Fig.3-11. Make a Small Pitch Correction
for an Altitude Deviation of less than 100 ft High.*

Conversely, a small descent in a stable cruise will usually be accompanied by a slight gain in airspeed. A deviation of 100 ft or less beneath the
desired altitude can be corrected by a slight adjustment to pitch
attitude, say by raising it one half bar width on the Attitude Indicator to
regain altitude (and airspeed). Once at or near altitude, the pitch attitude
can then be lowered slightly to maintain level flight. No power
alterations should be required.

Fig.3-12. Pitch Correction for an Altitude Deviation of less than 100 ft Low.

Larger Deviations from Altitude

To correct a large deviation from altitude (say in excess of 100 ft) will require an **attitude change** and possibly a **power change** as well.

Even if the altitude is changing rapidly, the correction made to pitch attitude by the Pilot should still be smooth, with light control pressures, and can be thought of in two stages: one to stop the movement of the altimeter needle and reduce the VSI indication to zero, and a further pitch correction to return the aeroplane towards the desired altitude. The **total** pitch correction required still may be only one or two bar widths.

Fig.3-13. Attitude and Power Corrections for a Significant Deviation Below Altitude.

Following a large deviation below altitude, a significant climb back to the desired altitude of 100 ft or more will probably require increased power for the period of the climb if airspeed is to be maintained. Once back on height at the desired airspeed, cruise power can be reset to maintain that airspeed.

Conversely, a significant descent to regain the desired altitude will require a lower pitch attitude, and a temporary reduction in power to avoid an unwanted airspeed increase. Once back on height with the correct pitch attitude set and at the desired airspeed, cruise power can be reset to maintain that airspeed.

Fig.3-14. Attitude and Power Corrections for a Significant Deviation Above Altitude.

ENERGY TRANSFER IN STRAIGHT AND LEVEL FLIGHT

Maintaining both a steady height and a steady airspeed can be thought of in terms of energy management. An aeroplane in flight has *Kinetic Energy* in the form of airspeed and *Potential Energy* in the form of height. It is possible to convert between these two forms of energy either by **zooming** to a greater height and converting airspeed to height, or by **diving** and converting height to airspeed. Additional energy, if required, can be supplied to the aeroplane by adding power with the throttle.

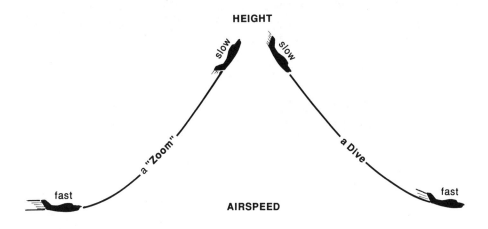

Fig.3-15. Converting Airspeed to Height, and Vice Versa.

If, for instance, the aeroplane is below the desired altitude with the airspeed well in excess of that desired, then the Pilot can convert the excess airspeed to altitude without the use of additional power. If there is no excess airspeed, however, then additional engine power will be required to maintain airspeed. Conversely, excess height can be lost by lowering the pitch attitude with elevator and either accepting an airspeed increase or reducing power with the throttle to maintain airspeed.

Scanning the vertical performance instruments will tell the Pilot what he should do. As in all flight, the performance of the aeroplane depends upon both a combination of attitude and power but, in Straight and Level flight, it is easiest for the Pilot to think in terms of controlling:
- **height with elevator (pitch attitude); and**
- **airspeed with throttle (power).**

Possible deviations and remedies include the examples which follow.

Fig.3-16. Possible Deviations and Remedies.

RECOVERING FROM SLIGHTLY UNUSUAL ATTITUDES

It is possible, indeed even probable, that early during instrument training you will find the aeroplane in some slightly unusual attitudes.

The remedies are quite straightforward:

• If the aeroplane is banked, level the wings on the AI with the ailerons.

• If the nose is too high or too low, ease it into the correct attitude on the AI with elevator.

• If the airspeed is excessively high or low, or if large alterations to height are required, some adjustment of power may be necessary.

Fig.3-17a. Nose High and Turning Left.   Fig.3-17b. Nose Low and Turning Left.
Lower the Pitch Attitude   Level the Wings
and Level the Wings.   and Raise the Pitch Attitude.

COPING WITH A FAULTY ATTITUDE INDICATOR

The Attitude Indicator is the Master Instrument for the Pilot and, if it is not functioning correctly, his task is made that much harder. There are situations where it may fail totally, and others where its indications are not perfectly correct, but are still usable.

Re-setting the Model Aeroplane

A symbol of the real aeroplane appears as a Model Aeroplane, or **Index Aeroplane**, in the centre of the Attitude Indicator. Its position can be adjusted, when required, using a small adjustment knob. **The Index Aeroplane should be positioned so that, during normal cruise flight, it will appear in line with the horizon bar**. The Pilot should always check this on the ground with the aeroplane in a level attitude before every instrument flight.

If the pre-flight check of the AI shows that the Model Aeroplane is not properly aligned, then it should be adjusted immediately. If, for some reason, it requires re-setting in flight, then the Pilot should establish straight and level flight (monitored on the other instruments), and then reset the Index Aeroplane against the Artificial Horizon. After resetting, the AI will give its normal indications in all attitudes.

*Fig.3-18. Set the Index Aeroplane in the Attitude Indicator
with the Aeroplane in the Straight and Level Attitude.*

Coping with a Faulty Wings-Level Indication

Occasionally a Pilot will come across an AI that gives a faulty wings-level indication, due to either a lopsided Index Aeroplane or an Artificial Horizon Line that is not perfectly horizontal. It may also be due to small gyroscopic precession errors following strenuous manoeuvres, but these will correct themselves and only be short-lived.

The clue to a Pilot that the AI is not indicating bank correctly is that, with the wings held level according to the AI and with the Balance Ball centred, the Direction Indicator shows a gradually changing heading, and the Turn Coordinator shows a turn.

To cope with a suspected faulty wings-level indication on the Attitude Indicator, the Pilot should:
- keep the aeroplane in balance with rudder pressure (ball centred);
- hold the Desired Heading with reference to the Direction Indicator; and
- accept the slightly erroneous *lopsided* AI indication.

*Fig.3-19a. A Faulty Wings-Level
Indication on the AI.*

*Fig.3-19b. Maintaining Heading
with a Faulty AI.*

A complete failure of the Attitude Indicator is possible, although unlikely, since it is generally a very reliable instrument. For instance, a vacuum pump failure to a vacuum-driven AI, or an electrical failure to an electrically-driven AI, or even an internal gyroscopic failure, will make the AI unusable as the gyroscope runs down.

Any failure of the AI prior to flight should be detected during the pre-flight checks of the instruments whilst the aeroplane is still on the ground. The rare event of the AI failing in flight, causing the Pilot to fly on instruments without reference to the most important one of all, is considered later under the title of *Flying on a Limited Panel*.

CHANGING AIRSPEED IN STRAIGHT AND LEVEL FLIGHT

Normal cruise involves setting cruise power, holding cruise altitude, and accepting the airspeed that is achieved, which should be close to the figure published in the Pilot's Operating Handbook.

On occasions, however, there is a need to fly at other than normal cruise airspeed. This will require a different pitch attitude and a different power setting. To slow the aeroplane down, the Pilot will throttle back and gradually raise the pitch attitude to maintain height; to increase airspeed, the Pilot will advance the throttle, and gradually lower the pitch attitude to maintain height.

Once the desired airspeed is achieved, the Pilot will adjust the power to maintain it. **The precise power required for steady flight** will depend upon the amount of Total Drag, which on the cruise varies with angle of attack and airspeed. High power will be required for:

- high speed cruise (when Total Drag is high mainly due to Parasite Drag); and
- low speed cruise (when Total Drag is high mainly due to Induced Drag).

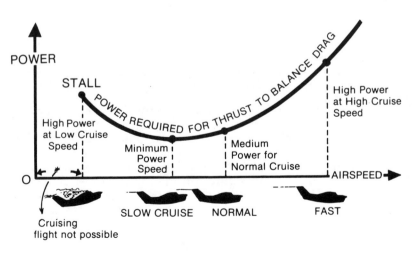

Fig.3-20. The Power Curve.

Medium power will be required for normal cruise. The ASI will confirm whether or not correct power is set. If not, do something about it. **The ASI is the primary performance guide to power requirements during level flight.**

Practising airspeed changes on the cruise is **excellent instrument flying practice** since pitch, bank, balance and power changes must all be coordinated to maintain constant height and heading. When the Pilot changes power, a single-engined propeller-driven aeroplane will tend to move around all three axes of movement. If the propeller rotates clockwise as seen from the cockpit, which is the usual case, adding power will cause the nose to pitch up and yaw left, with a tendency for the aeroplane to bank left.

The Pilot, of course, can counteract this by applying forward elevator pressure to avoid the nose pitching up, with right rudder and aileron pressure to overcome the tendency to yaw and roll left. The converse applies when reducing power, i.e. hold the nose up and apply left rudder pressure. Refer to the AI to keep the wings level and hold the pitch attitude, and refer to the Balance Indicator to remain in balance.

Some hints on changing cruising speed follow. The Attitude Indicator gives a direct picture of pitch and bank attitudes. The Balance Ball gives a direct indication of balance. Useful performance instruments are the Altimeter and VSI to ensure that height is being maintained, and the Direction Indicator to ensure that Heading is being maintained. The Air Speed Indicator will indicate the power requirements. If too slow, add more power; if too fast, reduce power.

The **scan rate** of the Flight Instruments during the power change needs to be reasonably smart to counteract the pitch/yaw effects smoothly and accurately. For this reason, it is good to develop the skill of judging power changes by throttle movement and engine sound, rather than only by observation of the Power Indicator. This will allow concentration on the Flight Instruments until after the power change has been made, at which time a quick glance at the Power Indicator for fine adjustment will suffice.

If the Pilot memorises the approximate power settings necessary to maintain the various cruise speeds, then power handling and airspeed changes become simpler to manage.

Small airspeed changes (say a few knots either way) can generally be handled by a single small power change, and then allowing the aeroplane to gradually slow down or accelerate to the desired speed. Large airspeed changes, however, are most efficiently achieved within a few seconds by '**underpowering**' on the initial power change for a speed decrease, or '**overpowering**' on the initial power change for a speed increase. This allows more rapid deceleration or acceleration to the desired speed, at which time the necessary power to maintain that airspeed is set.

The degree of over- or under-powering will depend upon how fast the Pilot wishes to achieve the desired speed (typically 2–300 rpm, or

3–4" MP), and also on engine limitations (which must not be exceeded). Once the desired airspeed is achieved and suitable power is set, the ASI will indicate if further fine adjustment of power to maintain airspeed is required. In level flight, the ASI is the primary guide to power requirements.

To Increase Speed in Level Flight

A small airspeed increase, 5 kt for instance, may be achieved by a small power increase that allows the airspeed to gradually increase by the desired amount. To achieve a large airspeed increase without delay, however, excess power should be applied to accelerate the aeroplane quickly, and then adjusted when the desired airspeed is reached. This can be thought of as *overpowering* on the initial power change, a typical amount being 200–300 rpm (or 3–4" MP for CSUs).

- Increase power with the throttle (*overpower* for large speed increases). Hold forward pressure to maintain height, referring to the VSI and Altimeter; balance with rudder pressure referring to the Balance Ball; keep wings level with aileron and check DI for Heading.
- Lower the pitch attitude slightly on the AI to maintain height (VSI and Altimeter), and allow airspeed to increase to the desired value (ASI).
- At or approaching the desired airspeed, adjust the power to maintain it (ASI).
- Hold the pitch attitude (AI) using elevator, and trim off the elevator pressure.

Fig.3-21. Increasing Speed in Level Flight.

To Decrease Speed in Level Flight

A small speed decrease can be achieved with a single small power change, but a large speed decrease without delay is best achieved with *underpowering.* Once the aeroplane has decelerated to the desired airspeed, power can be increased to maintain it.

- Decrease power with the throttle (*underpower* for large speed decreases). Hold backward pressure to maintain height referring to the VSI and Altimeter; balance with rudder pressure referring to the Balance Ball; keep wings level with aileron and check DI for Heading.
- Raise the pitch attitude slightly on the AI to maintain height (VSI and Altimeter), and allow airspeed to decrease to the desired value (ASI).
- At or approaching the desired airspeed, adjust the power to maintain it (ASI).
- Hold the pitch attitude (AI), and trim.

Fig.3-22. Decreasing Speed in Level Flight.

Once approximate level flight is achieved:
- the Height can be accurately maintained with elevator; and
- the Air Speed can be accurately maintained with power.

CHANGING CONFIGURATION IN LEVEL FLIGHT

On occasions it is necessary to change the configuration of the aeroplane whilst maintaining level flight, for instance when lowering some flap or lowering the undercarriage while manoeuvring prior to landing. Before a Pilot makes any changes in configuration, however, he must ensure that any limitations are satisfied, for instance the airspeed must be less than V꜀ᴇ before flaps are lowered, or below Vʟᴇ in a retractable undercarriage aeroplane before the landing gear is extended.

Lowering the flaps or landing gear in most aeroplanes will cause an increase in Total Drag and therefore a tendency to lose airspeed, as well as a pitch change. With familiarity, the Pilot will be prepared to counteract these tendencies smoothly and comfortably. Unwanted pitch changes can be counteracted using elevator pressure, with reference to the Attitude Indicator, Altimeter and VSI. Airspeed control is achieved using the throttle, with reference to the Air Speed Indicator, additional power being required to counteract the increased Drag if airspeed is to be maintained. If, however, a further airspeed reduction is required, application of additional power can be delayed.

To Maintain Height and Airspeed as Flap is Lowered:
- Ensure IAS is at or below V꜀ᴇ with reference to the ASI;
- Lower the Flaps, maintaining height with elevator pressure (monitoring the VSI and Altimeter), and maintaining airspeed with power (monitoring the ASI). A lower pitch attitude and higher power can be expected.

Fig.3-23. Maintaining Height and Airspeed as Flap is Lowered.

To Maintain Height and Airspeed as Flap is Raised:
- Ensure IAS is at or below V$_{FE}$;
- Raise the Flaps, maintaining height with elevator back pressure, and airspeed with reduced power. If an airspeed increase is desired, then the power can be adjusted, if necessary, to achieve this.

Fig.3-24. Maintaining Height and Airspeed as Flap is Raised.

To Maintain Height and Airspeed as Landing Gear is Lowered:
- Ensure IAS is at or below V$_{\text{LE}}$;
- Lower the Undercarriage, maintaining height with elevator pressure, and airspeed with additional power.

This manoeuvre typically is used in instrument flying as the aeroplane is flown level towards the descent point for an ILS approach.

Fig.3-25. Maintaining Height and Airspeed as Landing Gear is Lowered.

To Maintain Height and Airspeed as Landing Gear is Raised
- Ensure IAS is at or below V$_{\text{LE}}$;
- Raise the Undercarriage, maintaining height with elevator pressure, and airspeed with power.

Usually the undercarriage is raised during the initial climb-out after take-off, although there are occasions when it may be required to raise the gear from the extended position at other times, for instance when manoeuvring in level flight and deciding to discontinue an approach to land.

4

THE STRAIGHT CLIMB AND DESCENT

With the correct power and attitude, the aeroplane should achieve the desired performance, which in this case is a straight climb. The **Control Instruments** for the climb are the same as for all manoeuvres:
- the **Power Indicator**, used by the Pilot to set power with the throttle; and
- the **Attitude Indicator**, used to set pitch attitude with the elevator (typically one or two bar widths above the cruise position).

TO ENTER A CLIMB ON INSTRUMENTS

As in visual flight, the procedure for entering the climb on instruments is P-A-T: Power–Attitude–Trim.
- Set climb **power** using the throttle (with the mixture *RICH* if necessary).
- Select the climb **attitude** with reference to the AI using elevator.
- Trim.

In the typical single-engined propeller-driven aeroplane there will be a tendency for the nose to pitch up and yaw left as power is applied. To ensure that heading is maintained, the wings are kept level on the AI with aileron, and the Balance Ball kept centred with rudder pressure.

Hold the attitude and allow the airspeed to settle on the ASI, then make fine adjustments to the attitude with elevator to achieve the desired climbing speed precisely, and finally **trim** off any steady control pressure. It is a good idea to make a coarse trim adjustment initially, followed by a finer trim adjustment as the precise climb speed is achieved and maintained.

Fig.4-1. Enter the Climb with Power, Attitude and Trim.

Once established in the climb, the climbing performance of the aeroplane, i.e. its **vertical performance**, is monitored on:
• the Altimeter;
• the Vertical Speed Indicator; and
• the Air Speed Indicator.

With a smooth transition from level flight to a climb, the VSI will show an upward trend, and then the Altimeter reading will start to increase. The VSI will eventually indicate a rate appropriate to the stabilised climb airspeed and pitch attitude for the power set.

MAINTAINING THE CLIMB ON INSTRUMENTS

Keeping the wings level with aileron and the ball centred with rudder pressure will ensure that Heading is maintained, which can be verified on the Direction Indicator. With climb power set (and this is often full power in light aircraft), the Pilot achieves the desired climbing airspeed precisely with slight adjustments to pitch attitude on the AI using elevator. **The Air Speed Indicator is the primary performance instrument in the climb to ensure that pitch attitude is correct.**

Situation: AIRSPEED LOW
Remedy: LOWER THE PITCH ATTITUDE

Situation: AIRSPEED HIGH
Remedy: RAISE THE PITCH ATTITUDE

Fig.4-2. Make Minor Pitch Attitude Adjustments to Maintain Climbing Airspeed.

Once established in the climb, any fine adjustments to pitch attitude should be confined to just one quarter or one half bar width on the AI. **If the climbing airspeed is correct, then the pitch attitude is correct.** If the airspeed is low, then the pitch attitude is too high and should be lowered slightly. Conversely, if the airspeed is too high, then the pitch attitude should be raised slightly. Once the airspeed has settled to its new value, any steady control pressure can be trimmed off.

Heading is maintained by keeping the wings level on the AI and the Balance Ball centred, and **direction can be monitored on the DI.** Small heading corrections can be made with gentle coordinated turns.

Clearing turns (that are made in visual flight every 500 ft or so to look for other aircraft) are meaningless in cloud and nil visibility but, if you happen to be in visual conditions (which is often the case during an instrument flight), clearing turns may be made. During training, your Instructor will probably restrict your outside vision to simulate instrument conditions, but he will require clearing turns to be made periodically for him to adequately perform his function as Safety Pilot.

Engine temperatures and pressures should be checked periodically on the climb, since the engine is working hard and the cooling airflow is less, but do not be distracted from your scan of the flight instruments for more than a few seconds at a time.

As the desired cruising altitude is approached, the Altimeter should be increasingly brought into the scan, and its subscale checked to ensure that the correct subscale setting (Regional QNH, 1013, Aerodrome QNH or QFE) is wound in.

LEVELLING OFF FROM THE CLIMB

As for visual flight, the procedure for levelling off from a climb on instruments is A-P-T: Attitude–Power–Trim. As the desired altitude is approached, the focus for changes in pitch attitude shifts from the Air Speed Indicator to the Altimeter – the aim being to lower the pitch attitude to **capture the desired altitude.** Levelling off should be commenced before actually reaching the altitude, a suitable lead-in height being "10% of the Rate of Climb", which at RoC 500 ft/min would be 50 ft before reaching the desired altitude.

Commencing at the lead-in height, **gradually lower the pitch attitude** towards the level flight position on the AI. The VSI will show a gradually reducing climb rate, and movement of the Altimeter needle will slow down. The aim is to reduce the Rate of Climb to zero just as the desired altitude is captured.

Normally, climb power is retained after levelling off to allow the aeroplane to accelerate to the cruise speed. Once at the desired airspeed, **reduce to cruise power**, holding the desired pitch attitude with elevator, and then **trim**.

Fig.4-3. Levelling off from a Climb.

Heading is monitored on the DI, and will remain constant if the wings are kept level and the Balance Ball centred. Heading corrections can be made using shallow coordinated turns. Minor adjustments to pitch attitude using the elevator will be required to maintain the exact height. If a particular cruise airspeed is desired, then power adjustments may also be required.

CLIMBING AT DIFFERENT AIRSPEEDS

With climb power set, climbing airspeed is selected with pitch attitude on the AI, a higher pitch attitude resulting in a lower airspeed. Different climb airspeeds are used to achieve different objectives, for instance:

- the **Best Angle of Climb** airspeed (Vx) to clear obstacles;
- the **Best Rate of Climb** airspeed (Vy) to gain height as quickly as possible;
- the **Cruise-Climb** airspeed, sacrificing Rate of Climb for a higher airspeed, often used to provide faster journeys, better aeroplane control because of the increased airflow over the control surfaces, better engine cooling, and a more comfortable (lower) aeroplane attitude.

61

MAX ANGLE CLIMB   CRUISE-CLIMB

Fig.4-4. Different Climbing Airspeeds to Achieve Different Objectives.

The precise values of Vx and Vy may be found in the Pilot's Operating Handbook. To achieve the desired airspeed, the Pilot simply adjusts the pitch attitude on the AI, the Air Speed Indicator being the primary performance instrument to verify that pitch attitude is correct.

VARIATIONS ON ENTERING THE CLIMB

The technique used to enter the climb from level flight will depend upon the level airspeed and the desired climb speed. If the same airspeed is to be used both cruising and climbing, then **simultaneously apply power and gently raise the pitch attitude** to maintain the airspeed and then, once settled into the climb, **trim** off any steady pressure.

If, however, the climb airspeed is to be less than the cruising airspeed (which is generally the case), then the Pilot can either:
• apply power and raise the pitch attitude, allow the airspeed to wash-off to climb speed, and then make pitch adjustments to maintain the desired climb speed (i.e. the usual P-A-T); or
• raise the pitch attitude and allow the speed to wash-off before applying power to maintain the desired climb speed (i.e. A-P-T).

In general, the order P-A-T is acceptable, however your Instructor will advise you if he prefers the second method.

CLIMBING AT A PARTICULAR RATE

Controlling the Rate of Climb to a specific value in most light aircraft is not generally required, because of their moderate performance capabilities even at full power. High-powered aeroplanes, however, may occasionally be required to climb at a particular rate.

The airspeed in a climb is controlled by small alterations in pitch attitude using elevator, with the Air Speed Indicator as the primary performance instrument for climb speed. The Pilot has a measure of **Rate of Climb** from either:

• the Vertical Speed Indicator (VSI); or
• the Clock and the Altimeter combined.

CLIMBING AT 500 ft/min USING CLOCK & ALTIMETER

Fig.4-5. Monitoring Rate of Climb.

The VSI, after it has stabilised, is normally the primary performance instrument for Rate of Climb but, if turbulence causes the VSI to fluctuate, then the Pilot can either estimate the average reading of the VSI or use the Clock and Altimeter to time the climb. In the above case, the aeroplane has climbed 125 ft in 15 seconds (1/4 minute), a rate of 500 ft/min.

Power can be adjusted until the desired Rate of Climb is achieved precisely, accompanied by minor adjustments of pitch attitude on the AI to hold airspeed. For instance, as illustrated below, a decrease in power to reduce the Rate of Climb from 900 ft/min to 500 ft/min will require a slight lowering of the pitch attitude to maintain a constant airspeed of 80 kt.

Fig.4-6. Establishing a Precise Rate of Climb.

Conversely, the Rate of Climb can be increased at a constant airspeed by adding power and raising the pitch attitude. If, however, maximum power is already being used (as is often the case in light aircraft), the only way of improving Rate of Climb is to fly closer to Vᵥ, the Best Rate of Climb airspeed.

Be warned that raising the pitch attitude too high, and reducing the airspeed to **below** Vᵥ, will lead to a poorer Rate of Climb.

In an extreme case, the aeroplane may simply *stagger* along in a nose-high attitude with a poor Rate of Climb (if any), facing the possibility of a stall, and with the risk of poor engine cooling because of the high power and reduced cooling airflow.

CLIMBING INTO CLOUD AFTER TAKE-OFF

The actual take-off ground run and lift-off will be made with external visual reference to the runway and its surroundings. Once airborne and climbing away from the ground, however, it is possible that visual reference to ground objects and to the natural horizon will be lost. This will occur if the aeroplane enters cloud, but it may also occur in conditions of poor visibility (e.g. mist, haze, smog, rain, snow or dust), or at night. **Between take-off and loss of external reference, the Pilot must have transferred his attention to the instruments.**

The importance of the instrument checks made prior to take-off is obvious, since these may now suddenly become the *only* source of attitude and performance information to the Pilot.

When instrument conditions are expected to be entered shortly after becoming airborne, carry out a visual take-off and stabilise the aeroplane in the climb-out, with climb power and climb attitude set, and with the aeroplane in trim for the climb speed. In other words, **make a normal visual take-off**. Then, *prior* to entering cloud or otherwise losing visual reference, **transfer your attention from external references to the instrument panel**.

Fig.4-7. Transfer Attention to the Instrument Panel shortly after Take-Off.

- Maintain pitch attitude and wings level on the AI, with the ball centred.
- Hold airspeed on the ASI with small pitch changes on the AI.
- Keep in trim.
- Maintain heading on the DI with small coordinated turns.
- Monitor climbing performance on the Altimeter and VSI.

Transferring attention to the Flight Instruments shortly after lift-off and when established in the climb-out is especially important at night, when there is little ground lighting or when low cloud might be encountered unexpectedly.

THE STRAIGHT DESCENT

With the correct power and attitude, the aeroplane should achieve the desired performance, which in this case is a straight descent. The **Control Instruments** for the descent are the same as for all man-oeuvres:
- the **Power Indicator**, used by the Pilot to set or remove power with the throttle;
- the **Attitude Indicator**, used to set pitch attitude with the elevator (slightly below the horizon bar for a powered descent, and typically one or two bar widths below the horizon bar for the glide).

TO ENTER A DESCENT

As in visual flight, the procedure for entering a descent on instruments is P-A-T: Power–Attitude–Trim. Reduce the **power** by placing the Mixture Control to *RICH* (fully in), the Carburettor Control to *HOT* (fully out) if the power reduction is significant, and smoothly move the throttle out until the desired descent power is set. Back pressure on the control column and rudder pressure will be required to counteract the "pitch down/yaw right" tendency as power is reduced. Keep the wings level with aileron, and the Balance Ball centred with rudder pressure, to ensure that heading is maintained.

Hold height until airspeed reduces to that desired, and then lower the **pitch attitude** one or two bar widths beneath the horizon bar to maintain airspeed. (If descent speed is to be the same as the level speed, then the power reduction and the lowering of pitch attitude on the AI should be simultaneous.) Hold the pitch attitude and allow the airspeed to settle, then make any minor pitch adjustments required, and **trim**. It is a good idea to make an initial coarse trim adjustment after the power and attitude have been selected, followed by a finer trim adjustment once the precise airspeed is achieved and maintained.

Descent Power, Hold Height ▪ ▪ At Descent Speed, Lower Pitch Attitude, and Trim ▪

Fig.4-8. Enter the Descent with Power Reduction, Attitude and Trim.

The descent performance, i.e. the **vertical performance**, is monitored on:
• the Altimeter;
• the Vertical Speed Indicator; and
• the Air Speed Indicator.

With a smooth transition from level flight to a descent, the VSI will show a downward trend, and then the Altimeter reading will start to decrease. The VSI will eventually indicate a rate appropriate to the stabilised descent airspeed and pitch attitude for the power set.

Fig.4-9. Monitoring Descent Performance.

MAINTAINING THE DESCENT

Keeping the wings level with aileron and the ball centred with rudder pressure will ensure that Heading is maintained, which can be verified on the Direction Indicator. With descent power set (and this is often throttle fully closed), the Pilot achieves the precise descent airspeed desired with slight adjustments to pitch attitude on the AI using elevator. **The Air Speed Indicator is the primary performance instrument in the descent (as in the climb) to verify that pitch attitude is correct.**

Situation: AIRSPEED LOW	Situation: AIRSPEED HIGH
Remedy: LOWER THE PITCH ATTITUDE	Remedy: RAISE THE PITCH ATTITUDE

Fig.4-10. Make Minor Pitch Attitude Adjustments to Maintain Descent Airspeed.

Once established in the descent, any fine adjustments to pitch attitude should be confined to just one quarter or one half bar widths. **If the descent airspeed is correct, then the pitch attitude is correct.** If the airspeed is low, then the pitch attitude is too high and should be lowered slightly. Conversely, if the airspeed is too high, then the pitch attitude should be raised slightly. Once the airspeed has settled to its new value, any steady control pressure can be trimmed off.

If the power is kept constant, then a pitch attitude change is the only way of achieving a change in airspeed, and this will be accompanied by a change in the Rate of Descent. If a precise Rate of Descent is required, as well as a precise airspeed, then a combination of power and attitude is used (see later in the chapter).

In a prolonged descent with low power, thought should be given to clearing the engine every 1000 ft or so by applying 50% power for a few seconds. This will keep the engine and oil warm, avoid carbon fouling on the spark plugs, and ensure that the Carburettor Heat is still supplying warm air. Be prepared to counteract the pitch/yaw tendencies as power is changed.

As the desired altitude or flight level is approached, the Altimeter should be increasingly brought into the scan, and the subscale checked to ensure that the correct subscale setting (Regional QNH, 1013, Aerodrome QNH or QFE) is wound in.

LEVELLING OFF FROM A DESCENT ON INSTRUMENTS

The procedure for levelling off from a descent is P-A-T: Power–Attitude–Trim. As the desired altitude is approached, the focus for changes in pitch attitude shifts from the Air Speed Indicator to the Altimeter, the aim being to raise the pitch attitude to **capture the desired altitude**, and to use power to achieve the desired cruise speed. A suitable lead-in height is "10% of the Rate of Descent", which at RoD 400 ft/min would be 40 ft before reaching the desired altitude.

Commencing at the lead-in height, **smoothly apply cruise power (Carburettor Heat *COLD*), and gradually raise the pitch attitude** towards the level flight position on the AI, keeping the aeroplane in balance with rudder pressure. The VSI will show a gradually reducing descent rate, and movement of the Altimeter needle will slow down. The aim is to reduce the Rate of Descent to zero just as the desired altitude is captured. A fairly quick scan rate will help to make this a smooth and comfortable manoeuvre. Once established in level flight at the desired airspeed, **trim** off any steady pressures.

Apply Power, and Raise the Pitch Attitude

Hold Height, then Trim

Fig.4-11. Levelling off from a Descent.

Heading is monitored on the DI, and will remain constant if the wings are kept level and the Balance Ball centred. Heading corrections can be made using shallow coordinated turns. Minor adjustments to pitch attitude using the elevator will be required to maintain height. If a particular cruise airspeed is desired, then power adjustments may also be required.

If the cruise airspeed is significantly greater than the descent airspeed, then power can be added a little earlier than usual, say 100 ft before reaching the desired altitude, and the aeroplane can commence accelerating to be at or near the higher cruise speed just as levelling-out is completed.

CLIMBING AWAY FROM A DESCENT ON INSTRUMENTS

This is a very important instrument manoeuvre, since it is used when a Pilot elects to go-around from a missed approach to land, as well as at any other time he or she wishes to go directly from a descent into a climb. The procedure is still P-A-T: Power–Attitude–Trim, except that it is **climb power** and **climb attitude** that are selected, and the change in control pressures and **trim** will be much greater than in previous manoeuvres.

ON FINAL APPROACH

Apply Power,
select Attitude,
and Trim

Fig.4-12. Climbing away from a Descent.

A greater pitch/yaw tendency can be expected with the large power increase in the go-around, and this must be counteracted. In a genuine go-around, full power will probably be used (with Carburettor Heat *COLD* and Mixture *RICH*). Once established in the climb, it is acceptable to make a coarse trim adjustment, and then fine tune the trim as the aeroplane settles down in the climb.

For a go-around off final approach (perhaps because unexpected cloud has been encountered at a low level) then, associated with the application of climb power and the selection of a suitable pitch attitude, the Pilot may also have to think about retracting the undercarriage and raising the flaps.

DESCENDING AT A PARTICULAR RATE

Airspeed in the descent at constant power is controlled with small pitch attitude changes, using the ASI as the primary performance instrument. Rate of Descent is shown directly on the VSI, or can be determined from the Clock and Altimeter.

The desired **airspeed** and **Rate of Descent** can be achieved by using a combination of **power** and **attitude**. Again, it is the interplay of power and attitude that determines the performance of the aeroplane. If the Rate of Descent is too great, it can be reduced by raising the pitch attitude and increasing power to maintain the same airspeed. Retrimming to relieve steady control pressures will be necessary once the aeroplane has settled into the new descent.

Fig.4-13. Reducing the Rate of Descent.

Conversely, the Rate of Descent can be increased by simultaneously lowering the pitch attitude and reducing power to maintain the same airspeed.

If the Pilot cannot reduce power because the throttle is already fully closed, then the Rate of Descent can be increased by other means:
- by lowering the pitch attitude and accepting a higher airspeed; or
- by increasing Drag, which can be achieved by lowering flaps, lowering the landing gear, or deploying spoilers if fitted.

THE PRECISION APPROACH

The Precision Approach will most likely be covered in the latter stages of your instrument training. It follows from what has just been discussed to provide a general description here.

The Precision Approach is a very precise instrument descent towards the touchdown zone on a runway. If the runway is not sighted by a certain minimum altitude, then a go-around is made; if the runway is sighted and the aeroplane is in a position to be landed, then a landing may be made.

The most common Precision Approach in instrument flying is achieved using the electronic Instrument Landing System (ILS) that provides:

- guidance in azimuth (left or right of the extended runway centreline); and

- approach slope guidance (referred to as the *glideslope* even though the aeroplane will not in fact be gliding, but in a powered descent).

The ILS glideslope is an inclined surface, typically 3° or 1:20 to the horizontal, that intersects the runway in the touchdown zone, usually about 300 metres in from the threshold. It is generally intercepted 2000 ft or 3000 ft Above Aerodrome Level, some 7 to 10 nm from the aerodrome and in line with the runway. The position of the glideslope relative to the aeroplane is displayed to the Pilot in the cockpit on an instrument associated with the VHF-NAV radio.

Fig.4-14. The Glideslope onto the Touchdown Zone of a Runway.

Maintaining the glideslope at the desired airspeed during an instrument approach is one of the major tasks of an Instrument Pilot, but this task is very similar to maintaining straight and level cruise flight. In both cases, the Pilot is trying to direct the aeroplane along a particular surface (horizontal for level flight, sloping for the approach) whilst maintaining a particular airspeed. The easiest control technique in both cases is:
- hold the glideslope (or height) with elevator;
- hold the airspeed with throttle.

As always, *power* and *attitude* (controlled by throttle and elevator respectively) determine the *performance* of the aeroplane. Often a change in one will necessitate a change in the other, but it is still easier to separate the functions in your own mind as stated above – maintain glideslope with attitude and airspeed with power.

Fig.4-15. An Accurate Approach to Land.

5

TURNING ON INSTRUMENTS

The aim of a turn is to change heading. This is achieved by banking the aeroplane and tilting the Lift force produced by the wings. The horizontal component of the tilted Lift force (known as the centripetal force) pulls the aeroplane into the turn.

If height is to be maintained, the vertical component of the tilted Lift force must be increased to equal the Weight. This is achieved with back pressure on the control column to increase the Angle of Attack (i.e. raise the pitch attitude), thereby increasing the Lift generated by the wings.

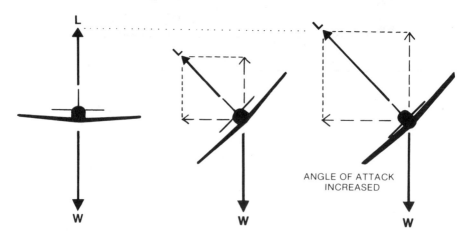

Fig.5-1. Lift must be increased to maintain Height in a Level Turn.

A consequence of the increased Lift is increased Induced Drag. The aeroplane will therefore slow down unless power is applied. In a medium turn, the loss of a few knots is usually acceptable, and so additional power is not normally applied. The airspeed loss is regained fairly quickly once the aeroplane is returned to straight and level flight.

BANK ANGLE AND RATE OF TURN

The Standard Rate of turn in instrument flying is **Rate 1**, with the heading of the aeroplane changing at **3°/sec**. At Rate 1, it will therefore take 30 seconds to turn through a heading change of 90°, 1 minute to turn through 180°, and 2 minutes to turn through 360°.

The rate of turn is a function of airspeed and bank angle, a higher airspeed requiring a greater bank angle to achieve the same rate of turn. A very quick method of estimating the bank angle required for a Rate 1 turn is 'airspeed/10 + 7'. For instance, at an airspeed of 80 kt, the bank angle for a Rate 1 turn is '80/10 + 7' = 8 + 7 = 15° bank angle, whereas at 150 kt it is 22°. If you prefer, you can simply **drop the last numeral of the airspeed and then add 7**. For instance, at 125 kt, the bank angle required for a Rate 1 turn is 12 + 7 = 19°.

It is permissible to use a turn in excess of Rate 1, but it is strongly advised not to exceed a bank angle of 30° in instrument conditions (although your Instructor may use steep turns during your training to give you practice in coordination of eyes, hands and feet).

BE IN TRIM BEFORE COMMENCING THE TURN

A turn is usually commenced from straight flight. It can be flown more accurately if the aeroplane, prior to being banked, is exactly on height, on speed, and **in trim**. There is no requirement to retrim during the turn, since it will only be a transient manoeuvre and the aeroplane will most likely be returned to straight flight fairly quickly.

IN VISUAL CONDITIONS, KEEP A GOOD LOOK OUT

A good Look Out is essential in visual flight but, in cloud with zero visibility, there is little point. A surprising amount of a typical instrument flight will occur in visual conditions, however, and a good Look Out then shows good airmanship. During training, the Instructor will act as Safety Pilot and maintain a good Look Out for you.

ROLL-IN AND ROLL-OUT RATE

All instrument flying should be smooth and unhurried. Turns should be entered at a comfortable rate with coordinated aileron and rudder pressure, with time allowed to check the Attitude Indicator for bank angle and the Balance Ball for balance. As training progresses, and the rate of scanning and interpreting the instruments increases, roll-in and roll-out of turns can occur at a faster rate if desired. **Strive to achieve a fairly constant rate of roll-in and roll-out for all turns**, which will make it easier to judge when to commence the roll-out onto a precise heading.

Part (i) – THE MEDIUM LEVEL TURN

ROLLING INTO A MEDIUM LEVEL TURN ON INSTRUMENTS

Note the position of the Index Aeroplane on the Attitude Indicator in steady straight and level flight before entering the turn, and then **roll into the turn at a comfortable roll rate with coordinated aileron and rudder pressure.** At the desired bank angle, the roll-in can be stopped by neutralising the ailerons and keeping the ball centred with rudder pressure, and then holding a steady bank angle.

Early in the roll in, the pitch attitude can remain the same as before entry but, as the bank angle increases, a height loss will be seen on the VSI and Altimeter unless **the pitch attitude is raised slightly with back pressure.** The VSI is the best guide in smooth air for correct pitch attitude in the level turn, since it will show a tendency to depart from height before the Altimeter registers any change. In rough air, however, the VSI fluctuates and is of less value, the Altimeter then becoming the primary guide to correct pitch attitude.

Fig.5-2. Rolling into a Level Turn.

MAINTAINING A MEDIUM LEVEL TURN ON INSTRUMENTS

Bank angle and pitch attitude are maintained on the AI, which is a **control** instrument, and the ball is kept centred. The *bank pointer* on the AI will give an accurate indication of the degrees of bank angle.

Turning performance can be confirmed on the **Turn Coordinator**, which is graduated to indicate a Rate 1 turn of 3°/sec. Small bank angle corrections, when required, can be made on the AI using aileron. There is generally no need to check the **Direction Indicator** until well-established in the turn and approaching the desired heading (which at Rate 1 will be 30 seconds away for a 90° change of heading).

Fig.5-3. Maintaining a Level Turn on Instruments.

Confirm **vertical performance** on the VSI and Altimeter, making any small pitch corrections on the AI using elevator. In general, a slight back pressure will be required, increasing as the bank angle becomes steeper.

Confirm **balance** with the Balance Ball, and keep it centred with rudder pressure. Confirm **airspeed** with the Air Speed Indicator and be prepared for a loss of several knots. If a constant airspeed is required, then increase power slightly.

It is difficult to hold bank angle, height and balance perfectly, but a good Instrument Pilot will notice trends very quickly and act to correct them. **Aim for perfection**, and at least stay well within the limits of +/–5° bank angle and +/–100 ft of altitude during the turn. Remember that the **performance instruments** (VSI, Altimeter, Turn Coordinator) may indicate a need for change, but that these changes should be made with reference to the **control instruments**. In particular, **use the Attitude Indicator for any pitch attitude or bank angle changes**. The throttle can be used for airspeed control in the level turn, if required.

ROLLING OUT OF A LEVEL TURN ON INSTRUMENTS

Commence the roll-out a few degrees before the desired heading. A suitable lead is by one half of the bank angle. For example, if the bank angle in the turn is 20°, commence roll-out 10° before reaching the desired heading. Aim to level the wings just as the desired heading is reached.

Roll out of the turn at a comfortable roll rate with coordinated aileron and rudder pressure. The **Attitude Indicator** is monitored for control of the bank angle during the early part of the roll-out, with the **Direction Indicator** being monitored to check that the desired heading is being achieved.

Vertical performance is confirmed on the **VSI and Altimeter**, with small pitch adjustments on the AI to maintain height. The back pressure applied on entering the turn can now be released, and the pitch attitude lowered slightly.

Commencing Roll-Out ▪▪▪ ▮ Wings Level, and Height Maintained ▬

Fig.5-4. Rolling Out of a Turn.

After the roll-out, the scan should revert to the normal straight and level scan:
- use the AI to set the pitch attitude and hold the wings level;
- keep the Balance Ball centred; and confirm:
- vertical performance on the VSI and Altimeter (hold height with elevator);
- directional performance on the Direction Indicator and Turn Coordinator (adjust heading with gentle coordinated turns if necessary); and
- monitor airspeed on the ASI (controlling with power if necessary).

The few knots of **airspeed** that were lost in the turn will gradually return. If additional power was applied in the turn to maintain airspeed, however, it should be removed in the roll-out to avoid an unwanted airspeed increase.

INSTRUMENT TURNS ONTO A SPECIFIC HEADING

Turns onto a particular heading can be achieved using:
- the Direction Indicator;
- Timed Turns, with the Clock and Turn Coordinator, knowing that Rate 1 is 3°/second; or
- the Magnetic Compass.

The primary source of direction information in the aeroplane is the Magnetic Compass, but this is an awkward instrument to use, especially when the aeroplane is turning and causing it to read incorrectly. Since directional information is very important in a turn, Pilots are provided with a more stable instrument, the **Direction Indicator**, driven by a gyroscope and **not** subject to turning errors. The DI occupies a position within the main area of the Instrument Panel where it can easily be scanned by the Pilot, whereas the Magnetic Compass is well away, generally somewhere above the cockpit coaming panel near the windscreen, not out of sight, but certainly outside the primary scanning area.

Using the Direction Indicator

Unlike the Magnetic Compass, the DI does **not** automatically align itself with Magnetic North. For its reading to be meaningful, **ensure that the DI is realigned with the Magnetic Compass during steady straight and level flight every 10 or 15 minutes**.

Before commencing a turn, the DI can be used to decide whether to turn left or right onto the new heading. Usually, the turn is made in the shorter direction, but not always. In a *teardrop* turn carried out in certain instrument manoeuvres, the turn is made in the longer direction and exceeds 180°.

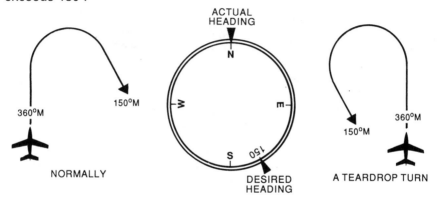

Fig.5-5. Orientate Yourself, and decide which Way to turn.

Having decided which way to turn, the DI need not be scanned until the aeroplane is approaching the desired heading. The roll-out should be commenced a few degrees before the desired heading is reached. **Anticipate the heading by half the bank angle.** For instance, if the bank angle is 20°, commence rolling out 10° before the required heading is reached – the roll-out for a right turn onto 150°M commencing as the DI passes through 140°. Aim to level the wings just as the desired heading is reached.

Settle into normal straight flight, checking direction on the DI and height on the VSI and Altimeter. Hold the desired heading accurately by making small coordinated turns as needed. Aim for perfection, and certainly stay within the limits of +/–5° of heading.

Timed Turns using the Turn Coordinator and Clock

Timed Turns are very useful in instrument flying. It is good habit to develop the skill of estimating **time to turn**, as explained at the beginning of the chapter. Rate 1 is 3°/second, so a 45° turn at Rate 1 will take 15 seconds. A Rate 1 turn is achieved at a particular bank angle dependent on airspeed (airspeed/10 + 7, i.e. 16° bank angle at 90 kt), and can be monitored on the Turn Coordinator (or Turn Indicator).

A 15° change of heading at Rate 1 will therefore require 15/3 = 5 seconds (or a little longer allowing for roll-in and roll-out), 30° will take 10 seconds, 45° will take 15 seconds, 90° will take 30 seconds, 180° will take 1 minute, and 360° will take 2 minutes. By establishing a Rate 1 turn on the **Turn Coordinator** and measuring the time on a **Clock**, very accurate turns can be made without reference to the DI or Magnetic Compass.

Fig.5-6. Timed Turns with the Clock and Turn Coordinator can be very Accurate.

It is usual to use Rate 1 turns in instrument flying but, especially if the heading change required is only small, Rate 1/2 on the Turn Coordinator could be used in which case the heading would change at only 1.5°/sec, a 12° heading change requiring 8 seconds.

To carry out a Rate 1 timed turn:

1. Calculate heading change and divide by 3 (e.g. a right turn from 340°M onto 100°M is 120° change at 3°/sec = 120/3 sec = 40 sec);

2. Start the stopwatch or note the reading of the second hand (say against 12, 3, 6 or 9 to make it easier for you), and roll into the turn with the coordinated use of aileron and rudder, achieving the estimated bank angle for a Rate 1 turn.

3. Confirm **turning performance** is Rate 1 on the Turn Coordinator, and make slight adjustments to bank angle on the AI if required. Confirm **vertical performance** on the VSI and Altimeter.

4. Commence the roll-out when the second hand reaches the calculated number of seconds. If the roll-in and roll-out rates are approximately the same, they will compensate each other, and will not require consideration.

5. At the end of the timed turn, with the wings level and the Balance Ball centred, check heading on the Direction Indicator, or on the Magnetic Compass once it settles down. Make minor adjustments to heading with gentle coordinated turns.

Calibration of the Turn Coordinator

The accuracy of the Turn Coordinator can be checked by banking the aeroplane until the Turn Coordinator indicates Rate 1 precisely, and then timing the rate of actual heading change using the Direction Indicator and Clock. In 10 seconds, if the turn is exactly at Rate 1, the heading should change by 30°. If the aeroplane only turns through 27° in this time, then the Pilot knows that the Turn Coordinator is over-reading in that direction, and to increase bank until the Turn Coordinator is indicating slightly more than Rate 1 for a Rate 1 turn in fact to occur.

Conversely, if the heading changes say 34° in the 10 seconds, then the Pilot knows to decrease bank until the Turn Coordinator indicates slightly less than Rate 1 for a Rate 1 turn in fact to occur. The Pilot can make allowances for any known peculiarities of his particular Turn Coordinator.

Using the Magnetic Compass

This is the least preferred method of making accurate turns, since the Magnetic Compass suffers considerable indication errors in a turn. It can, however, be used to achieve at least an approximate heading, which can then be checked once the Compass has settled down in steady straight flight and the oscillations have ceased.

The construction of the Magnetic Compass is such that, when an aeroplane is turning (especially through North or South), it will give false indications of magnetic heading. To allow for Magnetic Compass errors **in the Northern Hemisphere**, observe the following:

(a) When turning onto Northerly Headings, roll out when the Magnetic Compass indicates approximately 30° **before** the desired heading (i.e. undershoot on North).

(b) When turning onto Southerly Headings, roll out when the Magnetic Compass indicates approximately 30° **past** the desired heading (i.e. overshoot on South).

These allowances should be reduced when turning onto headings well removed from North and South (in fact when turning onto East or West no allowance at all need be made).

NOTE: In the Southern Hemisphere, these allowances must be reversed (i.e. overshoot on North, and undershoot on South).

Part (ii) – CLIMBING TURNS

The technique of flying a climbing turn is the same as for a level turn, except that airspeed (rather than height) is maintained.

ROLLING INTO A CLIMBING TURN ON INSTRUMENTS

Note the position of the Index Aeroplane relative to the horizon on the **AI**, and then roll into the turn with coordinated aileron and rudder until the estimated bank angle is reached. Monitor the **ASI**, and be prepared to lower the pitch attitude slightly to maintain a constant climbing airspeed. There will be a natural tendency for the aeroplane to drop its nose when it is banked, so (even though the pitch attitude in the climbing turn is slightly lower than when the wings are level) slight back pressure may have to be applied to prevent the nose dropping too far.

Fig.5-7. Entering a Climbing Turn.

MAINTAINING A CLIMBING TURN ON INSTRUMENTS

The **AI** is used to maintain bank angle and pitch attitude, with the Balance Ball kept centred with rudder pressure. Airspeed is monitored on the **ASI** and, if the airspeed is slightly lower than desired, the pitch attitude should be lowered slightly on the AI. The ASI is the primary indicator in the climb that correct pitch attitude is being held.

The **vertical performance** will be less than in the straight climb, indicated by a reduced Rate of Climb on the VSI, and slower movement of the Altimeter needle.

The **turning performance** can be monitored on the Turn Coordinator, with the bank angle being altered with reference to the AI to achieve the desired rate of turn. The Balance Ball is kept centred with rudder pressure. The Direction Indicator should be brought increasingly into the scan as the desired heading is approached.

ROLLING OUT OF A CLIMBING TURN

As the desired heading on the DI is approached, roll off bank with coordinated aileron and rudder, aiming to level the wings on the **AI** just as heading is reached. Monitor airspeed on the **ASI**, and select a slightly higher pitch attitude on the AI to maintain climbing airspeed.

Fig.5-8. Maintaining a Climbing Turn. Fig.5-9. Rolling Out of a Climbing Turn.

Part (iii) – DESCENDING TURNS

The technique of flying a descending turn is the same as for a level turn, except that airspeed (rather than height) is maintained. This makes the ASI an important performance guide to the correct pitch attitude.

ROLLING INTO A DESCENDING TURN

Note the position of the Index Aeroplane relative to the horizon on the **AI**, and then roll into the turn with coordinated aileron and rudder until the estimated bank angle is reached. Monitor the **ASI** and be prepared to lower the pitch attitude slightly to maintain a constant descent airspeed. There will be a natural tendency for the aeroplane to drop its nose when it is banked, so (even though the pitch attitude in the descending turn is slightly lower than when the wings are level) slight back pressure may have to be applied to stop the nose dropping too far.

Fig.5-10. Entering a Descending Turn.

MAINTAINING A DESCENDING TURN

The **AI** is used to maintain bank angle and pitch attitude, with the Balance Ball kept centred with rudder pressure. Airspeed is monitored on the **ASI** and, if the airspeed is slightly lower than desired, the pitch attitude should be lowered on the AI. If the airspeed is slightly high, then the pitch attitude should be raised.

The ASI is the primary indicator that correct pitch attitude is being maintained in the descent.

The **vertical performance** of the aeroplane can be monitored on the VSI, and Altimeter. An increased Rate of Descent in a descending turn is to be expected but, if desired, this can be reduced by the addition of power and the selection of a slightly higher pitch attitude.

The **turning performance** can be monitored on the Turn Coordinator, with the bank angle being altered with reference to the AI to achieve the desired rate of turn. The Balance Ball is kept centred with rudder pressure. The Direction Indicator should be brought increasingly into the scan as the desired heading is approached.

ROLLING OUT OF A DESCENDING TURN

As the desired heading on the DI is approached, roll off bank with coordinated aileron and rudder, aiming to level the wings on the **AI** just as heading is reached. Monitor airspeed on the **ASI**, and select a slightly higher pitch attitude on the AI to maintain descent airspeed.

Fig.5-11.
Maintaining a Descending Turn.

Fig.5-12.
Rolling Out of a Descending Turn.

Part (iv) – STEEP TURNS

Rate 1 is the typical instrument flying turn but, on occasions, turns up to 30° bank angle may be used when required. Any turn steeper than this in instrument flying may be considered a **steep turn.**

It is poor airmanship to exceed a 30° bank angle in normal operations, since the required coordination of hands, eyes and feet makes accurate flying more difficult. The end result, if it gets out of hand, could be a spiral dive.

Steep turns under instrument conditions with an Instructor on board, however, can be good practice in:
- improving basic flying skills;
- speeding up the scan rate; and
- recovering from flight attitudes neither usual, nor desirable, in normal instrument flight (see later chapter on Unusual Attitudes).

THE STEEP LEVEL TURN

Tilting the Lift force as the aeroplane banks will reduce its vertical component. **Back pressure** on the control column is therefore required to increase the angle of attack of the wings and increase the magnitude of the Lift force so that its vertical component will still balance the Weight and avoid a loss of height (monitored on the VSI and Altimeter).

The Load Factor (Lift/Weight) increases significantly in a steep turn – two consequences being a greater g-loading on the aeroplane and Pilot, and a higher stalling speed.

The increased angle of attack in a steep turn means not only increased Lift, but also greatly increased Drag. Airspeed will decrease significantly unless **additional power** is applied (monitored on the ASI).

Stall speed increases
40% in a 60° banked turn

Maintain airspeed with
added power

Fig.5-13. A Steep Turn requires Increased Lift to maintain Height, and Increased Power to maintain Airspeed.

PRIOR TO ENTERING A STEEP LEVEL TURN

Achieve straight and level flight at the desired height and airspeed, and be in trim. Note the heading on the Direction Indicator, and decide which way you will turn and onto what heading. Ask the Safety Pilot to check outside for other aircraft.

ROLLING INTO A STEEP LEVEL TURN ON INSTRUMENTS

Roll into the steep turn with coordinated aileron and rudder the same as you would for a medium turn except that, as the bank angle increases through 30°:
- progressively increase back pressure to raise the pitch attitude on the AI to maintain height;
- progressively add power to maintain airspeed.

Fig.5-14. Entering and Maintaining a Steep Turn.

MAINTAINING A STEEP LEVEL TURN ON INSTRUMENTS

Increase your scan rate of the instruments as the turn steepens, to cope with all of the variables. The secret of an accurate steep level turn on instruments is to:

- have a good scan;
- hold the correct bank angle and pitch attitude on the Attitude Indicator; and
- maintain airspeed with power.

Control of the bank angle and balance is achieved with coordinated use of aileron and rudder, with reference to the **Attitude Indicator** and the **Balance Ball**. The Turn Coordinator is of little use, since the steep turn will be well in excess of Rate 1, however it is still useful as an indication of the direction of the turn, left or right. The desired bank angle is held on the AI.

Pitch Control is more difficult to achieve than bank control, because of the considerably increased back pressure required (and also, for some people, the slightly unpleasant g-forces that increase as back pressure is applied). The pitch attitude is higher in the steep turn than in level flight. **Vertical performance** can be monitored on the VSI and Altimeter to ensure that height is being maintained. **The primary performance indicator that the pitch attitude held on the AI is correct is the Altimeter, supported by the VSI.**

Airspeed control is achieved with the throttle. If insufficient additional power is applied, then airspeed can diminish quite rapidly. The power should be increased progressively as the bank angle steepens during the roll-in, and the Pilot should imagine that there is a direct link from the Air Speed Indicator to his hand on the throttle – any hint of an airspeed loss requiring an immediate increase in power. **The primary performance indicator for power in level flight (including turns) is the ASI.** There is no need to monitor the Power Indicator directly unless there is a possibility of exceeding limitations.

Loss of height will result if insufficient back pressure is applied as the steep turn is entered, the nose will drop, the VSI and Altimeter will indicate a rapid loss of height, and the ASI will indicate an increasing airspeed. Simply increasing back pressure at a steep bank angle when the nose has dropped will only tighten the turn without raising the nose.

The recommended technique if height is lost is:
- reduce bank angle with aileron;
- raise pitch attitude with elevator (back pressure); and
- re-apply bank.

Fig.5-15. Regaining a Height Loss in a Steep Turn.

If **height is being gained**:
- relax some of the back pressure, and lower the pitch attitude slightly; and/or
- steepen the bank angle slightly.

Extreme cases of nose high or nose low attitudes are considered shortly under the heading of Unusual Attitudes. They can result from a poorly flown steep turn, especially under instrument conditions, and especially when the Pilot has a slow scan rate or is not prepared to exert his authority over the aeroplane and make it do what exactly he wants.

ROLLING OUT OF THE STEEP LEVEL TURN ON INSTRUMENTS

If the aim is to roll out onto a particular heading, then approximately 30° lead should be allowed because of the high rate of turn. Roll out of the steep turn using coordinated aileron and rudder. Gradually release the back pressure on the control column and lower the pitch attitude on the AI to maintain height (as monitored on the VSI and Altimeter). Gradually reduce power to maintain the desired airspeed (as monitored on the ASI).

Fig.5-16. Rolling out of a Steep Level Turn.

STEEP DESCENDING TURNS

The steep descending turn is never flown in normal instrument flight operations, but it may be used during your training (with your Flying Instructor on board as Safety Pilot) as a practice manoeuvre to improve coordination. Note that there is no steep climbing turn, since this is beyond the performance capability of most training aircraft, and a useful Rate of Climb could not be maintained.

It is usual to allow airspeed to increase in a steep descending turn in order to maintain an adequate safety margin over the stalling speed (which increases during a turn). Typical speed increases, controlled by use of the elevator, are:

- 10 kt for a 45° bank in a steep descending turn; and
- 20 kt for a 60° bank in a steep descending turn.

ROLLING INTO A STEEP DESCENDING TURN ON INSTRUMENTS

From a steady descent, roll on bank with coordinated aileron and rudder. Keep the Balance Ball centred with whatever rudder pressure is required; in a gliding turn, there will be more rudder pressure required one way compared to the other because of the lack of a slipstream.

Lower the pitch attitude slightly on the AI, using elevator to maintain the desired nose position to achieve the higher airspeed. The nose will tend to drop in a descending turn and so, even though the pitch attitude on the Attitude Indicator will be lower to achieve a higher airspeed, some back pressure on the control column will be needed to stop the nose dropping too far.

MAINTAINING A STEEP DESCENDING TURN

Increase your scan rate as the turn steepens to cope with all of the variables. Hold the desired pitch attitude and bank angle with reference to the AI, and monitor the ASI closely. Control bank angle with coordinated use of aileron and rudder. Control pitch attitude on the AI with elevator to achieve the desired airspeed. The ASI is the primary indicator that pitch attitude is correct.

Fig.5-17. Maintaining a Steep Descending Turn.

If the pitch attitude is too low and the airspeed becomes excessive:
• reduce the bank angle on the AI using ailerons;
• raise the pitch attitude on the AI with elevator to reduce airspeed on the ASI; and
• re-apply the bank.

If the bank angle is not reduced, then simply applying back pressure may only serve to tighten the turn without decreasing airspeed, and the g-loading may increase beyond acceptable limits. A spiral dive can result if pitch attitude, bank angle and airspeed are not kept within acceptable limits.

The Rate of Descent in a Steep Descending Turn will increase significantly, not only because of the lower pitch attitude for the higher airspeed, but also because the tilting of the Lift force reduces its vertical component. If desired, the Rate of Descent can be controlled with power, and monitored on the VSI and Altimeter. Increasing power, and raising the pitch attitude to maintain airspeed, will result in a reduced Rate of Descent.

ROLLING OUT OF A STEEP DESCENDING TURN

With reference to the Attitude Indicator, roll-off bank with coordinated aileron and rudder, and select the slightly higher pitch attitude with elevator required for the straight descent. Monitor the ASI and adjust pitch attitude on the AI to achieve the desired airspeed. The ASI is the primary guide to a correct pitch attitude. If the aim is to roll out onto a particular heading, then approximately 30° lead should be allowed because of the rapid rate of turn.

A steep descending turn that is not monitored carefully can result in a spiral dive, an unusual attitude best avoided. How to recover from a spiral dive is covered in the section on Unusual Attitudes.

6

UNUSUAL ATTITUDES

An *Unusual Attitude* in instrument flying is any attitude not normally used during flight solely on instruments, including:

- bank angles in excess of 30°;
- nose-high attitudes with a decreasing airspeed; and
- nose-low attitudes with an increasing airspeed.

An unusual attitude may result from some **external influence** such as turbulence, or it can be induced by **pilot error**. For instance, if a Pilot becomes disoriented or confused (where am I?, which way is up?), or becomes preoccupied with other cockpit duties (such as radio calls, or the study of charts) at the expense of an adequate scan rate, or if he over-reacts or under-reacts on the controls, interprets the instruments incorrectly, or follows an instrument that has (unbeknowns to him) failed, then the aeroplane may enter an unusual attitude.

Whatever the cause of the unusual attitude, the immediate problem is to recognise exactly what the aeroplane is actually doing, and to return it safely to normal acceptable flight (generally straight and level flight). Analysis at a later time as to what lead to the event, however, should lead to avoidance of any reoccurence.

In unusual attitudes, the physiological sensations may be disconcerting, but do not allow these to influence either the recognition of the attitude, or the subsequent recovery action.

RECOGNISING AN UNUSUAL ATTITUDE

If you notice any unusual instrument indication or rate of change not expected in the normal gentle instrument flight manoeuvres, or if you experience unexpected g-forces or air noise, assume that the aeroplane could be in (or about to enter) an unusual attitude. **Increase the scan rate** to determine the attitude and/or if any instrument has malfunctioned.

If all instruments are functioning normally, then an **excessive bank angle** will be indicated *directly* on the AI, supported by an excessive rate of turn on the Turn Coordinator, and a rapidly turning DI. Which way the wings are banked can be determined from the AI, supported by the Turn Coordinator. (Be aware that some Attitude Indicators can topple and become unusable when the aeroplane is in an extreme attitude. This is discussed shortly.)

Fig.6-1. An Excessive Bank Angle.

A nose-low attitude will be indicated by a low pitch attitude on the AI, supported by descent indications on the Altimeter and VSI, and an increasing airspeed on the ASI. An excessive bank angle will often lead to a nose-low attitude as well, since the nose tends to drop naturally when the wings are banked. The result could be a spiral dive – a most undesirable unusual attitude that, uncorrected, can result in tragedy.

Fig.6-2. Nose-Low Unusual Attitudes.

If all instruments are functioning correctly, **a nose-high attitude** will be indicated by a high pitch attitude on the AI, supported by climb indications on the Altimeter and VSI, and a decreasing airspeed on the ASI. In an extreme nose-up attitude, however, a stall could result, with the VSI and Altimeter indicating a descent, and the ASI a low airspeed.

NOSE-HIGH AND BANKED   NOSE-HIGH AND STALLED

Fig.6-3. Nose-High Unusual Attitudes.

If any instrument has failed, then a **cross-check** of the others should enable the Pilot to isolate it and disregard its indications. For instance, if limits are exceeded the AI could topple and become unusable, which can happen in some aircraft as a result of the unusual attitude. Similarly, a suction failure in some aircraft can lead to both the AI and DI becoming unusable (a situation considered later in *Instrument Flight on a Limited Panel*). In such a case:

• nose-high or nose-low information can be derived from the ASI, Altimeter and VSI; and

• bank information can be derived from the Turn Coordinator.

Fig.6-4. Unusual Attitudes indicated by a Limited Panel.

In recognising an unusual attitude, the key points to establish are:

1. Is the aeroplane nose-high or nose-low?
2. Is it banked?

HAVING RECOGNISED THE UNUSUAL ATTITUDE FOR WHAT IT IS, DO NOT OVER-REACT

It is easy for an inexperienced Pilot to over-react to an unusual attitude with rapid and excessive control movements, since he does not expect to find himself in an unusual attitude during normal instrument flight. Over-reaction can lead to a worsened situation and, possibly, an overstressed airframe.

One purpose of instrument training, therefore, is to place the aeroplane into unusual attitudes on purpose and to develop recovery techniques that allow the Pilot, having recognised the nature of the unusual attitude, to return the aeroplane to normal flight calmly, quickly and safely.

Each unusual attitude, and the recovery, should be practised:
• in fully visual conditions with external references;
• on a full panel of instruments; and then
• on a limited panel of instruments.

It is possible that some AIs may topple during an unusual attitude and become unusable. The Pilot may suddenly have to revert to Limited Panel techniques quite unexpectedly. For this reason, we have included Limited Panel recovery techniques in this chapter for ease of reference after your training has been completed. During your training, however, your Flying Instructor may prefer to consider the Full Panel techniques alone at this stage, and then return to the Limited Panel later.

NOSE-LOW ATTITUDES WITH INCREASING AIRSPEED

If the pitch attitude is too low, then the airspeed will start to increase. In an extreme situation, the aeroplane may end up in a steep dive, either straight or spiral. If not corrected, the aeroplane may exceed VNE (the never-exceed speed shown on the ASI as a red line), possibly suffering excessive airframe stress in the dive and, if not handled correctly, in the recovery.

To reduce the rate at which the airspeed is increasing, and to avoid unnecessary loss of height, **reduce the power** with the throttle, even closing it completely if necessary. As well as reducing the Thrust as an accelerating force, this will increase Drag as a result of the now windmilling propeller, further reducing the tendency for airspeed to increase.

A steep bank angle and a nose-low attitude may develop into a spiral dive. If the control column is simply pulled back to raise the nose whilst the aeroplane is still steeply banked, then the spiral dive will be tightened without the descent being stopped. Therefore, **it is most important to level the wings** using the AI and the Turn Coordinator, changing a banked or spiral dive into a straight dive, before raising the pitch attitude to ease the aeroplane out of the dive.

Throttling back and rolling the wings level can be done simultaneously, with the aeroplane being kept in balance with rudder pressure. Once the wings are level, the aeroplane will be in a straight dive. Then, **to ease the aeroplane out of the straight dive, smoothly raise the pitch attitude** through the level flight position on the AI.

There is a danger of overstressing the airframe at high airspeeds with large and sudden elevator control movements (see the V-n diagram in APM Vol 4), hence the instruction to 'ease' the aeroplane out of the dive with firm elevator pressure rather than with sudden and large movements of the elevator control.

On reaching the level flight attitude, the airspeed will 'check' (i.e. stopping increasing), and the Altimeter will move from a descent indication to a level (or even climbing) indication. The VSI initially may be erratic and unusable due to the large change in attitude (possibly showing a reversed reading), although it will settle down fairly quickly to a steady and usable reading once the recovery is completed.

After the initial recovery actions have been taken, the rate of scanning the flight instruments should be increased to ensure that there is no over-controlling, which is a possibility especially since the control pressures at the start of the recovery (when the airspeed is high) may be quite heavy.

Fig.6-5. Regaining Normal Flight using the Full Panel.

To regain lost height after recovering from a spiral dive or a straight dive, apply power, raise the pitch attitude to the climbing attitude and commence a normal climb.

Once in steady straight flight, the Direction Indicator should be checked to ensure that it is aligned with the Magnetic Compass.

NOTES:

1. The airspeed will continue to increase until the aircraft passes through the level flight attitude, when it will check (i.e. stop increasing).

2. Unless the wings are fairly level when the Pilot raises the pitch attitude with back pressure, the Turn Indicator will show an exaggerated turn rate, and the spiral will tighten. This is undesirable. **Always level the wings before easing out of the dive**.

3. With the fairly large initial pitch up control movement to achieve the level flight attitude, the VSI may **initially** show a reverse indication, i.e. an initial increase in the Rate of Descent, even though the reverse is in fact occurring. Excessive attitude corrections can cause VSI indication reversal, and so this instrument should be disregarded in the first few seconds following a large pitch change.

On only a **Limited Panel**, with no usable information available from the AI, the indication of a nose-low attitude will be an increasing airspeed on the ASI, with secondary information from the Altimeter and VSI showing a high and possibly increasing Rate of Descent, and with bank angle (if any) indicated on the Turn Coordinator.

The recovery manoeuvre is the same visually on a Full Panel or on a Limited Panel, the only difference being the instruments available from which to derive information. On a Limited Panel:
- reduce power;
- level the wings (using the Turn Coordinator on a Limited Panel);
- ease out of the dive (level pitch attitude indicated on the Limited Panel when the airspeed checks, and the Altimeter stabilises).

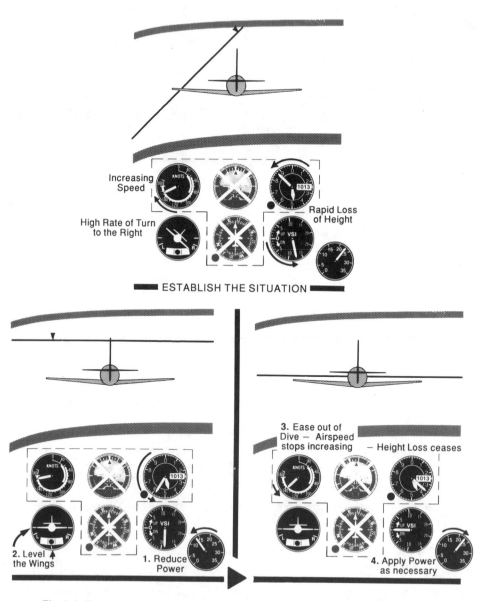

Fig.6-6. Recovery from 'Nose-Low and High Airspeed' on a Limited Panel.

NOSE-HIGH ATTITUDES WITH DECREASING AIRSPEED

If the pitch attitude is too high, then the airspeed will start to decrease. A high pitch attitude will be shown on the AI, with the ASI indicating a decreasing airspeed, and the Altimeter and VSI showing a climb (depending upon the power used). Whether the wings are level or not will be shown on the AI and the Turn Coordinator.

In an extreme situation the aeroplane may stall, either wings level or with a wing drop, and the Altimeter and VSI will show a descent. The nose attitude may be high to begin with, but may drop, depending upon the aeroplane. A vigilant Instrument Pilot, however, will never allow the aeroplane to inadvertently approach a stall. Recovery action will have been initiated well ahead of the stall occurring.

The recovery manoeuvre when the aeroplane is in a **nose-high/airspeed reducing** attitude, but not in or near a stalled condition, is to **simultaneously increase power, lower the pitch attitude and roll the wings level on the AI with coordinated use of aileron and rudder**. Which wing (if any) is low, is indicated by the AI and the Turn Coordinator.

The level flight attitude, when this has been achieved, will be shown directly on the AI. It will also be indicated by the fact that the airspeed change is checked, i.e. it stops decreasing. The Altimeter reading will also stabilise. Following a large pitch attitude change, however, the VSI may be erratic, and even show a reversed reading, so it should initially be disregarded.

Fig.6-7. Regaining Normal Flight Using the Full Panel.

Having regained normal steady straight flight following recovery from an unusual attitude, the Pilot should check the Direction Indicator against the Magnetic Compass, to ensure that it is aligned.

Using only a **Limited Panel** with no usable information available from the AI, the indication of a nose-high attitude will be:
• a decreasing airspeed on the ASI, with supporting information from the Altimeter and VSI; and with
• bank angle (if any) indicated on the Turn Coordinator.

Recovery is the same, with the level pitch attitude being indicated on the ASI when the airspeed is checked and stops decreasing, and the Altimeter stabilises. The wings-level bank attitude is achieved when the wings are level on the Turn Coordinator.

Fig.6-8. 'Nose-High and Decreasing Airspeed' on the Limited Panel.

NOSE HIGH, AND APPROACHING THE STALL

A 'nose-high/airspeed decreasing' situation can result ultimately in a stall. In this situation, it should be possible to regain normal flight, with the maximum loss of altitude being 50 ft or less.

Fig.6-9. Recovering from the Incipient Stall.

There is little danger of overstressing the airframe at low airspeeds with large elevator control movements, because the aeroplane will stall before any load limits are reached (see the V-n diagram in APM Vol 4).

However, if the recovery from a nose-high attitude is not followed through correctly and the aeroplane placed into a normal acceptable flight condition, a nose-low attitude could develop, resulting in either a straight or spiral dive with rapidly increasing airspeed, from which recovery action from a 'nose-low/airspeed increasing' situation (as previously discussed) will be required.

Using only a **Limited Panel**, with no usable information available from the AI, the indication of a nose-high attitude approaching the stall will be a decreasing airspeed on the ASI, with secondary information from the Altimeter and VSI (which may show a decreasing Rate of Climb or even a descent). Any departure from wings level will be indicated by deflections on the Turn Coordinator.

The recovery procedure is the same. Simultaneously:
- lower the nose to the level pitch attitude (or lower if necessary – with the level pitch attitude on a Limited Panel being indicated when the airspeed checks and stops decreasing, and the Altimeter stabilises); and
- apply full power.

- Prevent further yaw with rudder and, once certain flying speed is achieved on the ASI, level the wings on the Turn Coordinator with coordinated aileron and rudder.

Fig.6-10. Stall Recovery on a Limited Panel.

7

NORMAL INSTRUMENT FLIGHT ON A LIMITED OR PARTIAL PANEL

For the exercises on the *Limited (or Partial) Panel,* one or more of the flight instruments is assumed to have failed. It is possible to cope with this situation quite comfortably because, even though there is less information available, the aeroplane will fly exactly the same and respond in exactly the same way to any Pilot inputs.

CROSS-CHECK AVAILABLE INSTRUMENTS

If any instrument has failed, then a **cross-check** of the other instruments should enable the Pilot to isolate it and disregard its indications. The AI is the *Master Instrument,* and its loss is perhaps the most difficult to cope with. The AI could be lost as a result of its power source failing (electrical or suction), or its gyroscope could topple and become unusable during an extreme unusual attitude.

SUCTION FAILURE

In many aircraft, both the AI and DI are powered by suction. Their gyroscopes are driven by an airflow induced through them by the vacuum system. A suction failure could lead to the loss of both of these instruments. This is the common Limited Panel situation (unusable Attitude Indicator and Direction Indicator). In such a case, the aircraft is controlled by reference to the **performance instruments**:

1. Nose-high or nose-low information can be derived from the ASI, Altimeter and VSI.
2. Bank information can be derived from the Turn Coordinator, with the Magnetic Compass available to supply heading information.
3. Balance, as always, is shown by the simple Balance Ball that never suffers a power failure.

ELECTRICAL FAILURE

An **electrical failure** may make electrically-driven instruments unusable. This could include the Attitude Indicator, the Direction Indicator and the Turn Coordinator. An electrical failure could also make the Pitot Heater unavailable, leading to icing problems with the pitot-static system unless the Pilot avoids icing conditions.

Electrical failure will make the radios unusable unless there is an emergency source of power available (e.g. the battery). Instrument navigation without VHF-NAV or the ADF is difficult. Radar assistance may be requested, but this requires VHF-COM to be working.

Following an electrical failure, check that the Master Switch is *ON,* and check any circuit breakers or fuses for the particular item. Do not interrupt your scan of the operating flight instruments for more than a few seconds at a time. If an electrically-powered instrument has indeed failed and cannot be restored, then cross-checking the other instruments will help to cover its loss.

PITOT TUBE BLOCKAGE

A *damaged* pitot tube will affect the Air Speed Indicator. So will an *iced-up* pitot tube, but the use of electric Pitot Heat in icing conditions will generally prevent the occurrence of icing problems in the pitot-static system. A more serious situation is a *pitot cover* that has not been removed prior to flight. As well as probably being impossible to remedy in flight, it indicates that the Pilot has been derelict in his duties at the pre-flight stage.

Pre-flight checks of the pitot tube are very important. Remove the pitot cover, and check the pitot tube for damage and blockages, possibly by insects.

If the ASI is unusable, then all is not lost. Selecting a suitable *attitude* on the AI and suitable *power* on the Power Indicator should result in the desired *performance*, even though airspeed information is not available.

STATIC VENT BLOCKAGE

A damaged or blocked **static system** will affect the Air Speed Indicator, the Altimeter, and the VSI. If totally blocked, a constant static pressure may be trapped in the system. The Altimeter indication will not alter and the VSI will remain on zero as the aeroplane changes height. In cloud or at night, this could be very dangerous. The ASI will indicate an incorrect airspeed. The Indicated Air Speed is a measure of 'dynamic pressure = pitot (total) pressure − static pressure'; therefore, as the aeroplane climbs, the too-high static pressure trapped will cause the ASI to read too low. The danger on the climb is to follow the false ASI reading and speed up, possibly exceeding V$_{NE}$.

Conversely, on descent the trapped static pressure will be too low, causing the ASI to read too fast. The danger on descent is to follow the false ASI indication and slow up, possibly to the point of stalling.

A blocked static system may be tackled by switching to the alternate static source that most aircraft have and, hopefully, the affected instruments will become usable again.

As a last resort if both normal and static sources are unusable (a most unlikely event), the instrument glass of the VSI could be broken to admit cabin static pressure into the whole static system. Cabin pressure in an unpressurised aircraft is slightly lower than the external static pressure because of the venturi effect caused by the aeroplane's motion through the air. This slightly lower static pressure would cause the Altimeter to read 50–100 ft too high, and the ASI to read 5 kt or so too high.

ADAPT TO SUIT THE SITUATION

Whatever instrument fails, the resourceful Pilot should be able to cope, using whatever resources remain, and adapting his control of the aircraft to suit the situation. For instance, without the aid of the Attitude Indicator, the effects of inertia appear to be more marked than usual. Therefore, when using only a Partial Panel, the Pilot must develop the ability to make smooth and gentle changes using the '**Change – Check – Hold – Adjust – Trim**' technique, using the instruments that are available, and avoiding chasing the needles.

Because the immediate and direct presentation of attitude changes on the Attitude Indicator is missing on a Limited Panel, and because performance instruments like the ASI, Altimeter and VSI suffer some **lag**, it is even more important that the Pilot *holds* any new attitude to **allow time for the performance instruments to stabilise**, before further adjustments are made.

Therefore, in a Limited Panel situation, **reduce the rate and extent of control movement** compared to when operating on a Full Panel. The lag in readings will be less severe, and there will be less tendency to over-react by chasing the needles. Small control movements should be made, then checked and held whilst the performance instruments catch up with the change and settle into their correct readings. Then, fine-tune with further adjustments if necessary, before trimming off any steady control pressures.

The scan for each manoeuvre when using a Limited Panel will need to be modified to increase reference to the now more-important instruments, and to bypass the unusable instruments. This is easier to do than what it sounds. Simply look at the instrument that will give you the information you want. If it is bank angle you want, and the AI is not usable, then refer to the Turn Coordinator. It will not tell you bank angle directly, but it will tell you if the aeroplane is turning and, if it is, which way and at what rate. From this information, you can gain some idea of bank angle.

INTERPRETING PITCH ATTITUDE ON A LIMITED PANEL

The **Attitude Indicator** is a control instrument. It is the best guide to pitch attitude, since it gives a direct and immediate picture of the attitude of the aeroplane relative to the (artificial) horizon. However, for practice in flying on a Limited Panel, it may not be available. If the Attitude Indicator is indeed unusable, then the Pilot can determine the pitch attitude of the aeroplane using the three air pressure instruments which derive their information from the pitot-static system. They are the Air Speed Indicator, the Altimeter and the Vertical Speed Indicator.

Fig.7-1. Using the Pitot-Static Instruments to Determine Pitch Attitude (without the Attitude Indicator).

The **Altimeter** not only indicates height, but can also provide information regarding pitch attitude. If height is remaining constant, then the pitch attitude is correct for level flight at that power setting, whereas increasing or decreasing height would indicate a pitch attitude that is too high or too low.

The **Air Speed Indicator**, as well as indicating airspeed, can also provide information regarding pitch attitude. If the ASI shows that the desired airspeed is being maintained, then the pitch attitude for the power set is correct. If it indicates an increasing airspeed, or an airspeed that is too high, then the pitch attitude is too low for the power set. Conversely, if the ASI indicates a decreasing airspeed, or an airspeed that is too low, then the pitch attitude is too high for the power being used.

Used in conjunction with the Altimeter, the ASI is an extremely valuable guide to pitch attitude, but it should be remembered that, because of its inertia, an aeroplane will take some time to change speed and, therefore, the ASI indication must have settled before it can confidently be regarded as an accurate indication of pitch attitude. In other words, *hold any new attitude for a few seconds* to allow the airspeed and the ASI to settle.

The **VSI** not only indicates the Rate of Climb or Descent, but also can provide information regarding pitch attitude. If the VSI indication remains approximately zero, then the pitch attitude is correct for level flight at that power, whereas a significant and sustained departure from zero would indicate a pitch attitude that is either too high or too low for level flight. In a climb or descent, a steady and fairly constant VSI reading can be used to support information on pitch attitude from the other performance instruments. Remember that large or sudden changes in pitch attitude may cause the VSI to initially give reverse indications − another reason for avoiding dramatic attitude changes when flying on a limited panel.

Fig.7-2a. Pitch Attitude Too High.   Fig.7-2b. Pitch Attitude Too Low.

INTERPRETING BANK ATTITUDE ON A LIMITED PANEL

The Attitude Indicator is the best guide to bank attitude, since it gives a direct picture of the attitude of the aeroplane relative to the (artificial) horizon. However, for practice in flying on a limited panel, it may not be available. If the Attitude Indicator is indeed unusable, then the Pilot can determine the bank attitude from the Turn Coordinator and Balance Ball, and the Direction Indicator (if it is working, which it may not be) or the Magnetic Compass.

For the purpose of this exercise, the Direction Indicator is assumed to be unusable (say because the suction has failed both to it and the Attitude Indicator). If, in a real situation, the DI is working, then use it.

If the aeroplane is in balanced flight (i.e. the Balance Ball centred), **any indication of turning will mean that the aeroplane is banked**.

A steady Zero reading on the **Turn Coordinator**, with the **Balance Ball centred**, will mean that the wings are level. If the Turn Coordinator reading is not zero and the ball is centred, then the direction and rate of turn will be indicated. In most instrument flying, the normal rate of turn is Rate 1, which is a change of heading at 3°/second.

Fig.7-3. Determining Bank Attitude on a Limited Panel.

Whilst most modern aircraft are fitted with a Turn Coordinator, there are some still fitted with a Turn Indicator. The modern Turn Coordinator is a superior instrument in that, as well as indicating 'rate of turn' as does the Turn Indicator, **the Turn Coordinator also shows 'rate of bank'** because its gyroscope is mounted slightly angled. It will respond immediately an aeroplane banks, even before the aeroplane actually starts turning. It is therefore an easier instrument to use when trying to keep the wings level.

Remember that, even though it has symbolic wings to indicate banking and turning, **the Turn Coordinator does not give pitch information**.

Fig.7-4. Determining Bank Attitude on a Limited Panel with a Turn Indicator.

If, for some reason, the Turn Coordinator or Turn Indicator is not working, then bank information can be derived from the **Direction Indicator or Magnetic Compass. If the heading is constant and the Balance Ball centred, then the wings are level**. If the heading is changing at 3°/sec (i.e. 15° heading change in 5 seconds) and the ball is centred, then the wings are banked sufficiently to give a Rate 1 turn (bank angle = airspeed/10 + 7).

Fig.7-5. Determining Bank Attitude on a Limited Panel.

STRAIGHT AND LEVEL FLIGHT ON A LIMITED PANEL

Setting cruise *power* and placing the aeroplane in the cruise *attitude* will provide cruise *performance,* with the aeroplane in straight and level flight.

To **achieve straight and level flight** at a particular altitude on a Limited Panel without the use of the AI:

- set cruise power on the Power Indicator;
- hold the wings level with reference to the Turn Coordinator, with the Balance Ball centred; and
- adjust the pitch attitude with reference to the Altimeter and VSI; and then
- trim.

Fig.7-6. Achieving Straight and Level Flight on a Limited Panel.

To maintain straight and level flight at the chosen altitude, once it has been achieved:

- Maintain **heading** by keeping the wings level using the Turn Co-ordinator, and the ball centred. Heading can be checked on the Direction Indicator if it is working, otherwise on the Magnetic Compass.

  Any corrections to heading should be made with gentle coordinated turns (Rate 1/2 on the Turn Coordinator, which is 1.5°/sec, should be more than adequate). The Direction Indicator, if usable, will indicate heading directly but, if the Magnetic Compass is used, then some allowance will be needed to *undershoot* on Northerly headings and *overshoot* on Southerly headings.

- Any tendency to drift off **altitude** due to a slightly incorrect pitch attitude will first be shown on the VSI, and minor adjustments with the elevator can be made almost before any change is registered on the Altimeter. In turbulent conditions, however, the VSI will tend to fluctuate, in which case the Altimeter will be the more useful instrument. Aim to stay right on altitude. Minor deviations of less than 100 ft can generally be corrected with very small pitch alterations; any deviation in excess of 100 ft may also require a small power change as well as an attitude change. Keep in trim to make the task easier.

- **Airspeed** is normally just accepted on the cruise, once cruise power has been set. If, however, precise airspeed control is desired, then this can be achieved with power. Once cruise speed is achieved, ensure that the aeroplane is in trim.

Fig.7-7. Maintaining Heading and Height.

To **change airspeed** in straight and level flight, a coordinated change of both power and pitch attitude will be required. Greater precision using only a limited panel of instruments can be achieved if these changes are gradual and smooth.

A *higher* speed will require more power and a lower pitch attitude. Remember that a power increase will cause a 'pitch up/yaw left' tendency in most aircraft, and this should be resisted with gentle control pressures. Therefore, as power is slowly increased with the throttle **to achieve a speed increase**, monitor the VSI (backed up by the Altimeter) to determine the small increases in forward pressure required on the control column to maintain height, and keep the ball centred with a slight increase in (right) rudder pressure.

Refer to the Turn Coordinator to ensure that wings are kept level, so that heading is maintained. Power adjustment may be required to maintain the desired airspeed. Once stabilised at the desired speed, retrim the aircraft. The Direction Indicator (if available) or the Magnetic Compass (once it has settled down) can be checked to verify heading.

Fig.7-8. Changing Airspeed on a Limited Panel.

To reduce the airspeed will require less power and a higher pitch attitude. The power reduction will cause a 'pitch down and yaw right tendency', which the Pilot should be ready to counteract. The VSI can be used to avoid any tendency to lose altitude, prevented by use of the elevator, and the Turn Coordinator and Balance Ball can be used to prevent any tendency to drift off heading. Once the desired lower airspeed is achieved, minor power adjustments with the throttle may be required. The aeroplane should then be retrimmed.

CLIMBING ON A LIMITED PANEL

The procedure to enter a climb using only a partial instrument panel is the same as with a Full Panel: P-A-T, Power–Attitude–Trim. Smoothly apply climb *power* (mixture *RICH* if necessary), keeping the wings level on the Turn Coordinator and the ball centred to maintain heading, and raise the pitch *attitude* slightly. There will be a pitch up tendency as power is applied, so probably only a slight back pressure on the control column will be required.

116

Hold the new pitch attitude until the **Air Speed Indicator** stabilises. The VSI will show a climb and, once you are familiar with the particular aeroplane, this will provide useful backup information to the ASI regarding correct pitch attitude. An initial trim adjustment will assist in maintaining the new attitude. Once the airspeed has settled, minor adjustments can be made with the elevator to fine tune the airspeed, and then the aeroplane can be trimmed precisely to maintain the desired climbing speed.

To maintain a straight climb on a Limited panel, hold the pitch attitude with reference to the **ASI**, which is the primary indicator of correct pitch attitude during the climb. Maintain heading by keeping the wings level on the **Turn Coordinator** and the **ball centred**. Heading can be checked on the **Direction Indicator or Magnetic Compass**.

It is good airmanship to periodically check engine temperatures and pressures on the climb, since the engine is working hard and the cooling airflow is less, but this should not take more than one or two seconds and should not distract you from your main scan of the flight instruments. Being in trim will make life easier.

Fig.7-9. Entering a Climb on a Limited Panel.

Fig.7-10. Maintaining the Climb on a Limited Panel.

To level off at a particular height, it is important that the Altimeter has the correct setting in its subscale (Regional QNH, 1013, or Aerodrome QNH or QFE as the case may be). The **Altimeter** should be increasingly brought into the scan as the desired height is approached, and the focus for pitch control shifted to it from the ASI. Levelling off should be commenced smoothly before the desired height is actually reached, a suitable lead-in being 10% of the Rate of Climb (say 40 ft before the height for a Rate of Climb of 400 ft/min).

The procedure to level-off is A-P-T, Attitude–Power–Trim. Gradually **lower the pitch attitude** towards the level flight position, noting a decreasing climb rate on the VSI, and **capture the desired altitude with reference to the Altimeter**. Keep the wings level and the ball centred to maintain heading. Once the **airspeed** has increased to the desired cruising value on the ASI, **smoothly reduce power**, and then **trim** the aircraft.

Fig.7-11. Levelling Off from a Climb on a Limited Panel.

Once the aeroplane is stabilised, the scan becomes that for normal straight and level flight, although particular attention should be paid to the ASI in the early stages to ensure that adequate power is set to maintain the desired airspeed.

DESCENDING ON A LIMITED PANEL

A descent will require less power and a lower pitch attitude than for level flight. **To enter a descent**, the procedure is P-A-T, Power-Attitude-Trim. Smoothly reduce the power (Mixture Control *RICH*, Carburettor Heat *HOT* if necessary) with the throttle. Hold the wings level and the ball centred to maintain heading, and hold the pitch attitude with slight back pressure until the desired descent airspeed on the **ASI** is almost reached in level flight, at which time the nose can be gently lowered slightly to maintain airspeed.

If the descent airspeed is to be the same as the level airspeed, then the pitch attitude should be lowered simultaneously with the power reduction. Remember that there will be a natural tendency for the nose to drop and yaw as power is reduced.

The **VSI** can be used to monitor any vertical tendencies. An initial coarse trim adjustment as soon as the descent attitude is adopted is acceptable to remove most of any steady control pressure, followed by fine adjustments to the pitch attitude to maintain the desired airspeed and a final fine trim adjustment.

Fig.7-12. Entering a Descent.

To maintain the descent on a Limited panel:

- maintain **heading** with wings level on the Turn Coordinator and the Balance Ball centred, checking heading against the Direction Indicator or the Magnetic Compass;
- maintain **airspeed** with gentle changes in pitch attitude, using the **ASI** and **VSI** – if a particular rate of descent is required, then coordinated use of power and attitude can be used to achieve it, with the airspeed being monitored on the ASI, and the Rate of Descent being monitored on the VSI.

Fig.7-13. Maintaining a Descent on a Limited Panel.

In a prolonged descent with low power, thought should be given to clearing the engine every 1000 ft or so by applying 50% power for a few seconds to keep the engine and oil warm, to avoid carbon fouling of the spark plugs and to keep warm air available to the Carburettor Heat.

Applying the extra power, and then removing it, should not distract you from scanning the flight instruments for more than a few seconds. Be prepared to counteract pitch/yaw tendencies as the power is changed.

To level off from a descent at a particular height, it is important that the Altimeter has the correct setting in its subscale. As the desired height is approached, the focus for pitch attitude control should shift from the ASI to the Altimeter, and the levelling off manoeuvre commenced before the height is actually reached (a suitable lead-in being 10% of the Rate of Descent).

The procedure to level-off from a descent is P-A-T, Power–Attitude–Trim. Smoothly increase power to the cruise setting and raise the pitch attitude, noting that the VSI shows a reducing Rate of Descent, and aim to capture the desired height precisely on the **Altimeter**. Trim the aeroplane. Revert to the normal straight and level scan, checking the Altimeter for height, and initially checking the ASI to ensure that the desired airspeed is indeed being maintained.

Fig.7-14. Levelling off from a Descent on a Limited Panel.

To enter a climb from a descent, such as in a go-around, is a more demanding manoeuvre on a Limited Panel than on a Full Panel, since a large and fairly rapid power increase, accompanied by a higher pitch attitude, will be required. The large pitch attitude change may cause the VSI to give a reversed reading initially, so it must be disregarded until its reading has stabilised. Practising a go-around on a Limited Panel is, perhaps, an exercise for the more advanced student.

TURNING ON A LIMITED PANEL

To turn onto a specific heading, the best instruments to use for directional guidance are (in order):
- the Direction Indicator;
- the Clock (for timed turns – Rate 1 being 3°/sec); or
- the Magnetic Compass (with its turning and acceleration errors).

If the **Direction Indicator** is used, then it must first have been aligned with the Magnetic Compass whilst in steady straight flight.

If the DI is not usable, then a **timed turn** with Clock and Turn Coordinator is the preferred method. This method can be quite accurate. Once established in straight flight on the new heading, the Magnetic Compass will settle down and allow the heading to be checked.

If, however, the **Magnetic Compass** has to be used during the turn, then the roll-out should occur *BEFORE any desired Northerly heading* is indicated on the Compass (by about 30° in a Rate 1 turn), and *AFTER any desired Southerly heading* is indicated. No allowances need be made when using the Magnetic Compass to turn onto Easterly or Westerly headings, and lesser corrections for intermediate headings.

Prior to commencing a turn, ensure that you are comfortable in straight and level flight, exactly on height, on speed, and in trim. Check the Direction Indicator (if available) or the Magnetic Compass for the present heading, establish which way to turn, left or right, to take up the new heading, and what rate of turn will be used. Rate 1 is suitable for significant heading changes, but just a few degrees of heading change can be achieved satisfactorily at Rate ½. Calculating time to turn, even if using the DI or Compass, provides a very convenient backup. The ASI, Altimeter and VSI should all be fairly steady before rolling into a level turn using partial panel.

To enter a level turn, note the time in seconds on the Clock (or set the Stop Watch going), roll on bank in the desired direction using coordinated aileron and rudder until the **Turn Coordinator** shows Rate 1, at which point the ailerons should be neutralised to stop further banking, and the **Balance Ball** kept centred with rudder pressure. Height can be maintained by counteracting any trend on the **VSI** with elevator, which will probably require a slight back pressure. In turbulent conditions, the Altimeter may be more useful than the VSI which could be fluctuating. Neutralising the ailerons will hold the bank angle fairly constant, but minor corrections will have to be made continually to **maintain Rate 1 on the Turn Coordinator**.

Fig.7-15. Entering and maintaining a Level Turn using a Limited Panel.

To maintain a level turn, hold Rate 1 on the **Turn Coordinator** using the ailerons, and keep the ball centred with rudder pressure. Hold height on the Altimeter, by picking up any trend on the **VSI** and counteracting it with elevator. The **Altimeter** will confirm that the precise height is being maintained. The ASI will show the expected loss of several knots, which is acceptable, unless a constant airspeed is desired, in which case the addition of some power is required. It is not usual to trim in the turn, since it is a transient manoeuvre and straight flight will shortly be resumed. As the desired heading is approached, bring the heading indicator (DI, Clock or Compass) increasingly into the scan.

To roll out of a level turn, anticipate the desired heading by some degrees and roll off bank with coordinated aileron and rudder until the **Turn Coordinator** shows wings level. Hold height using the **VSI** and **Altimeter**, smoothly relaxing any back pressure held during the turn. Allow the Magnetic Compass to settle down in steady straight flight, then check it for heading and make any necessary adjustments with small coordinated turns.

THE CLIMBING TURN ON A LIMITED PANEL

The climbing turn is normally entered from a straight climb, and is more easily achieved if the aeroplane is first well-established and trimmed in the straight climb. Climbing **airspeed** should be maintained in the climbing turn, therefore the primary performance guide to pitch attitude is the ASI.

To enter a climbing turn, roll on bank with coordinated aileron and rudder until the desired rate of turn is indicated on the **Turn Coordinator**. Adjust the pitch attitude with reference to the **ASI**. It will be slightly lower than in the straight climb.

Fig.7-16. Entering and Maintaining a Climbing Turn.

Maintain the climbing turn with reference to the **Turn Coordinator** and the **ASI**, and bring the heading indicator (DI, Clock or Magnetic Compass) into the scan as the desired heading is approached.

Roll out of the climbing turn into a straight climb with coordinated aileron and rudder, achieving wings level with the **Turn Coordinator**, **Balance Ball** centred, and maintaining climbing airspeed with reference to the **ASI**.

THE DESCENDING TURN ON A LIMITED PANEL

The descending turn is normally entered from a straight descent, and is more easily achieved if the aeroplane is well-established and trimmed in the straight descent. Descent **airspeed** should be maintained in the descending turn, therefore the primary performance guide to pitch attitude is the ASI.

To enter a descending turn, roll on bank with coordinated aileron and rudder until the desired rate of turn is indicated on the **Turn Coordinator**. Adjust the pitch attitude with reference to the **ASI**. Pitch attitude in a descending turn will be slightly lower than in the straight descent.

Fig.7-17. Entering and maintaining a Descending Turn on a Limited Panel.

To maintain the descending turn, hold bank angle with reference to the **Turn Coordinator**, and hold pitch attitude with reference to the **ASI**. Bring the heading indicator (DI, Clock or Magnetic Compass) into the scan as the desired heading is approached.

Roll-out of the descending turn into a straight descent with coordinated aileron and rudder, achieving wings level with the **Turn Coordinator**, **Balance Ball** centred, and maintaining descending airspeed with reference to the **ASI**.

☐ **The Exercises on Section 1, Instrument Flying,** should now be completed. (These are located at the rear of the manual).

Intentionally Blank

2

RADIO NAVIGATION AIDS

Intentionally Blank

8

INTRODUCTION TO RADIO NAVIGATION AIDS

Having achieved a high standard in Attitude Flying using the Flight Instruments, it is now time to apply this ability to cross-country flying on instruments.

It is, in fact, possible to fly cross-country using Attitude Flying only, without referring to any Radio Navigation Instrument in the cockpit, simply by following instructions passed to you by a Radar Controller. Instructions such as:
Turn Onto Heading Three Four Zero, and *Descend Now To Eight Hundred Feet,* can be followed, even to the point of a cloudbreak for a straight-in landing on a particular runway.

Radar is the first of the Radio Navigation Aids that we consider in this Section, since it does not involve a great deal of understanding before you can benefit from it. As well as explaining how radar can be of use to you, we have also discussed its theory, including the **Transponder** in the aircraft, so that this manual may serve as a serious reference for you in the future.

It is possible that your Instructor will wish to follow an order of study different to that presented here. If so, then simply bypass the other chapters and proceed to the one desired. Each chapter stands fairly well alone, and a reading of the earlier chapters is not necessary for an understanding of the content of a later one.

VHF Direction Finding (VDF), which also does not require additional instrumentation in the cockpit, may be used for cross-country flying. By requesting ATC to provide you with a *magnetic bearing to the station,* known as a QDM, which can be determined at some aerodromes by detecting the direction from which your **VHF radio communications** are received, a track to or from the station can be flown. The procedure used is a little more complicated than simply steering radar headings, and so we have left it until towards the end of this Section.

Radio Navigation Aids that **do** have instruments in the cockpit, and which will be thoroughly covered, include the **Non-Directional Beacon (NDB) and Automatic Direction Finder (ADF) combination**, the ADF having various presentations such as the Relative Bearing Indicator (RBI) or the Radio Magnetic Indicator (RMI).

The **VHF Omni Range (VOR)** is also covered, as is the **Distance Measuring Equipment (DME)**, and the **Instrument Landing System (ILS)**. It may sound a little complicated at this stage, but careful consideration of each of these Radio Navigation Aids one at a time will make it easy for you.

There is a certain amount of *jargon* associated with instrument flying (for instance, who else but a Pilot would know what an ILS is?), but it will not take long before you are familiar with all the terms.

The main function of this Section of the manual is for you to understand how the aids work, and how to use them, especially for **tracking** to or from a ground station. The following Section (Section 3), considers the slightly more advanced aspects of instrument flying, such as Instrument Departures, Instrument Holding, Instrument Approaches to land, and Visual Manoeuvring at the end of a successful Instrument Approach. These depend to a large extent upon the lessons learnt in this Section 2. A good Instrument Approach, for instance, consists mainly of accurate attitude flying and accurate tracking.

9

RADAR

Most air traffic control in busy airspace occurs in a **radar environment**. This means that the Air Traffic Controller has a radar map of the area showing the position of the various aeroplanes within it, bringing enormous advantages such as:

- a significant reduction in the amount of air-ground communication: for instance, there is no need for a Pilot to transmit regular Position Reports;
- an ability to handle an increased number of aeroplanes in the same airspace, with reduced, but still safe, separation distances;
- an ability to **radar vector** an aeroplane along various tracks by passing headings to steer to the Pilot; and
- an ability to feed aeroplanes onto final approach to land, either to the commencement of an instrument approach such as an ILS (Instrument Landing System) or until the Pilot becomes visual, without the need for excessive manoeuvring, and with more than one aeroplane on the approach at any one time.

This use of radar is known as **Surveillance Radar**. Surveillance Radar, although extensively used in Air Traffic Control, is not confined to controlled airspace. Wide areas of the UK have radar coverage, and a Pilot, even if operating in uncontrolled airspace, may take advantage of services such as the Lower Airspace Radar Advisory Service (LARS).

Most aeroplanes are now fitted with a Secondary Surveillance Radar **Transponder**, which transmits a unique signal in response to a radar signal from the ground, thereby allowing the Radar Controller to identify a particular aeroplane on his Radar Screen. You are probably familiar with the operation of the Transponder – if not, it is considered in detail towards the end of this chapter. The name *Trans-ponder* is developed from *Transmitter/Responder*.

Fig.9-1. A Typical SSR Transponder.

131

At certain aerodromes, the Surveillance Radar Controller can provide tracking guidance and desired height information down final approach in what is called a Surveillance Radar Approach (SRA). This is a common approach for an IMC-rated Pilot.

A completely different set of ground-based equipment available at only a small number of aerodromes, known as Precision Approach Radar (PAR), enables a Radar Controller to provide to a Pilot extremely accurate approach guidance to land on a particular runway. PAR voice guidance is given in both azimuth (horizontal navigation) and slope (vertical navigation). The PAR is a rare approach for an IMC-rated Pilot. PAR is *not* available at civil airfields, but is readily available at selected military airfields.

In this chapter, we first consider Radar Vectoring, and then look at a Surveillance Radar Approach. There is no need for you to understand the theory of radar to be able to fly according to instructions from a Radar Controller, although towards the end of this chapter the Theory of Radio (including Radar) is considered.

RADAR VECTORING

Radar Vectoring is when a Radar Controller passes a Heading to steer to a Pilot with an instruction such as:

Charlie Delta
Steer Heading Two Five Zero.

Bear in mind that the Radar Controller is trying to get you to achieve a particular track over the ground and, because he does not know precisely what the wind at your level is and the amount of drift that it is causing, he will occasionally request a modification to your heading whilst radar vectoring your aeroplane.

No radio navigation instruments are required in the aeroplane for it to be radar vectored, but radio communication is necessary. The Pilot concentrates on attitude flying (maintaining the desired heading, altitude and airspeed), whilst the Radar Controller concentrates on the aeroplane achieving the desired track over the ground. This is not to say that the Pilot should not be very aware of where this track is taking him, especially if high terrain is in the vicinity, and he should always maintain a picture of where the aeroplane is with respect to the aerodrome. This is essential in case of radio communication failure.

The termination of radar vectoring is indicated by the phrase:

Resume Own Navigation.

Radar Vectoring is a very useful procedure in busy terminal areas where an aeroplane may be vectored quite efficiently onto final approach to land. Radar Vectoring by the Controller may cease once the aeroplane is established on a visual approach or on an instrument approach such as an ILS (Instrument Landing System), or it may continue down a Surveillance Radar Approach (SRA).

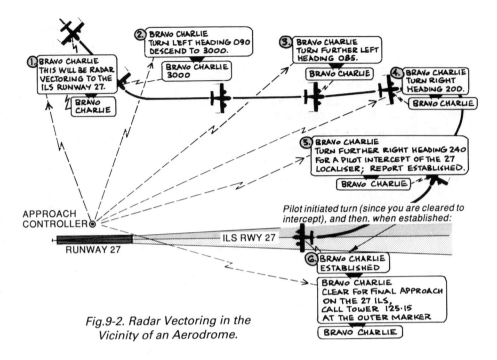

Fig.9-2. Radar Vectoring in the Vicinity of an Aerodrome.

SURVEILLANCE RADAR APPROACH (SRA)

A Surveillance Radar Approach is carried out by the Pilot under guidance from the Radar Controller on the VHF-COM radio who passes:

- horizontal navigation (tracking) instructions in the form of turns to make and headings to steer; and

- vertical navigation (descent) instructions in the form of Range to touchdown and desired height at that range.

The usual instrument approach slope is 3° to the horizontal, a slope of 1 in 20. (The 1 in 60 rule is useful here, 3° being approximately equal to 3 in 60, or 1 in 20.)

To achieve a 3° descent, for each 1 nm (approximately 6,000 ft) travelled horizontally, an aeroplane must descend 1/20th of this, i.e. 300 ft. Therefore **a 3° slope is approximately 300 ft/nm.**

Fig.9-3. The Usual Instrument Approach Slope is 3°.

Since the landing aeroplane should pass 50 ft above the runway threshold, it is quite simple to develop a *height/distance* profile. Working backwards from 50 ft above the runway threshold, the aeroplane should pass through a *window* 300 ft higher for each 1 nm further back from the runway.

The figures shown above are what the Pilot would aim to achieve with **QFE** set in the altimeter subscale.

On a Surveillance Radar Approach, the Controller will radar vector the aeroplane onto final and advise the pilot:

- when to commence a 3° descent;
- the appropriate height for the aeroplane's distance from touchdown; and
- what heading to steer if the aeroplane diverges from the approach track.

Phrases used will be similar to:
Range 5 Miles – Height Should Be 1550.

Track guidance will be given in a form such as:
Turn Right Five Degrees – Heading One Eight Five.

How to initiate a 3° Descent

There is no instrument in the cockpit that indicates descent in terms of feet/nm; such an instrument would make it easy to set a descent of 300 ft/nm to give a 3° approach slope. What the Pilot does have, however, is a Vertical Speed Indicator that measures the rate of descent in ft/min, and an Air Speed Indicator that measures Indicated Air Speed in knots (nm/hr).

The approach slope is measured in **ground** nautical miles (and not air nautical miles), so a Pilot estimate of Ground Speed taking into account the wind strength will increase the accuracy of an estimate of the desired descent rate.

- With a Ground Speed of 60 kt, an aeroplane will travel 1 nm in 1 minute and to achieve a slope of 300 ft/nm would require a descent rate of 300 ft/min.
- With a Ground Speed of 120 kt, an aeroplane will travel 2 nm in 1 minute and to achieve a slope of 300 ft/nm would require a descent rate of 600 ft/min.
- With a Ground Speed of 90 kt, an aeroplane will travel 1.5 nm in 1 minute and to achieve a slope of 300 ft/nm would require a descent rate of 450 ft/min.

Example 1: An aeroplane has an approach speed of TAS 75 kt. To achieve a 3° slope of 300 ft/nm, the required rate of descent is:

(a) in nil wind, TAS 75 kt, GS 75 kt, 375 ft/min;
(b) in 15 kt headwind, TAS 75 kt, GS 60 kt, 300 ft/min;
(c) in 30 kt headwind, TAS 75 kt, GS 45 kt, 225 ft/min;
(d) in 15 kt tailwind, TAS 75 kt, GS 90 kt, 450 ft/min; in this case, however, I would be wary of continuing the approach in case the tail wind limitation for landing was exceeded.

Perhaps an easier means of quickly determining an approximate descent rate to achieve a 3° slope is:

Rate of Descent (ft/min) **for a 3° approach slope = 5 x Ground Speed** (kt)

Example 2: At GS 80 kt, required RoD = 5 x 80 = 400 ft/min.

Surveillance Radar Approach (SRA) guidance may be given to a distance of 2 nm (i.e. approximately 650 ft above the runway elevation), or, if the ground equipment is satisfactory and the Radar Controller has only one aircraft on approach, to $\frac{1}{2}$ nm, where the height above the runway should be approximately 200 ft. The minimum for an IMC-Rated Pilot, however, is much higher than this – 600 ft AAL at least. (This is fully discussed in Chapter 19.)

For SRAs that terminate at 2 nm, calls will be given each 1 nm; for SRAs that terminate at $\frac{1}{2}$ nm, calls will be given at each $\frac{1}{2}$ nm.

OTHER INFORMATION PASSED TO THE PILOT

1. Prior to the commencement of the SRA, the *radar controller* will pass the Aerodrome QFE to the pilot which, when set in the altimeter subscale, will cause the altimeter to read height above aerodrome elevation. Threshold QFE may alternatively be given, which would cause the altimeter to read height above threshold elevation. Height information, such as an instruction to descend to the intermediate approach height, or as included in the 'range/height' calls down final approach, will then refer to height above the airport or runway threshold.

NOTE: If the pilot requests it, Aerodrome QNH will be passed. QNH set in the subscale will cause the altimeter to read altitude (height above mean sea level) rather than above runway elevation, and the radar controller will have to modify his calls to be altitudes rather than heights. For instance, at an aerodrome of elevation 700 ft, the call:

- *"Range Three Miles; Height Should Be Nine Five Zero"* – based on QFE, will become:
- *"Range Three Miles; Altitude Should Be One Six Five Zero"* – based on QNH.

2. The Obstacle Clearance Height (OCH) will also be passed as a height above the aerodrome or threshold elevation (i.e. based on QFE), and the pilot will be reminded to check his Decision Height.

> *"Golf Delta Sierra*
> *This Will Be A Surveillance Radar Approach*
> *Terminating At One Half Mile From ....*
> *Obstacle Clearance Height ...... Feet*
> *Check Your Minima."*

As mentioned above, calculating your own particular minima (height and visibility) is discussed in Chapter 19, however the Surveillance Radar Approach minimum height must not be less than 600 ft AAL for an IMC-Rated Pilot. Obstacles in the vicinity may require it to be higher. Required visibility is at least 1800 metres. Further information on SRA minima is found in the UK AIP RAC 4-1 and 4-2, and on Radar Approach Procedure Charts.

HOW RADAR WORKS

The remainder of this Chapter discusses the theory of *Radio Waves* and of *Radar*. It is not essential knowledge but it will help your understanding of Radio, Radar and Radio Navigation Aids.

Radar is part of the electromagnetic spectrum, and operates in the *radio frequencies.* The ability to transmit electromagnetic energy from one place to another in the form of radio waves has existed for almost a century, and this idea of *radio* has played a vital role in the development of aviation.

Waves of electromagnetic energy emanating from a Radio Transmitter, and identical to light waves except for frequency, can carry information out into the surrounding space. Radio Receivers tuned to the particular frequency may detect these signals, often at quite some distance from the Transmitter.

Common uses for radio in aviation are:
• air/ground voice communication; and
• radio navigation (the ADF/NDB combination, VOR and ILS).

Fig.9-4. Radio is the Transmission of Electromagnetic Energy and the Reception of it at a Distant Location.

THE REFLECTION OF RADIO WAVES

Electromagnetic radiation can be reflected from certain surfaces. Light waves, for instance, will be reflected by the metallic coating on a mirror. Similarly, radio waves of certain frequencies will be reflected from metallic and other surfaces, some of the radio energy returning to the point from which it was transmitted as a return **echo**. Other surfaces and objects, such as wood, may not cause reflection of the radio waves which will simply pass through like X-rays pass through a body.

Fig.9-5 Light Waves reflected from a Mirror.   *Radio Waves reflected from an Object.*

RADAR

Detection of the **reflected** radio waves at the point from where they were originally transmitted is known as **Radar**. The principle of radar has been known since the mid-1930s, and was used with devastating effect during World War 2 (1939-45) to **detect** objects such as aeroplanes and measure their **range**. Indeed, the name *RADAR* was devised from *RAdio Detection And Ranging*.

Fig.9-6. Radar is the Transmission of Electromagnetic Radio Energy and the Detection of some of the Reflected Energy back at the Point of Transmission.

The combined *Transmitter-Receiver* used in radar is usually a parabolic dish that is very efficient both in transmitting radio energy in a particular direction and then receiving the reflected radio energy from the same direction. The best results are obtained with ultra high frequency radio energy. The whole sky can be scanned systematically, if desired, simply by slowly rotating the radar dish.

Fig.9-7. A Typical Radar Antenna.

THE RELATIONSHIP OF TIME AND DISTANCE

All electromagnetic energy travels at the speed of light, 300,000 kilometres per second (162,000 nautical miles per second), the equivalent of almost eight journeys around the world in one second. Some common forms of electromagnetic energy are Light, Radio Waves, X-Rays, Ultra-Violet Radiation and Infra-Red Radiation.

By measuring the elapsed **time** between the transmission of a bundle or *pulse* of radio energy and the reception back at the source of its reflected echo, it is a simple mathematical calculation (knowing velocity) to determine the **distance** or *range* of the object causing the echo.

$$\frac{distance}{time} = speed$$

Multiplying both sides of this equation by *time* gives us an expression for *distance* in terms of the known speed of light and the measured elapsed time.

distance = speed x time

Fig.9-8. Radar converts an Elapsed Time to a Distance.

During the elapsed time between transmission of the pulse and reception of its reflection (measured electronically at the radar site), the distance between the radar site and the object will of course have been travelled twice – once out and once back – so the elapsed time needs to be halved, and this is also done electronically.

The speed of light, being so great, means that the times involved are extremely short. This allows a stream of pulses to be transmitted, with only short time intervals between the pulses when no transmission occurs, to allow for reception of any echo. As a matter of interest, the time taken for a radar pulse to travel to and from a reflector 20 nm away (i.e. a total of 40 nm) is 0.000250 seconds, or 250 millionths of a second.

40 nm (2x20) at the speed of light 162,000 nm/sec = 40/162,000 sec
= 0.000250 sec

- If the measured elapsed time interval is 250 millionths of a second, then the object is 20 nm distant.
- If the measured elapsed time interval is 750 millionths of a second, then the object is 60 nm distant.
- If the measured elapsed time interval is 125 millionths of a second, then the object is 10 nm distant.
- If the measured elapsed time interval is 12.5 millionths of a second, then the object is 1 nm distant, i.e. a time interval of 12.5 millionths of a second (or *microseconds)* can be thought of as a *radar mile.*

AT WHAT RANGE CAN RADAR DETECT TARGETS?

Radar uses Ultra-High Frequency (UHF) transmissions, which are basically *line of sight*, and so propagation will be interrupted by buildings, high terrain and the curvature of the earth. These will cause radar shadows, and objects in these shadow areas may not be detected.

Bearing in mind the curvature of the earth, the higher an aeroplane is flying the greater the distance at which it can be detected by radar. An approximate maximum distance in nautical miles is given by the relationship:

$$\text{Radar Range} = \sqrt{1.5 \times \text{height AGL in feet}} \text{ (nautical miles)}$$

NOTE: $\sqrt{1.5 \text{ height}}$ is the same as $1.22\sqrt{\text{height}}$, which some people prefer. It is a similar expression, since the square root of 1.5 is 1.22.

Example 3: At 5000 ft AGL over flat terrain with no obstructions, an aeroplane will be detected up to approximately 87 nm.

$$
\begin{aligned}
\text{Radar Range} &= \sqrt{1.5 \text{ ht}} \text{ nm} & \text{or} \quad & 1.22 \sqrt{\text{ht}} \text{ nm} \\
&= \sqrt{1.5 \times 5000} \text{ nm} & &= 1.22 \sqrt{5000} \text{ nm} \\
&= \sqrt{7500} \text{ nm} & &= 1.22 \times 71 \text{ nm} \\
&= 87 \text{ nm} & &= 87 \text{ nm}
\end{aligned}
$$

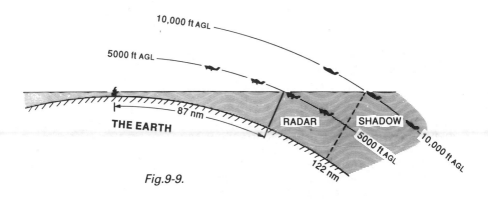

Fig.9-9.

Example 4: At 10,000 ft AGL over flat terrain with no obstructions, an aeroplane will be detected up to approximately 100 nm.

$$
\begin{aligned}
\text{Radar Range} &= \sqrt{1.5 \text{ ht}} \text{ nm} & \text{or} \quad & 1.22 \sqrt{\text{ht}} \text{ nm} \\
&= \sqrt{1.5 \times 10,000} \text{ nm} & &= 1.22 \sqrt{10,000} \text{ nm} \\
&= \sqrt{15,000} \text{ nm} & &= 1.22 \times 100 \text{ nm} \\
&= 122 \text{ nm} & &= 122 \text{ nm}
\end{aligned}
$$

NOTE: These are expected ranges under ideal conditions; in reality, the range of a radar may be significantly less than this, and it may experience *blind spots* and *radar shadows*.

Radar Range may be increased if the radar antenna is sited at a high elevation, both to raise it above nearby obstacles that would cause shadows, and to allow it to see further around the curvature of the earth. Hence radar dishes are to be seen on the tops of hills and buildings. The range at which an aeroplane can now be detected by a radar sited well above a uniform surface is given approximately by:

Radar Range $= \sqrt{1.5 \text{ height of radar dish}} + \sqrt{1.5 \text{ height of aeroplane}}$

  or $1.22 \sqrt{\text{height of radar dish}} + 1.22 \sqrt{\text{height of aeroplane}}$

Example 5: At 5000 ft AGL over flat terrain with no obstructions, an aeroplane will be detected up to approximately 99 nm if the radar dish is elevated 100 ft above a uniform surface.

$$\text{Radar Range} = \sqrt{1.5 \times 100} + \sqrt{1.5 \times 5000} \text{ nm}$$
$$= \sqrt{150} + \sqrt{7500} \text{ nm}$$
$$= 12 + 87 \text{ nm}$$
$$= 99 \text{ nm}$$

Fig.9-10. Radar Range is Increased if the Radar Dish is Elevated.

If the radar dish can be elevated 400 ft, then its range will increase by:
$\sqrt{1.5 \times 400} = 24$ nm.

Another technical design feature (apart from the positioning of the radar dish) that determines the range of a radar is the interval existing between pulse transmissions to allow the Transmitter to act as a Receiver. The greater the time interval, the greater the range from which echoes can be received. Greater time intervals between pulses means that fewer pulses per second may be transmitted, which is referred to as a lower *Pulse Repetition Rate* (PRR).

Fig.9-11. Short-Range Radar;   Long-Range Radar.

Radar that makes use of **reflected** radio energy is known as **Primary Radar**, and it is used for a number of purposes in aviation including:

- Surveillance Radar to provide an overview of a whole area, and used in Surveillance Radar Approaches (SRA) for azimuth and height guidance on final approach to land; and

- Precision Approach Radar (PAR) for extremely accurate azimuth and slope guidance on final approach to land.

DIRECTION BY RADAR

If the **direction** from which the reflected signal comes can be determined, as well as its **range**, then the **position** of the object can be pinpointed. This is achieved by slowly rotating the radar dish, a typical rate being two revolutions per minute, during which time it will have fired out many millions of pulses in its radar beam and received almost instantaneously any reflected returns. The **angle** of the radar antenna compared to north at the time the return echo is received indicates the horizontal direction (or *azimuth*) of the object. These *returns* are displayed as *blips* on a screen.

PRIMARY SURVEILLANCE RADAR

Surveillance Radar is designed to give a Radar Controller an overview of his area of responsibility. It does not transmit pulses in all directions simultaneously, but rather as a beam, which is slowly rotated. For an aeroplane to be detected, the beam must be directed roughly towards it. If the Radar Controller has his radar *tilted* up, then it may miss lower aircraft at a distance; conversely, nearby high aeroplanes may not be detected if the tilt is down.

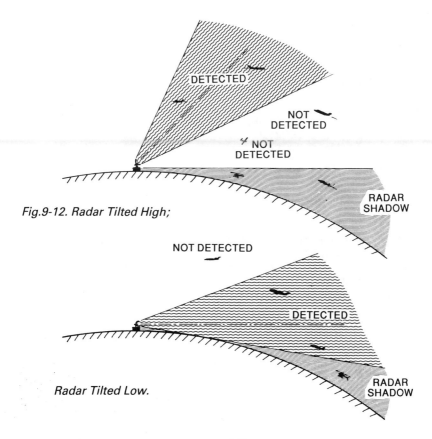

Fig.9-12. Radar Tilted High;

Radar Tilted Low.

THE RADAR SCREEN

Most Radar Screens are simply Cathode Ray Tubes (CRT) that resemble circular television screens. Using the same principle as television, a beam of electrons is directed onto the fluorescent coating of the CRT to provide a radar picture. Radar Controllers generally have circular displays showing the position of the radar antenna in the centre, with range marks to aid in estimating distance. The Radar Screen is also known as a *Plan Position Indicator* (PPI).

The actual radar dish may be located away from the position of the Radar Controller, possibly on a nearby hill or tower. As the radar antenna rotates slowly, the small electron beam in the Controller's CRT also rotates, leaving a faint line or trace on the screen in a direction aligned with the direction of the antenna at that moment. Any radar return signal appears as a *blip* or *paint* at the appropriate spot on the screen.

An indication of North on the screen allows the Controller to estimate the direction of the target, and the range marks assist in estimating its distance. The *paint* of the target remains visible for some seconds after the small trace line has moved on, and will still be visible (but fading) as its next *paint* occurs in the following revolution. This fading trail of blips allows the Controller to determine the motion of the target in terms of direction and speed.

AN ADVANCING TARGET

A FAST MOVING
DEPARTING TARGET

Fig.9-13. A Radar Screen.

In areas of high traffic density, the radar responsibility may be divided between various controllers, each with their own screen and radio communications frequency, and will go under such names as:
• Approach Control; and
• Zone Control.

Other markings besides the Range Circles may be superimposed upon the screen as a video map to indicate the location of nearby Controlled Airspace, aerodromes, radio navigation aids such as VORs and NDBs, Restricted Areas, etc.

Fig.9-14. A Typical ATC Radar Screen.

Some Disadvantages of Primary Radar

Whilst a big advantage of Primary Radar is that no special equipment is required in an aeroplane, it does have some operational disadvantages including:
- **clutter** from precipitation and high ground;
- **uneven returns** from different aircraft; and
- **blind spots**.

The radio energy in the reflected signal received at the radar dish may be quite small, depending upon the strength of the original transmission, how good a reflector the target is, its distance from the radar antenna, and so on. A radar that is sensitive enough to pick up weak returns from targets may also pick up returns from terrain and precipitation, leading to *ground clutter* and *weather clutter* on the screen. During periods of heavy rain, Primary Radar may be significantly degraded.

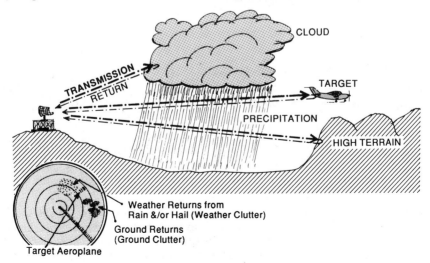

Fig.9-15. Primary Surveillance Radar is subject to Clutter.

Some radars incorporate an electronic sifting device known as a Moving Target Indicator (MTI) that only allows signals from *moving* targets to be shown on the screen, in an attempt to eliminate clutter from stationary objects.

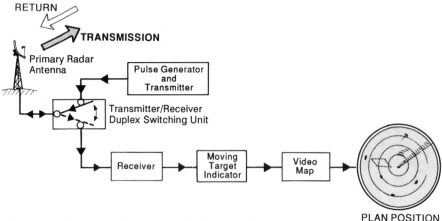

Fig.9-16. Diagrammatic Layout of a Primary Radar System.

With Primary Radar only, it is often difficult for the Radar Controller to distinguish between various signals, and he may have to request one aeroplane to carry out a manoeuvre such as a turn to distinguish its radar blip from that of another aeroplane. A typical request could be:

Golf Sierra Delta,
For Identification,
Turn Left Thirty Degrees,
Heading Zero Six Zero.

Once the Controller observes this turn on the screen:

Golf Delta Sierra,
Identified One Two Miles North-West of Exeter.

SECONDARY SURVEILLANCE RADAR (SSR)

Secondary Surveillance Radar removes most of the limitations of Primary Radar simply by **adding energy to the return pulse from the aeroplane**, using a device carried on board the aeroplane known as a **Transponder**.

Primary Radar detects radar energy passively reflected from a target and displays it as a *blip*, or fading series of blips, on a screen; this is a similar process to a searchlight operator at night seeing an aeroplane in the beam of the searchlight.

Secondary Radar is much more than this, and the target is far from passive. It is as if each time the searchlight strikes the target, the target is triggered to light itself up very brightly in response, and not just passively reflect some of the energy transmitted from the ground site. **Secondary Radar is really two sets of radar talking to each other.**

Because only a small amount of energy transmitted from the ground is required to act as a trigger for the airborne SSR Transponder, the Secondary Radar ground transmitter and antenna system can be quite small (unlike the large Primary Radar dish and powerful transmitter in a system which depend upon reflected echos proportional to the original power of transmission). A long and narrow Secondary Surveillance Radar antenna can often be seen above the large Primary Radar dish.

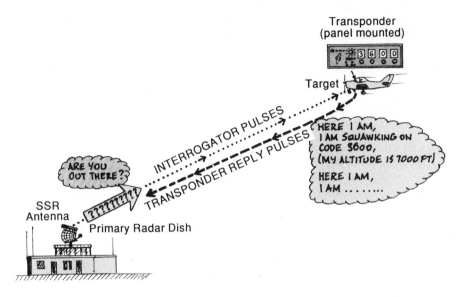

Fig.9-17. SSR is Two Radars talking to Each Other.

The SSR ground equipment consists of:

- an **interrogator** that provides a coded signal *asking* a transponder to respond;
- a highly directional rotating radar **antenna** that transmits the coded interrogation signal, then receives any responding signals, and passes them back to the interrogator; and
- a **decoder**, which accepts the signals from the interrogator, decodes them and displays them on the radar screen.

The SSR airborne equipment consists of a Transponder carried in the individual aeroplane.

The originating signal transmitted from the ground station triggers an **automatic response** from the aeroplane's transponder. It transmits a strong answering coded signal which is then received at the ground station. This response signal is much, much stronger than the simple reflected signal used in Primary Radar. **Even a very weak signal received in the aircraft will trigger a strong response from the Transponder.**

The secondary responding pulse from the aeroplane's Transponder can carry coding which can distinguish the aeroplane from all others on the radar screen. Depending upon the code selected in the Transponder by the Pilot, it can also carry additional information such as:
• the identity of the aeroplane;
• its altitude;
• any abnormal situation such as radio failure, distress, emergency, etc.

A significant advantage is that **SSR** is not degraded to the same extent as Primary Radar by weather or ground clutter, it presents targets of the same size and intensity to the Controller, it allows the Controller to select specific displays, and the system has minimal *blind spots*.

Unfortunately, not all aircraft are fitted with a transponder, yet they may be flying in the same airspace. For this reason, both Primary and Secondary surveillance radar information will be presented to a Radar Controller on the one screen.

SSR Symbols on the Radar Screen

We recommend that you visit a Radar Control Centre to see the system in action from the Air Traffic Controller's point of view. Understanding his task and how it interacts with yours as Pilot-in-Command will lead to greater professionalism.

Sometimes ATC wish to distinguish a particular aeroplane from others in its vicinity. This situation may arise with a number of aircraft holding in the one area, or with a light aircraft that is having navigational difficulties and has requested assistance. ATC will then assign a code (such as 1700 or 4000) to this particular aircraft.

Technological advances are being made and already many aeroplanes and some SSRs are equipped for altitude reporting and the like. For instance, some aircraft squawk specific codes, e.g. code 3916 applies to only one particular aeroplane, and on certain advanced SSR screens this will show up as that aeroplane, with a read-out of its Altitude and Ground Speed. Under less sophisticated radar coverage, the older SSR screens will show this only as belonging to the 3000 family, i.e. as a large circle.

All of these symbols are continually shown on the screen as a result of the coding selected on the aircraft transponder, except for the large *squawk* triangle which appears on the radar screen for 15 to 20 seconds only when a pilot presses his *IDENT* button.

Squawk IDENT is often requested by ATC when they want positive identification of an aeroplane on their screen. For this reason you should only press the *ident* button on your transponder when specifically requested to do so by ATC.

USING THE TRANSPONDER IN THE COCKPIT

Usually the Transponder is warmed-up in the *STANDBY* position during the taxi, the code to be used (a four-figure number) selected, and then switched ON just prior to take-off.

Even though Transponders produced by various manufacturers vary slightly in design, they are operated in basically the same manner. As a responsible Pilot, you will become familiar with your particular Transponder.

Fig.9-18. Transponders from Various Manufacturers.

The Function Selector Knob

This enables you to select the transponder to *OFF, ON, STANDBY,* etc., i.e. it allows you to operate it in one of its various modes. Typical transponder modes include:

OFF:

STANDBY: warmed up, and ready for immediate use. This is the normal position until you are ready for take-off, when you would select *ALT* or *ON* (if Transponder is to be used in flight).

ON: transmits the selected code in Mode A (aircraft identification mode) at the normal power level.

LO SENS: *low sensitivity*, transmits the selected code the same as in the *ON* position but at a lower power level. This may be requested by the Radar Controller to avoid over-strong blips on his screen from aircraft close to the interrogating antenna. After landing, a pilot would normally switch to *STANDBY* or *OFF* for the same reason.

ALT: *altitude,* which may be used if the altitude reporting capability (known as mode C) is installed in your aircraft. This is a special "encoding" altimeter which feeds your altitude to the transponder for transmission on to the ATC radar screen. (If not installed, the transponder still transmits in Mode A, i.e. aircraft identification without altitude reporting).

TST: *tests* that the transponder is operating correctly and if so, illuminates the reply monitor light. It causes the transponder to generate a self-interrogating signal to provide a check of its operation.

Code Selection

Knobs are provided for you to select the appropriate code for your transponder, the selected code being prominently displayed for you in digital form.

An important procedure to follow when selecting and altering codes is to avoid passing through vital codes (such as 7700 for emergencies, 7600 for radio failure) when the transponder is switched *ON.* This can be avoided by selecting *STANDBY* whilst the code is being changed. Your Flying Instructor will explain further.

The Reply-Monitor Light

The reply light will flash to indicate that the transponder is replying to an interrogation pulse from a ground station.

The Reply-Monitor Light will glow **steadily** when you:

- press the *TEST* button or move the function switch to the *TEST* position (depending upon the design of your particular transponder) to indicate correct functioning; or
- transmit an *IDENT* pulse.

The *IDENT* Switch or Button

When the *IDENT* button is pressed by the Pilot upon request from the Radar Controller to *SQUAWK IDENT,* a special pulse is transmitted with your transponder's reply to the interrogating ground station. This causes a special symbol to appear for a few seconds on the radar screen around the return from your aircraft's transponder, thus allowing positive identification by the Radar Controller.

NOTE: Your particular transponder may have minor variations to that described above, but will certainly be fundamentally the same. It may for instance have a separate Mode Selector to select Mode A (position reporting) or Mode C (position and altitude reporting). These variations are easily understood.

SQUAWK

The term *Squawk* that you will often hear is confined to transponder usage, and the instruction following squawk is usually quite clear, for instance: *"Squawk Ident"; "Squawk Code 4000"; "Squawk Mayday" (7700),* etc.

TYPICAL RADIO COMMUNICATIONS INVOLVING TRANSPONDER OPERATION

ATC: *". . . (callsign), Squawk Ident".*

Pilot response is to press the transponder *IDENT* button, allowing the Radar Controller to identify you positively on his screen.

ATC: *". . . (callsign), Squawk Code 7340".*

Pilot response is a read-back of the assigned Code: *". . . (callsign), CODE 7340",* and to select the transponder to that Code.

ATC: *". . . (callsign), Squawk Standby".*

Pilot response is to move the function switch to *STANDBY* from the *ON* or *ALT* position, for a temporary suspension of transponder operation (maintaining present Code).

ATC: *". . . (callsign), Squawk Normal".*

Pilot response is to reactivate the transponder from *STANDBY* to *ON* or *ALT*, as appropriate, retaining the existing Code.

Further information on SSR operating procedures may be found in UK AIP RAC 7-4.

☐ Now complete **Exercises 9 – Radar.**

10

DME

DME MEASURES SLANT DISTANCE

Distance Measuring Equipment (DME) can provide a Pilot with extremely useful information, his distance from a DME ground station. DME uses radar principles to measure this distance, which is the **slant distance** rather than the horizontal distance (or Range). For most practical purposes, the DME distance can be considered as Range, except when the aeroplane is within a few miles of the DME ground station.

Fig. 10-1. DME Measures Slant Distance.

Passing directly over the DME ground station, the DME Indicator in the cockpit will either show the height of the aeroplane in nautical miles (1 nm = 6000 ft approximately), or the DME indication will *drop out.*

Fig. 10-2. Passing Overhead a DME Ground Station.

DME COCKPIT DISPLAYS

DME distance is usually displayed in the cockpit as a digital read-out. The Pilot generally selects the DME using the VHF NAV radio (since most DMEs are paired with a VOR frequency or a Localizer frequency). Once the DME is *locked on,* and a DME reading and *IDENT* obtained, the DME indications can be used for distance information irrespective of whether the VOR (or Localizer) is used for tracking or orientation purposes.

Fig.10-3. A Digital DME Indicator.

Some airborne DME equipment is capable of computing the **rate of change of DME distance** (i.e. the *Rate of Closure* of the aeroplane with the DME ground station), and displaying this *Rate of Closure* on the DME cockpit instrument. If it is assumed that slant distance equals horizontal distance, and that the aeroplane is tracking either directly towards or directly away from the DME ground station, then the Rate of Closure read-out will represent **Ground Speed**, a very useful piece of information. Some DME Indicators can also display **Time to the Station** (TTS) in minutes at the current Rate of Closure, by comparing the GS with the DME distance.

Fig.10-4. Ground Speed Read-Outs.

If the DME equipment in the aeroplane does not give a Ground Speed read-out, then the Pilot can simply note the DME distance at two particular times, and carry out a simple calculation of GS = distance/time either mentally or on his Navigation Computer.

Example 1: A Pilot notes DME distance and time as he tracks towards a DME ground station. Calculate Ground Speed.

$$
\begin{array}{ll}
\text{DME 35} & \text{Time 0215 UTC} \\
\text{DME 25} & \text{Time 0220 UTC} \\
\phantom{\text{DME}}\text{10 nm} & \phantom{\text{Time 021}}\text{5 min} \quad = \quad \text{GS 120 kt}
\end{array}
$$

The DME provides a Circular Position Line.

If the DME reads 35 nm, for instance, then the Pilot knows that the aeroplane is somewhere on the circumference of a 35 nm circle centred on the DME ground station.

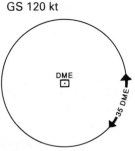

Fig.10-5a. A Circular Position Line from a DME.

Information from another radio aid may assist in **positively** fixing the position of the aeroplane, provided the two position lines give a good 'cut' (angle of intercept).

Fig.10-5b. Using Two Radio Navaids to Fix Position.

Some Instrument Approach Procedures (e.g. Carlisle NDB/DME) allow a **DME Arc** to be flown, prior to intercepting the final Approach track, by maintaining an approximately constant DME reading — achieved by keeping the other aid (e.g. the NDB) approximately on the wingtip.

Fig.10-6. Example of a DME Arc Manoeuvre.

Approaching 9 DME, turn to place the ADF needle "on the wingtip".

DME USES THE PRINCIPLE OF SECONDARY RADAR

Radar is covered thoroughly in its own chapter, where both Primary and Secondary Radar are discussed. Primary Radar detects one of its own transmissions that is *reflected* from some object; Secondary Radar detects a *responding transmission* from a **Transponder** activated by an *interrogation* signal.

Distance Measuring Equipment operates by the airborne transmitter (the *Interrogater*) sending out a stream of radio pulses in all directions on the receiving frequency of the DME Ground Station *Transponder*.

At the target DME ground beacon, these pulses are passed through an *electronic gate*. If the pulses and the *gate* match up, the DME ground beacon (or Transponder) is triggered, and responds by transmitting a strong answering signal. The airborne DME equipment detects this answering signal and measures the time between the transmission of the interrogating pulse from the aircraft and the reception of the ranging reply pulse from the DME ground station. It converts this time to a **distance in nautical miles** and the DME Indicator, when it displays this distance with the red *OFF* flag out of view, is said to have *latched on* or *locked on*.

NOTE: Do not confuse the DME Transponder at the DME ground station (and associated with the airborne DME equipment) with the SSR Transponder carried in the aircraft (operated by the Pilot and associated with the ground-based Secondary Surveillance Radar).

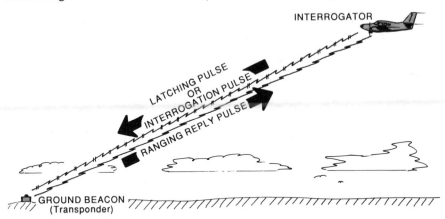

Fig. 10-7. Operation of the DME.

Each DME ground transponder can cope with about 100 different aeroplanes at any one time before becoming saturated, and the system is designed so that there is no possibility of interrogation pulses from one aeroplane causing an incorrect range indication in another aeroplane. Also, because the frequencies are carefully chosen so that stations with like frequencies are situated well apart geographically, there is no likelihood of interference from the wrong DME ground station. DME signals are line-of-sight transmissions (like VHF radio communications, Radar and VOR), with an approximate usable range in nautical miles of the square root of (1.5 x height in ft) nm.

DME FREQUENCIES

DME operates in the UHF (Ultra High Frequency) band from 962–1213 MHz which, with 1 MHz spacing, gives 252 possible frequencies. Each DME Channel consists of two frequencies (an interrogation frequency from the aeroplane and a paired response frequency from the ground station).

There are 126 channels currently in use, numbered from 1 to 126, and with an X or Y classification after them. You may see references such as DME Ch 92Y or DME CH 111X in the AIP, but there is no need for a Pilot to know these details, since these numbers are **not** used by the Pilot to select the DME – **the DME is automatically selected** on many types of VHF-NAV units when he selects the VHF NAV to an appropriate VOR or ILS frequency.

VOR/DME PAIRING

Each VOR frequency has a specific DME channel paired with it. For instance, VOR frequency 112.00 MHz has DME Channel 57X paired with it, so that the VOR's associated DME will automatically be interrogated when the Pilot selects the VOR frequency 112.00 on his VHF NAV. The purpose of this pairing is to reduce the Pilot's workload in the cockpit, with only one selection instead of two required, and to reduce the risk of a Pilot selecting the right VOR but the wrong DME station. It is normal for only **co-located** VORs and DMEs to be frequency paired. Co-located VORs and DMEs are situated within 800 metres of each other, and each will have the same morse code IDENT.

A paired VOR and DME give a very good position fix:
• the radial from the VOR; and
• the distance from the DME.

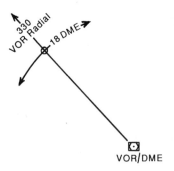

Fig.10-8. Fixing Position with VOR and DME.

Some VORs and DMEs are not sufficiently close to be co-located, but are sufficiently close to be considered *associated*, in which case the IDENT of the DME will have Z as its last letter, e.g. Machrihanish in Scotland has a VOR IDENT 'MAC' and a DME IDENT 'MAZ'.

ILS/DME PAIRING

Many Instrument Landing Systems (ILS) have their Localizer frequency paired with a DME located very close to the runway threshold. This provides the pilot with very useful information during an ILS or Localizer Approach to the runway – for example, distance fixes for key positions on the approach (such as the Final Approach Fix), as well as the distance-to-run to the runway threshold.

Fig. 10-9. Using a paired Localizer/DME.

INFORMATION ON DME STATIONS IN THE UK AIP

Further information on individual DME ground stations can be found in the UK Aeronautical Information Publication, COM section.

RADIO COMMUNICATION AND NAVIGATION FACILITIES

STATION	SERVICE	CALL SIGN OR IDENT	EM	TRANSMITS kHz	TRANSMITS MHz	RECEIVES kHz	RECEIVES MHz	HOURS OF WINTER PERIOD
1	2	3	4	5	6	7	8	9
Midhurst	VOR	MID	A9W	–	114.000	–	–	H24
	DME		P0N					

INFORMATION ONLY Not for Navigational Purposes

SERVICE SUMMER PERIOD	CO-ORDINATES	LOCATION MAG	LOCATION NM	OPERATING AUTHORITY AND REMARKS
10	11	12	13	14
H24	N5103.20 W00037.40	–	–	NATS. DOC 60 nm/50000 ft (100 nm/50000 ft in Sector 127° to 217° MAG). DME Ch 87X. Aerial Hgt 200 ft amsl.

Fig. 10-10. Information from AIP COM for the Midhurst DME Station.

❑ Now complete **Exercises 10 – DME.**

11a

THE NDB AND THE ADF

The Non-Directional Beacon (NDB) is the simplest form of radio navigation aid used by aircraft. It is a ground-based transmitter which transmits radio energy in all directions, hence its name – the **Non-Directional Beacon**

The ADF, or **Automatic Direction Finder,** fitted in an aeroplane has a Needle which indicates the direction from which the signals of the selected NDB ground station are being received. This is extremely useful information for a Pilot flying in Instrument Conditions and/or at Night. In days past, the combined ADF/NDB system was referred to as the *Radio Compass.*

Fig.11a-1. A Correctly Tuned ADF Indicates the Direction of the selected NDB from the Aircraft.

Flying to an NDB in an aeroplane is similar to following a Compass Needle to the North Pole – fly the aeroplane towards where the Needle points and eventually you will arrive overhead.

Fig.11a-2. Flying To a Station is Straightforward.

Flying away from the North Pole, however, with the Magnetic Compass Needle pointing behind, could take the aeroplane in any one of 360 directions. Similarly, flying away from an NDB using only the ADF needle will not lead the aeroplane to a particular point (unlike flying **to** an NDB). The aeroplane could end up anywhere! Further information is required.

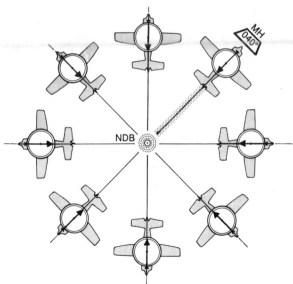

Fig.11a-3. Flying Away From a Station to Somewhere Else Requires Further Information than just the Needle on the Tail.

The ADF and the Direction Indicator are a very useful Combination

The extra information required by the Pilot, in addition to that supplied by the **ADF Needle**, comes from the Magnetic Compass and its *junior partner* the **Direction Indicator** (which is easier for a Pilot to use). Very accurate navigation can be carried out using these two references:
- an **ADF Needle** that points at an NDB ground station; plus
- a **Direction Indicator** that indicates the aeroplane's Magnetic Heading.

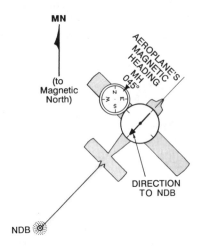

Fig. 11a-4. To Be Really Useful to a Pilot, the ADF/NDB Combination Needs Support From a Magnetic Compass (or DI).

NOTE: Since a Direction Indicator most probably will slowly drift out of alignment, it is vital that the Pilot periodically realigns it with the Magnetic Compass in straight flight at a steady speed, say every 10 minutes or so.

Fig. 11a-5. Periodically Realign the DI with the Magnetic Compass in Steady Flight.

What a Competent Pilot can do with the NDB/ADF Combination

Before using an ADF's indications of the bearing to a particular NDB, the aeroplane must be within the Promulgated Range of the NDB and the Pilot must have:

- correctly **selected** the NDB frequency;
- **identified** its morse-code ident; and
- test the ADF Needle to ensure that it is indeed **'ADFing'**;

If the NDB is 40° to the left of the aeroplane's Magnetic Heading, say MH 070°M, then the situation can be illustrated as shown below. The NDB, since it is 40° left of the nose, will have a Magnetic Bearing (MB) of 030°M from the aeroplane.

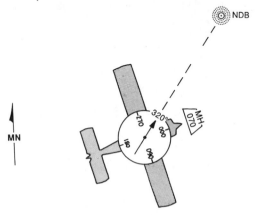

Fig.11a-6. A Diagrammatic Representation.

The ADF/NDB combination, in conjunction with the Direction Indicator, can be used by the Pilot:

- to **track** to the NDB on any desired track, pass overhead the NDB, and track outbound on whatever track is desired; or
- to **fix** the aeroplane's position.

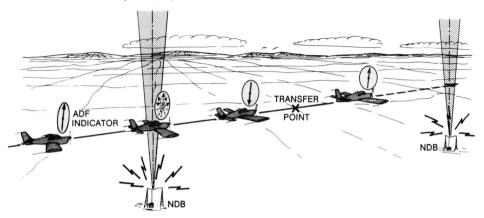

Fig.11a-7. Flying Towards, Over, and Past an NDB, and then On to the Next One.

The ADF in the aeroplane should, whenever possible, be selected to an NDB relevant to the desired path of the aeroplane. If tracking en route between two NDBs, the point of transfer from one NDB to the next would reasonably be the half-way point, depending of course upon their relative ranges. If the NDB is ahead, the ADF needle will point up the dial; if the NDB is behind, the ADF needle will point down the dial. As the aeroplane passes overhead the NDB, the ADF needle will become very sensitive and will swing from ahead to behind.

Excerpted from *E(LO)2* Enroute Chart by permission of JEPPESEN & CO. GmbH
© 1994 JEPPESEN SANDERSON INC.

Fig.11a-8. The Woodley NDB is used as a Tracking Aid, a Turning Point, and as a Reporting Point on the 'A47' Air Route.

The ADF can also be used for more advanced procedures such as:
- flying an accurate racetrack Holding Pattern based on the NDB; or
- using the NDB for guidance when manoeuvring in the vicinity of an aerodrome, either as a let-down or cloudbreak aid in its own right, or as a lead-in to a precision approach aid such as an ILS (Instrument Landing System).

NDBs with published approach procedures are referred to as Locators (L) (abbreviated *Lctr* on Jeppesen charts). The LUTON Locator (frequency 345 kHz), shown in figure 11a-9, is available as:
- a point over which to hold in a racetrack pattern;
- the sole tracking aid on an NDB let-down for Runway 26; or

- as an additional tracking guide when using the Runway 26 Instrument Landing System, and as an Outer Marker (LOM) or check point on this ILS approach.

NOTE: Approach Charts (or *Approach Plates,* as they are sometimes referred to) appear simpler as you become familiar with them.

Fig.11a-9. The Approach Chart for LUTON Rwy 26, using the ILS/DME or NDB.

Some NDBs are not available for Holding or for Instrument Approaches, but only for en route navigation. This information is available in the UK AIP COM section.

The NDB/ADF combination is the simplest form of radio navigation in theory, yet it takes a good Instrument Pilot to use it accurately. Other more advanced systems, such as the VOR, are more complicated in principle, but easier to use.

The NDB – What It Looks Like, and How It Works

The Non-Directional Beacon (NDB) is the ground-based part of the combination. It is named as being *non-directional* because no particular direction is favoured or differentiated in its transmissions; the NDB radiates identical electromagnetic energy in all directions. Each NDB transmits on a given frequency in the low-frequency or medium-frequency LF/MF bands (somewhere between 200 to 1750 kHz), the transmission mast being either a single mast or a large T-Aerial strung between two masts.

Fig.11a-10. Two types of NDB Transmitting Aerials.

To avoid confusion between various NDBs, and to ensure that the pilot is using the correct beacon, each NDB transmits its own particular identification signal (or *IDENT*) in the form of a two or three-lettered Morse Code signal, which should be monitored periodically in the cockpit by the pilot.

Example 1: The Perth NDB has a frequency of 388 kHz and is identified by the pilot listening to, and identifying the Morse Code symbols for **PTH,** which are: *"dit-dah-dah-dit dah dit-dit-dit-dit"* or ·——· — ····

The normal source of *frequency* and *IDENT* information for the Instrumet Pilot are the **Radio Navigation Charts** and/or the **Approach Charts,** which are carried in the cockpit.

Fig.11a-11. Information on Perth NDB found on Radio Navigation Charts.

As mentioned on the previous page, more detailed information is available in the UK AIP in the Radio Communications and Navigation Facilities section, known as **AIP COM**. The AIP is not usually carried in the aircraft, however. Additional information that is available in the AIP, and not available on the Radio Navigation Charts or Approach Charts, includes:

- hours of service;
- the operating authority;
- geographical location in latitude and longitude;
- the precise track and direction from the NDB to the aerodrome (useful information when flying to an aerodrome after locating the aeroplane over the NDB after an Instrument Approach);
- range; and
- any other relevant remarks.

COM 2-86 (17 Feb 94)

RADIO COMMUNICATION AND NAVIGATION FACILITIES

STATION	SERVICE	CALL SIGN OR IDENT	EM	TRANSMITS		RECEIVES	
				kHz	MHz	kHz	MHz
1	2	3	4	5	6	7	8
PERTH/Scone							
	L	PTH	NONA2A	388	–	–	–

	HOURS OF SERVICE		CO-ORDINATES	LOCATION		OPERATING AUTHORITY AND REMARKS
	WINTER PERIOD	SUMMER PERIOD		MAG	NM	
	9	10	11	12	13	14
			N5626.15 W00322.45	–	–	Air Services Training Ltd. On AD. Range 25 nm. Normally radiates H24.

Fig.11a-12. An Extract from the UK AIP COM showing details of Perth NDB.

The Range of an NDB

For long-range en route navigation where no other aids are available, a fairly strong NDB with a range of 100 nm or more is usually required. Some NDBs used for long distance overwater tracking, for instance in the Pacific area, may have a range of 400 nm. In the UK, however, where routes are relatively short and there are many navigation facilities, most NDBs have only a short range. *Radnor NDB,* for instance, on Airway B39 from London to Dublin, has a range of only 40 nm. The range of each Non-Directional Beacon (NDB) or Locator (L) may be found in AIP COM 2, and within this promulgated range the NDB should provide bearings accurate to within +/–5°. The promulgated range also provides guidance as to when you should shift your attention to the next aid.

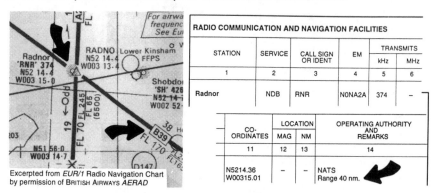

Excerpted from *EUR/1* Radio Navigation Chart
by permission of BRITISH AIRWAYS *AERAD*

Fig.11a-13. Many NDBs have only a Short Range.

For manoeuvring in the vicinity of aerodromes, only lower powered NDBs are required. NDBs used for approaches are referred to as Locators *(L,* or *Lctr,* Jeppesen), e.g. the *Manchester Locator,* IDENT *MCR.* If a Locator is co-located with an Outer Marker that serves to fix a position as an aircraft proceeds down an Instrument Landing System (ILS) approach, then it will be depicted on the ILS Approach Chart as **LOM** (Locator Outer Marker).

*Fig.11a-14.
The MCR Locator
is co-located with
the ILS Outer Marker,
shown as 'LOM', for
the Manchester
Rwy 06 ILS.*

The range of an NDB depends upon:
- the power of transmission (10–200 Watt);
- the frequency of transmission; and
- atmospheric conditions existing at the time – electrical storms, as well as the periods of sunrise and sunset, can distort or reflect the signals from an NDB.

The Accuracy of an NDB Signal

An ideal NDB signal received at an aeroplane may be accurate to $\pm 2°$, however various factors may reduce this accuracy considerably. These factors include:
- **Thunderstorm Effect**: causing the ADF needle to be deflected towards a nearby electrical storm (Cumulonimbus cloud) and away from the selected NDB.
- **Night Effect**: when strong skywaves from the NDB returning to earth from the ionosphere cause interference with the surface waves from the NDB, possibly resulting in a fading signal and a wandering ADF needle (most pronounced at dawn and dusk).
- **Interference**: from other NDBs transmitting on similar frequencies.
- **Mountain Effect**: due to reflections of the NDB signals from mountains.
- **Coastal Effect**: caused by the NDB signal bending slightly towards the coastline when crossing it at an angle.

IDENTIFYING AN NDB

Each NDB or Locator is identifiable by a two- or three-lettered morse code identification signal which is transmitted along with its normal signal. This is known as its **IDENT**. The Pilot **must** identify an NDB before using it for any navigational purposes within its Promulgated Range and, if using it for some length of time, then it should be periodically re-identified. The lack of an IDENT may indicate that the NDB is out of service, even though it may still be transmitting (say for maintenance or test purposes), and it must **not** be used for navigation. If an incorrect IDENT is heard, then those signals must not be used.

	L		L		
	"LUT" 345		"TD" 347.5		"NH" 371.5
Morse Code:	• — • •	• • —	—	— — • •		— • • • •

To identify most NDBs, the Pilot can simply select AUDIO on the ADF, listen to the morse code signal, and confirm that it is indeed the correct one (either from memory or from a morse code sheet, such as that included on the folder containing the *Aerad* Approach Charts or on the Legend of the ICAO 1:500 000 aeronautical chart series).

Different NDBs have different IDENT characteristics which are associated with the type of transmission.

All NDBs in the UK can now be identified with the ADF Mode Selector in the ADF position. In Continental Europe, however, there are still some NDBs that require the Pilot to select BFO (Beat Frequency Oscillator) to enable identification. The BFO imposes a tone onto the NDB Carrier

Wave to make it audible. Such NDBs are shown on charts without inverted commas, e.g. MP at Cherbourg and DEN at Dender, both in France.

Some NDBs carry voice transmissions, such as the Automatic Terminal Information Service (ATIS) at some aerodromes. It is also possible, in a situation where the communications radio (VHF COM) has failed, for ATC to send voice messages to the Pilot on the NDB frequency and for him to receive them on the ADF if AUDIO is selected.

NOTE: Broadcasting Stations such as the BBC and Commercial Stations may also be received by an ADF, since they transmit in the LF/MF bands. It is **not** good airmanship, however, to use a Broadcasting Station as a navigational aid, since they are difficult to identify precisely. Even if an announcer says "This is BBC Radio 2", it is possible that the transmission is coming, not from the main transmitter, but from an alternative or emergency transmitter located elsewhere, or even a relay station many miles away from the main transmitter. To use information from a radio broadcasting station, a Pilot must be absolutely certain of its geographical position — something which is difficult to determine. It is also **not** good airmanship to listen to a Broadcasting Station in flight, as this will distract a Pilot from his main operational tasks and responsibilities.

THE AUTOMATIC DIRECTION FINDER

The airborne partner of the NDB is the Automatic Direction Finder, usually referred to as the ADF. It operates on the *Radio Compass* principle whereby the ADF needle indicates the direction from which the signals are coming.

The Automatic Direction Finder has three main components:

- The **ADF Receiver**, which the Pilot tunes to the frequency of the desired NDB and verifies with the IDENT.

- The **aerial system** consisting of a **loop aerial** (or its modern equivalent), plus a **sense aerial**, which together determine the direction from which the signal is coming.

- The **ADF Cockpit Display**, either a Fixed-Card or a Rotatable Compass Card with a pointer or needle indicating the direction from which the signals are coming. The Cockpit Instrument is fitted into the instrument panel, usually to the right of the Attitude Flight Instruments, with the top of the dial representing the nose of the aeroplane, and the bottom of the dial representing its tail. Ideally, the ADF needle will point continually and automatically towards the NDB ground station.

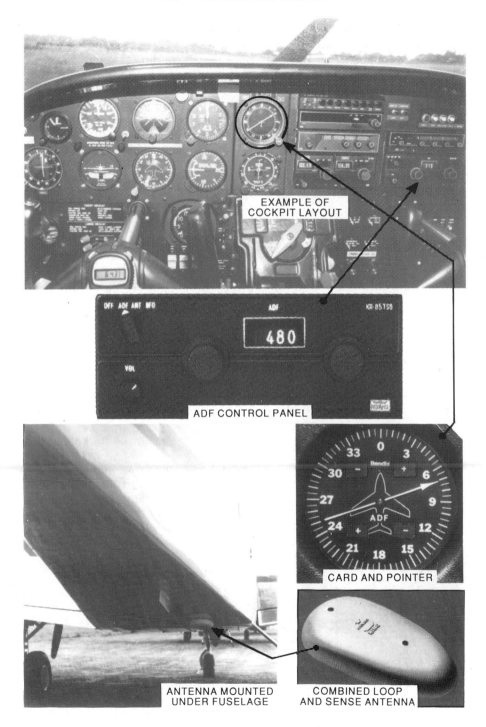

EXAMPLE OF
COCKPIT LAYOUT

ADF CONTROL PANEL

CARD AND POINTER

ANTENNA MOUNTED
UNDER FUSELAGE

COMBINED LOOP
AND SENSE ANTENNA

Fig.11a-15. The Airborne ADF Equipment.

Why Two ADF Aerials – the Loop Aerial and the Sense Aerial?

Improved reception on a portable radio is sometimes possible by rotating it to a particular position, because of the directional properties of its receiving antenna. The Automatic Direction Finder works on the same principle.

The loop aerial when it is aligned with the plane of a radio wave (in the position illustrated below) will have slightly different voltages induced either side of it because, at any instant, the two sides will be receiving different parts of the radio wave. This will cause a small electric current to flow from one side of the loop to the other, and this current is measurable. The size of the electric current will be greatest when the loop aerial is aligned with the radio wave, which occurs in two positions 180° apart.

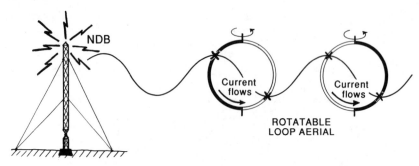

Fig.11a-16. The Loop Antenna Having a Maximum Electric Current Induced in It by a Radio Wave.

If the loop aerial is rotated until it is perpendicular to the Radio Wave, then each side of the loop will be receiving similar parts of the Radio Wave simultaneously, there will be no difference in potential, no voltage difference across the loop, and hence no current, i.e. a **null** position. The null positions can be thought of as the radio wave slipping through the loop. For one complete 360° rotation of the loop aerial, the *null* or zero signal will occur in two positions, 180° apart.

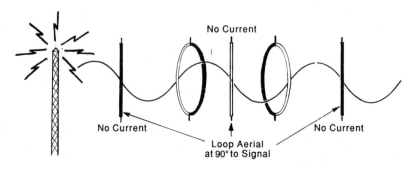

Fig.11a-17. The Loop Antenna in its Null Position, Having Zero Electric Current Induced in It by a Radio Wave.

168

For one 360° rotation of the loop aerial, the received signal will pass through two maximums and two nulls, with the nulls (zero current) being much more sharply defined than the maximums as illustrated below. Small angular deflections of the loop aerial near its null positions produce larger **changes** in current than similar angular changes near to the loops maximum positions. For this reason, a **null** position of the loop aerial, rather than a maximum position, is used for direction finding purposes.

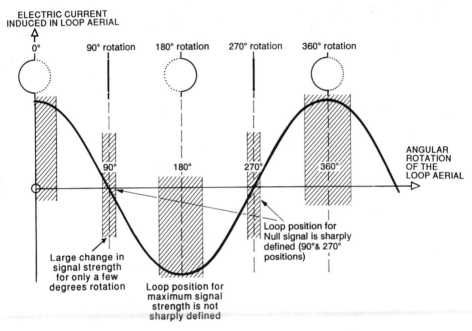

Fig.11a-18. The Nulls are Sharply Defined.

If a loop aerial is rotated into a null position where no current is generated, then the NDB transmitter is either directly ahead of the loop **or** 180° away and directly behind the loop. This is a very ambiguous situation, but it can be resolved using a **sense aerial**.

Fig.11a-19. Which Way to the NDB (using only a Loop Aerial).

The Sense Aerial

The sense aerial is a single stationary aerial. It has the same sensitivity as the loop in its maximum position and so it generates a continuous maximum current. Unlike the loop aerial, it has no directional properties.

By adding the steady signal from the sense aerial to the alternating signal from the loop signal as it rotates, there is now only one position as the loop rotates 360° at which there is zero current. This acts as a phase reference point, allowing the correct null position to be correctly identified. In other words, the 180° ambiguity has been removed, and the Pilot can be certain of the direction to the NDB.

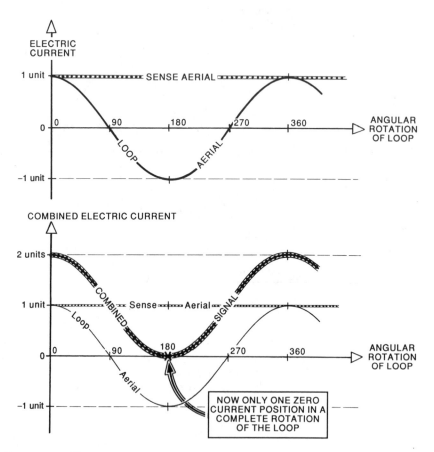

Fig.11a-20a. The Sense Antenna Removes the Ambiguity from the Loop Signal.

The Old Days

In days gone by, the loop had to be turned manually by the Pilot or Navigator for the Radio Compass needle to point towards the ground station. Then came a loop antenna that was rotated electrically, so that the ADF needle pointed continuously and automatically at the NDB.

Modern equipment uses a loop antenna that does not have to be rotated at all, but is rather a fixed loop antenna (or goniometer) that is directionally sensitive to radio signals. This has allowed the ADF aerial system to become very compact, especially if the sense aerial is internally mounted.

MODERN LOOP
ANTENNA HOUSING
(Low Drag)

COMBINED LOOP
AND SENSE ANTENNA

Fig.11a-20b. A Modern ADF Aerial System.

THE ADF CONTROL PANEL

There are various types of ADF that may be fitted to an aeroplane and, prior to flight, a Pilot must be familiar with the set that he will use.

Fig. 11a-21. Different Types of ADF Control Panels.

The Pilot must be able to select and positively identify the NDB that he wishes to use, and then verify that the ADF needle is indeed responding to the signals from that NDB. The correct procedure, any time a new NDB is to be used, is to confirm (verbally if so desired):
- **SELECTED;**
- **IDENTIFIED; and**
- **ADFing (and giving a sensible bearing).**

The Mode Selector or Function Switch

The Mode Selector has various positions depending upon the function that the Pilot wishes to use:

OFF: to switch the ADF OFF.

ADF: the normal position when the Pilot wants bearing information to be displayed automatically by the needle. Most NDBs can be identified with the Mode Selector in this position (and the VOLUME knob adjusted suitably).

ANT (sometimes **REC**): abbreviations for ANTENNA or RECEIVER. In this position, only the signal from the sense antenna is used, with no satisfactory directional information being available to the ADF needle. The reason for this function position is that it gives the best audio reception to allow easier identification, and better understanding of any voice messages. Never leave the mode selector in this position if you are navigating using the ADF − the ADF needle will remain stationary with no obvious indication that it is not responding! It is possible, however, to identify most NDBs with the Mode Selector in the ADF position (which is a safer position), and for the ANT position to be avoided.

BFO (sometimes **CW**): abbreviations for Beat Frequency Oscillator or Carrier Wave. This position is selected when identifying the few NDBs that use A0/A1 or A1 transmissions, which are unmodulated carrier waves whose transmission is interrupted in the pattern of the NDB's morse code identification. Since no audio message is carried on an unmodulated carrier wave, the BFO (as part of the airborne equipment) imposes a tone onto the carrier wave signal to make it audible to the Pilot so that the NDB signal can be identified. Again, do not leave the mode selector switch in this position when navigating using the ADF.

TEST: Placing the Mode Selector into the TEST position will deflect the ADF needle from its current position. Placing the Mode Selector back to ADF should cause the needle to swing back and indicate the direction of the NDB. This function should be tested everytime as part of the *SELECTED, IDENTIFIED, ADFing* tuning procedure. Some ADF sets have a separate TEST button which only needs to be pressed to deflect the needle, and then released to check the return of the needle.

NOTE: On some ADF equipment, the TEST function is achieved using the ANT/REC position, which drives the needle to the 090 position. Returning the Mode Selector to ADF should see the needle start "ADFing" again.

VOL: The VOLUME knob will probably be separate to the Mode Selector. With audio selected to the Pilot's headset or to the cockpit speakers, the VOL should be adjusted so that the IDENT or any voice messages on the NDB may be heard. If signal reception is poor in ADF, then try ANT/REC; if there is no signal reception, try BFO/CW. Remember to return the Mode Selector to ADF!

Frequency Knobs

NDBs transmit on a frequency in the range 200-1750 kiloHertz, the most common band being 200-400 kHz. To allow easier and accurate selection of any particular frequency, most modern ADFs have knobs that allow **digital** selection, in 100, 10 and 1 kHz steps. Some ADFs may have a Band Selector (200-400; 400-800; 800-1600 kHz), with either a Tuning Knob or Digital Selection for precise tuning.

THE ADF COCKPIT DISPLAY

The basic purpose of an Automatic Direction Finder in an aeroplane is for its needle to point directly towards the selected NDB ground station. The ADF Cockpit Display is a card or dial placed vertically in the instrument panel so that:
- if the ADF needle points up, the NDB is ahead;
- if the ADF needle points down, then the NDB is behind;
- if the ADF needle points to one side, then the NDB is located somewhere to that side of the fore-aft axis of the aeroplane.

To convey this information to the Pilot, various presentations are used, three of which we will consider:
- the Fixed-Card ADF, also known as the Relative Bearing Indicator (RBI);
- the Manually-Rotatable Card ADF (the *poor man's RMI*); and
- the Radio Magnetic Indicator (RMI).

1. THE FIXED-CARD ADF OR THE RELATIVE BEARING INDICATOR (RBI)

A Fixed-Card Display has an ADF needle that can rotate against the background of a fixed azimuth card of 360° with 000° (360°) at the top, 180° at the bottom, and so on. The Fixed-Card ADF is also known as the Relative Bearing Indicator (RBI), and is common in many General Aviation aircraft.

**On the Fixed-Card ADF, the needle indicates
the Relative Bearing of the NDB from the aeroplane.**

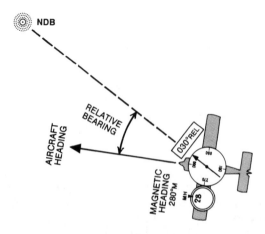

Fig.11a-22. A Fixed-Card ADF is a Relative Bearing Indicator (RBI).

The **Relative Bearing** of the NDB from the aircraft is the **angle** between the aircraft's **Heading** and the direction of the NDB. Usually Relative Bearings are described clockwise from 000° to 360°, however it is sometimes convenient to describe the bearing of the NDB relative to the nose or tail of the aeroplane.

Fig.11a-23. The RBI or Fixed-Card ADF shows Relative Bearings.

Each time the aeroplane changes its Magnetic Heading, it will carry the fixed card with it. Therefore:

**with each change of Magnetic Heading,
the ADF needle will indicate a different Relative Bearing (RB).**

Fig.11a-24. Each Time Heading is Changed, the Relative Bearing also Changes.

Orientation using the RBI or Fixed-Card ADF

The aeroplane can be orientated with respect to the NDB knowing:

- the **Magnetic Heading (MH)** of the aeroplane (from the Compass or Direction Indicator); plus
- the **Relative Bearing (RB)** of the NDB from the aeroplane.

In practice, Magnetic Heading is flown using the **Direction Indicator**, which should be realigned with the Magnetic Compass in steady flight every 10 minutes or so. Our illustrations will therefore display the DI instead of the Magnetic Compass.

In the illustration below, the aeroplane is heading 280° M, and the ADF indicates RB 030° to the BRISTOL Locator, i.e. MH 280 and RB 030.

Fig.11a-25. Orientation (Where Am I?) using an RBI.

MH 280	+	RB 030	=	310° M to NDB
Aircraft Magnetic Heading	+	Relative Bearing of NDB from aircraft	=	Magnetic Bearing of NDB from aircraft

QDM (the Magnetic Bearing to the NDB), and How to visualise it

The Magnetic Bearing of the NDB from the aeroplane is also known as **QDM**, and in this case is QDM 310.

A quick pictorial means of determining QDM using a Relative Bearing Indicator and a Direction Indicator is to translate the ADF needle onto the DI, by paralleling a pencil or by using your imagination.

Fig.11a-26. A Pictorial (but clumsy) Method of Finding QDM.

QDR (THE MAGNETIC BEARING FROM THE NDB), AND HOW TO VISUALISE IT

The Magnetic Bearing of the aircraft from the NDB, i.e. the reciprocal to QDM, is known as the **QDR**, and in the case illustrated above is QDR 130. QDR can be visualised as the Tail of the pencil (or needle) when it is transferred from the RBI onto the DI.

NOTE: An easier method of finding reciprocals than adding or subtracting 180°, is to either:
• add 200 and subtract 20; or
• subtract 200 and add 20.

Example 2:	QDM 310	QDM 270	QDM 085
	−200	−2—	+2—
	+20	+2–	−2–
	QDR 130	QDR 090	QDR 265

2. THE MANUALLY-ROTATED CARD ADF

The Manually-Rotated Card ADF is an advance on the Fixed-Card ADF, because it allows the Pilot to rotate the card so that the ADF needle indicates, not relative bearing, but **Magnetic Bearing to the NDB** (also known as **QDM**). The Pilot does this by aligning the ADF Card with the DI Compass Card each time the aeroplane's Magnetic Heading is changed.

To align a Manually-Rotated ADF Card:
• note Magnetic Heading on the Direction Indicator; then
• rotate the ADF Card, setting Magnetic Heading under the Index.

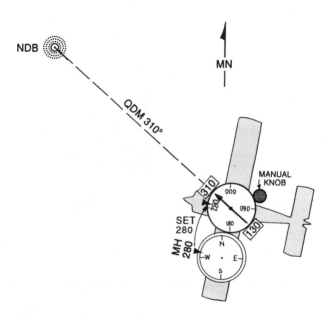

Fig.11a-27. Using a Manually-Rotated Card ADF.

When the ADF card is aligned with the DI, the ADF needle will indicate QDM, the Magnetic Bearing **to** the NDB. This eliminates any need for mental arithmetic, which is an advantage for the Pilot. Note also that the tail of the needle, 180° removed from its head, indicates **QDR**, the Magnetic Bearing of the aeroplane **from** the NDB.

Any time the aircraft changes Magnetic Heading, the Pilot should manually align the ADF card with the DI (ensuring, of course, that the DI is aligned with the Magnetic Compass).

If desired, the Manually-Rotated Card can still be used as a Fixed-Card simply by aligning 000 with the nose of the aeroplane and not changing it.

The next step up from a manually-rotated card is one that remains aligned automatically, i.e. the RMI.

3. THE RADIO MAGNETIC INDICATOR (RMI)

The RMI Display has the ADF needle superimposed on a card that is continuously and **automatically** being aligned with Magnetic North. It is, if you like, an automatic version of the Manually-Rotated Card ADF — an automatic combination of the Direction Indicator and RBI.

The RMI is the best ADF presentation, and the easiest to use, but unfortunately the most expensive and usually only encountered in the more sophisticated aircraft. In such aircraft, the RMI usually occupies the position in the instrument panel previously occupied by the manually-slaved DI.

- The RMI Needle will always indicate **QDM**, the Magnetic Bearing *to* the NDB; and
- The Tail of the RMI needle will indicate **QDR**, the Magnetic Bearing *from* the NDB.

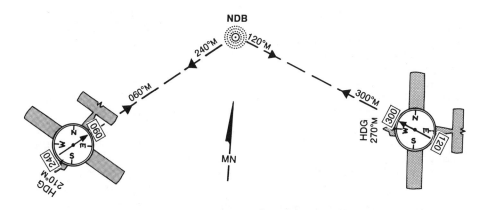

Fig.11a-28. The RMI Compass Card Remains Aligned with Magnetic North.

As an aeroplane turns and its Magnetic Heading alters, the RMI card (which automatically remains aligned with Magnetic North) will appear to turn along with the ADF needle. In reality, of course, it is the Compass Card and the RMI Needle that remain stationary, whilst the aeroplane turns about them. Before, during and after the turn, the RMI's needle will constantly indicate the current QDM.

Gyro-Stabilised Compass Equipment

In most aeroplanes fitted with an RMI, the initial Magnetic North reference to the RMI card is provided by a **Fluxgate** or **Fluxvalve**, a detector that is sensitive to Magnetic North, and situated in a fairly non-magnetic part of the aeroplane such as in a wingtip. A **Directional Gyroscope** is electrically slaved to this magnetic reference so that the Gyroscope is continually being aligned with Magnetic North, and it is this Directional Gyroscope that drives the RMI Compass Card in a process known as *slaving*.

FLUX VALVE
provides
Magnetic Reference to   DIRECTIONAL   which
                               GYRO   drives   RMI COMPASS CARD

Fig.11a-29. The RMI Compass Card is Driven by a Fluxvalve and DG.

Most gyro-stabilised compasses have an **Annunciator** near the compass card. This is a small needle, often triangular in shape, that oscillates when automatic slaving is in process (which should be all the time). The Annunciator being hard over to one side indicates that the Compass Card is a long way out of alignment; this can usually be remedied using a manual knob to quickly re-align the Compass Card with the Magnetic Heading of the aeroplane, after which the slower, automatic slaving should be sufficient to maintain alignment.

If slaving is not occurring because of some fault in the system (indicated by the Annunciator being stationary and not annunciating) then the Pilot can revert to using the RMI as a Manually-Rotated Card ADF (*poor man's RMI*) or as a Fixed-Card ADF (Relative Bearing Indicator).

SOME INDICATORS HAVE TWO POINTERS

Some aeroplanes are fitted with two ADF Receivers, and have two needles superimposed upon the one dial. Sometimes the indicator has a function switch that causes a Needle to point, not at an NDB, but at a VOR ground station. This gives the Pilot more flexibility in using his radio navigation aids.

Fig.11a-30. An Indicator with Two Needles.

WHAT IS TO FOLLOW

The next chapters consider the in-flight operation of:
- the Relative Bearing Indicator (RBI) or Fixed-Card ADF; and
- the Radio Magnetic Indicator (RMI), including the Manually-Rotatable Card.

☐ Now complete **Exercises 11a – NDB/ADF.**

11b

THE RELATIVE BEARING INDICATOR (RBI)

OPERATIONAL USE OF THE RBI

ORIENTATION – Using the RBI to Obtain a Position Line

A Line of Position is a line along which the aeroplane is known to be at a particular moment. A Line of Position (LoP) is also referred to as a Position Line (PL). A Line of Position may be obtained by a Pilot either visually, or by radio means.

Fig.11b-1. A Visual Position Line, and a Radio Position Line.

Two Position Lines that cut at a reasonable angle are needed for a fix. For the aeroplane to be on both Position Lines simultaneously, it must be at the point of intersection. The illustration below shows a **radio** fix obtained using two NDBs in an aeroplane fitted with two ADFs. It is possible to fix position using a **combination** of radio aids including ADF/NDB, VOR and DME.

Fig.11b-2. Two Position Lines with a Good Cut Can Provide a Fix.

A Position Line can be considered from two perspectives:

- **from the aeroplane** , i.e. the PL from the aeroplane to the NDB that a Pilot would see, as either a Relative Bearing (RB) or as a Magnetic Bearing to the Station (QDM); or

- **from the NDB ground station** (which is necessary if the aeroplane's position is to be plotted on a chart) as either a Magnetic Bearing from the Station (QDR) or as a True Bearing from the Station (known in the Q-Code as QTE).

Example 1: An aircraft has a Magnetic Heading of 015° M (i.e. MH 015). Its ADF needle points towards a Non-Directional Beacon 75° to starboard (i.e. to the right of the nose) on a Fixed-Card ADF (Relative Bearing Indicator). Magnetic Variation is 5°W. Calculate:

(a) the Relative Bearing (RB) of the NDB from the aeroplane;

(b) the Magnetic Bearing of the NDB from the aeroplane (MB or QDM);

(c) the Magnetic Bearing of the aeroplane from the NDB (QDR); and

(d) the True Bearing of the aeroplane from the NDB (TB or QTE).

Whilst it is possible to calculate all of this mentally, at this early stage it is a good idea to sketch a clear diagram to help visualise the situation.

    Step 1: Sketch the aeroplane on MH 015.

    Step 2: Indicate RB 075.

    Step 3: Draw in the Position Line to the NDB.

Fig.11b-3. Magnetic Heading 015°, Relative Bearing 075°.

MH 015	MB/QDM 090°M	Variation West,	QDR 270°M
+ **RB 075**	+ 180	Magnetic Best.	VARN –5
MB/QDM 090°M	**QDR 270°M**		**QTE 265°T**

Answers: RB 075; QDM 090; QDR 270; QTE 265.

A Small Note on QTE

Normally, an Instrument Pilot will not bother to actually plot positions on a chart. However, if for some reason he decides to, then the easiest method on a visual chart is to use True Bearings from a ground station, i.e. bearings from a ground station related to True North (as indicated on the chart by the Meridians of Longitude). In the 'Q-Code', this is known as **QTE** , a True Bearing from a Ground Station. QTE is easily calculated. In the UK, where Variation is West, it is simply:

QTE = QDR – West Variation.

Example 2: MH is 280. RB is 050. What is the True Bearing from the NDB (QTE)? Variation in the area is 6°W.

MH 280 + RB 050 =	QDM	330
		−2
		+2
	QDR	150
		−6 W Varn
	QTE	**144° TRUE**

Fig.11b-4. QTE = QDR 150 – 6°W Variation = 144°T.

NOTE: as a matter of interest, QTE can be supplied to a Pilot by the Radar Controller, although a prudent Pilot will calculate his own by subtracting West Variation from QDR.

Example 3: Magnetic Heading is 120°M. The needle indicates 290° on a Fixed-Card ADF. Variation is 7W. Calculate:

(a) the Relative Bearing (RB) of the NDB from the aeroplane;

(b) the Magnetic Bearing of the NDB from the aeroplane (MB or QDM);

(c) the Magnetic Bearing of the aeroplane from the NDB (QDR); and

(d) the True Bearing of the aeroplane from the NDB (TB or QTE).

*Fig.11b-5. Magnetic Heading 120°,
Relative Bearing 290°.*

```
        MH 120*      *after doing this, see below for a quicker method.
      + RB 290
      MB/QDM 410     MB/QDM 050°M   Variation West,   QDR 230°M
          –360           + 180      Magnetic Best.    VARN –7
      MB/QDM 050°M    QDR 230°M                       QTE 223°T
```

Answers: RB 290; QDM 050; QDR 230; QTE 223.

*AN EASIER METHOD OF VISUALISING QDM

A Relative Bearing, as well as being specified using the 360° method clockwise from the nose of the aeroplane, can be specified as either left or right of the nose (or the tail). For instance, a Relative Bearing of 290 may be thought of as –70, since the QDM will be 70° less than the Magnetic Heading. Similarly, RB 030 may be thought of as +30, since it will cause the QDM to exceed the MH by 30°.

For angles off the tail of the aeroplane, RB 160 may be thought of as –20 off the tail; and RB 210 as +30 off the tail. This builds up a **quadrantal** approach to Relative Bearing and QDM/QDR problems that will simplify your visualisation in flight.

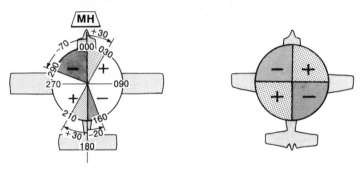

Fig.11b-6. 'Quadrants' for converting RBs to QDMs or QDRs.

Example 4: An aeroplane is flying on a Magnetic Heading of 340. The ADF needle shows RB 010. Determine the QDM.

MH 340
RB +10
QDM 350

Fig.11b-7. MH 340 + RB 10 = MB/QDM 350.

Example 5: An aeroplane is flying on a Magnetic Heading of 358. The ADF needle shows RB 352. Determine the QDM.

MH 358
RB −8
QDM 350

Fig.11b-8. MH 358 − RB 8 = MB/QDM 350.

Notice that, by coincidence, this aeroplane is on the same QDM as the one above. In fact, it may even be the same aeroplane which has simply altered Magnetic Heading by turning right from 340 to 358.

Example 6: An aeroplane is flying on a Magnetic Heading of 340. The ADF needle shows RB 190. Determine the QDR.

MH 340
+ 10 off the tail
QDR 350

Fig.11b-9. MH 340 + 10 off the Tail = QDR 350.

Example 7: An aeroplane is flying on a Magnetic Heading of 010. The ADF needle shows RB 160° Determine the QDR.

MH 010
−20 off the tail
QDR 350

Fig.11b-10. MH 010 − 20 off the tail = QDR 350.

Notice that, by coincidence, this aeroplane is on the same QDR as the one above. In fact, it may even be the same aeroplane which has simply altered Magnetic Heading by turning right from 340 to 010.

VISUALISING POSITION ON THE DIRECTION INDICATOR

Mentally transferring the RBI Needle onto the DI allows quick visualisation of QDM on the Head of the Needle, and QDR on its Tail. If the Pilot now imagines a model aeroplane attached to the Tail of the Needle, with the model aeroplane orientated with the actual Heading, he has a very good picture of the whole scene.

Example 8: Visualise the situation of MH 070 and RB 260.

Fig.11b-11. Visualising Position on the DI; QDM 330 and MH 070.

INTERCEPTING A TRACK

The Pilot, having orientated himself with respect to an NDB, knows the answer to the question **"Where am I?"** He now asks **"Where do I want to go?"** and **"How do I get there?"**

Step (1) is always to **orientate the aeroplane** relative to the NDB, and to the Desired Track.

Step (2) involves a **turn to take up a suitable intercept heading,** considering where it is that you want to join the track.

Step (3) involves maintaining the intercept heading and waiting:
• for the Head of the Needle to fall if inbound;
• for the Tail of the Needle to rise if outbound;
    to +/– 030 for a 30° intercept;
    to +/– 045 for a 45° intercept;
    to +/– 060 for a 60° intercept;
    to +/– 090 for a 90° intercept, etc.

Step (4) involves a **turn onto the Desired Track** and allowing for a suitable **Wind Correction Angle** to maintain it.

Fig.11b-12. Where Am I? Where Do I Want To Go? How Do I Get There?

VISUALISING WHERE YOU ARE, AND WHERE YOU WANT TO GO

The Direction Indicator (DI) can assist greatly in visualising the situation. In the previous example, the situation MH 070 and RB 260 was visualised, the aeroplane being on QDM 330. What now if the Pilot wishes to intercept a Track of 270 TO the NDB?

All that the Pilot needs to do is visualise the Desired Track on the DI. With a model aeroplane on the Tail of the Needle tracking as desired, it becomes quite clear what turns are necessary to intercept the Desired Track.

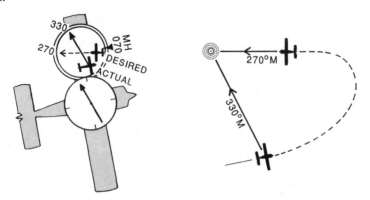

Fig.11b-13a. Visualising an Intercept on the DI.

The first turn to make is to the left onto a suitable intercept heading, say MH 360 for a 90° intercept of QDM 270 TO the NDB.

NOTE: If a Pilot becomes disoriented, a simple procedure is to take up the Heading of the Desired Track. Even though not on Track, the aeroplane will at least be parallel to it, and the ADF Needle will indicate which way to turn to intercept it.

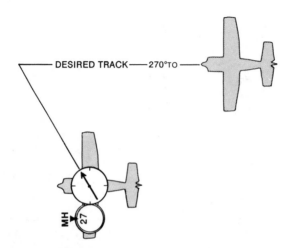

Fig.11b-13b. Paralleling Track to Help in Visualisation.

Suppose the situation is MH 340, RB 080, and the Pilot wishes to intercept a track of 090 TO the NDB. The current QDM is of course 060°M (MH 340 + RB 080).

Fig.11b-14a. Visualising the Intercept.

By continuing to head 340°M, the aeroplane will eventually intercept 090-TO, but it would be a rather untidy intercept, with a turn of 110° being required.

Fig.11b-14b.

A tidier and more efficient intercept could be achieved by turning onto an initial heading of 360°M for a 90° intercept; or a heading of 030°M for a 60° intercept. (Turning further right onto a heading of 060°M would of course point the aeroplane **at** the NDB and the 090-TO track would not be intercepted.)

Fig.11b-14c.

191

USING THE ADF TO INTERCEPT AN INBOUND TRACK

Example 9: An aeroplane is heading 355° M, and the RBI indicates 005 when tuned to a particular NDB. The Pilot is requested to track inbound on a Track of 340°M to the station, intercepting the track at 60°.

Step 1. Orientate the aeroplane.
MH 355 + RB 005 = QDM 360 or QDR 180.
The aeroplane is south of the NDB and heading 355.

ANGLES NOT
PRECISELY
TO SCALE

Fig.11b-15. Visualising Track.

The Desired Track is 340° M to the NDB (or 160° M from the NDB), which is to the right of the aeroplane.

Step 2. To intercept the Track 340 from the left at 60°, the aeroplane should be turned onto a Heading of (340 + 60 = 400 =) 040°M. As the aeroplane's heading alters, the ADF needle will continue to point at the NDB and so the Relative Bearing will change (in this case, even though it is not an important calculation, from 005 to – 040 or 320 with the 45° right turn).

Step 3. Maintain MH 040 and periodically observe the RBI as the Head of the Needle falls. Since it is a *plus 60* intercept, wait until the Head of the Needle falls to *minus 60* (or 300). You are: **heading plus 60, waiting for minus 60.**

Step 4. At QDM 340, or shortly before QDM 340 is reached, and as the Needle is falling to – 60, turn left to take up the Desired Track to the NDB, allowing for the estimated crosswind effect on tracking. In this case, a Wind Correction Angle (WCA) of 3° left is used. Maintain the Desired Track of 340°M to the station by continually checking that MH + RB = QDM 340.

NOTE: An aeroplane takes some distance to turn, and so a Pilot should anticipate the Desired Track by commencing the turn onto track just before QDM 340 is reached. He could do this by observing the rate at which the ADF Needle falls towards – 060, and commencing the turn accordingly.

Fig.11b-16. Intercepting 340°M Inbound, from South of the Station.

Example 10: An aeroplane is given a Radar Heading to steer of 010°M, and to intercept 055°M inbound to an NDB off that Heading.

Step 1. Orientate the aeroplane. With Radar Vector 010 to intercept 055 Inbound, the aeroplane must be south of 055 Inbound.

Step 2. The intercept has been organised by the Radar Controller so that the aeroplane will intercept track at 45° (055 − 010 = 45).

Step 3. Maintain MH 010 and periodically observe the RBI as the Head of the Needle falls. Since it is a minus 45 intercept, wait until the Head of the Needle falls to +045. **Heading minus 45, waiting for plus 45.**

Step 4. At QDM 055, or shortly before QDM 055 is reached and as the Needle falls onto +45, turn right to take up the Desired Track to the NDB, allowing for the estimated crosswind effect on tracking. In this case, a WCA of 5° right is used, by steering MH 060 with the RBI on − 005 (355). Maintain the Desired Track of 055°M to the station by continually checking that MH + RB = QDM 055.

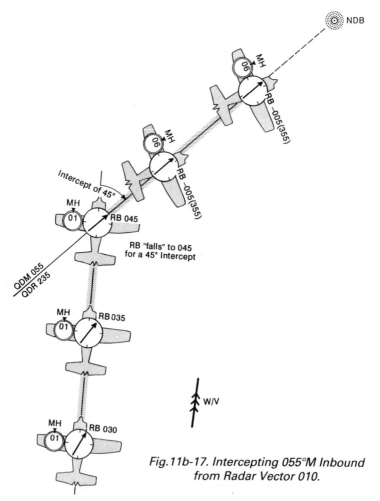

Fig.11b-17. Intercepting 055°M Inbound from Radar Vector 010.

Another means of achieving a smooth intercept is to reduce the closing angle as the Desired Track is approached, say from 45° to 30° to 15° and, finally, to zero as it is intercepted.

USING THE ADF TO INTERCEPT AN OUTBOUND TRACK

Example 11: The Radar Controller gives a Radar Vector of 340 to intercept an outbound track of 280.

Step 1. Orientate the aeroplane. It must be south of the Outbound Track. (*see Fig.11b-18 below*)

Step 2. Consider the intercept. A Radar Vector of 340 to intercept 280 Outbound means a +60° intercept.

Step 3. Monitor the intercept by steering a steady MH 340 and periodically checking the RBI to see the Tail of the Needle rising to – 060 (300). **Heading plus 60, waiting for minus 60.**

Step 4. As QDR (track outbound) of 280 is approached, indicated by the Tail of the Needle rising to – 060, turn left to pick it up, in this case allowing a WCA of 10° for the wind from the right, i.e. MH 290 and RB – 010 (350) = QDR 280.

Fig.11b-18. Visualising Track.

Fig.11b-19. Radar Vector 340 to Intercept 280 Outbound.

Example 12: An aeroplane is steering 120°M with RB 080. The Pilot wishes to track outbound from the NDB on 090°M, intercepting as soon as possible.

Step 1. Orientate the aeroplane.
MH 120 + RB 080 = QDM 200 or QDR 020
The aeroplane is North-North-East of the
NDB and heading 120°M.

The Desired Track is 090°M from the NDB,
which is to the right of the aeroplane.

Fig.11b-20. Visualising Track.

Step 2. Continuing on present MH 120 would give a 30° intercept of 090 Outbound. To intercept Track 090 Outbound as soon as possible, i.e. with a 90° intercept, the aeroplane should be turned onto a Heading of (090 + 90 =) 180°M.

Step 3. Maintain MH 180 and periodically observe the RBI as the Tail of the Needle rises. Since it is a *plus 90* intercept, wait until the Tail of the Needle rises to *minus 90* (270). **Heading plus 90, waiting for minus 90.**

Step 4. At QDR 090, or shortly before QDR 090 is reached and as the Tail of the Needle approaches −90, turn left to take up the Desired Track from the NDB, allowing for the estimated crosswind effect on tracking. In this case, with nil wind, steer MH 090. The Tail of the ADF Needle should be on 000. Periodically check that MH +/− ADF Tail = QDR 090.

Fig.11b-21. A 90° Intercept of 090 Outbound.

NOTE: With such a large intercept angle, the Pilot will have to watch the rate at which the Tail of the ADF needle rises, and anticipate the turn to intercept the Desired Track. If he does not anticipate the intercept, the aeroplane will fly through the track, which will then have to be re-intercepted from the other side – not a very tidy manoeuvre.

TRACKING

USING THE RBI TO TRACK INBOUND TO AN NDB

The ADF/NDB combination is often used to provide guidance for an aeroplane from a distant position to a position overhead the NDB ground position. This is known as *Tracking*. Just how the Pilot achieves this depends to a certain extent upon the wind direction and speed, since an aeroplane initially pointed directly at the NDB will be blown off course by a crosswind.

1. Tracking Towards an NDB, with No Crosswind Effect

With no crosswind, a direct track inbound can be achieved by heading the aeroplane directly at the NDB. This is achieved with a Heading that maintains the ADF Needle on the nose of the aeroplane (RB 000).

Fig.11b-22. Tracking Inbound, with No Crosswind.

If there is no crosswind to blow the aeroplane off track, then everything will remain constant as in the case illustrated above – the Magnetic Heading 096, the Relative Bearing of 000, and the QDM 096 will all remain constant. This will be the situation in:
- nil wind conditions;
- a direct headwind; or
- a direct tailwind.

2. Tracking Inbound with a Crosswind

(a) With **No Correction for Drift** made by the Pilot, and the aeroplane headed directly at the NDB so that the ADF needle indicates a Relative Bearing of 000, any crosswind will cause the aeroplane to be blown off track.

Time 0715	*Time 0725*
MH 096	MH 096
RB 000	RB 357 (i.e. −3)
QDM 096	QDM 093

Fig.11b-23. Crosswind Causes Drift.

In the case illustrated above, the wind, with a northerly component, has blown the aeroplane to the right of track. This is indicated by the ADF needle starting to move down the left of the dial. To return to track, the aeroplane must be turned towards the left, i.e. towards the direction in which the Head of the Needle is moving.

If the Pilot turns left to put the NDB on the nose again, i.e. RB 000, then after a short while the aeroplane will again have been blown to the right of track, and the ADF Needle will move to the left of the nose. A further turn to the left will be required – and the process will need to be repeated again and again.

In this way, the Track Made Good (TMG) to the NDB will be curved, the aeroplane finally approaching the NDB heading roughly into-wind, and a longer distance will be travelled compared to the direct track from the original position. This rather inefficient means of arriving overhead the NDB is known as *Homing* (keeping the NDB on the nose). It is not a very tidy procedure. Professional Pilots rarely use it!

(b) With **Correct Drift Correction** made by the Pilot – a far better procedure than Homing is to **track direct to the NDB** by heading into-wind and **laying off a Wind Correction Angle (WCA) to counteract drift** . If 5° left is indeed the correct WCA, the aeroplane can achieve a track of 096°M direct to the NDB by the Pilot steering MH 091.

Time 0715
MH 091
RB 005
QDM 096

Time 0725
MH 091
RB 005
QDM 096 (QDM = MH + RB).

Fig.11b-24. Tracking Direct to the NDB.

Different Winds Require Different Wind Correction Angles. An aeroplane is on Track when the Relative Bearing is Equal and Opposite to the difference between the actual Magnetic Heading and the Desired Track. This is illustrated in the figure below. In each situation, the aeroplane is on the Desired Track of 010°M, but using a different Wind Correction Angle to counteract the drift under different wind conditions.

(MH minus 8, RB plus 8)   (MH minus 4, RB plus 4)   (MH 0, RB 0)   (MH plus 20, RB minus 20)

Fig.11b-25. Laying Off Drift to Achieve The Desired Track.

If the precise wind effect is not known, then use a "best guess" WCA estimated from the available information as an initial WCA. For the same crosswind, slower aeroplanes will need to allow a greater WCA than faster aeroplanes.

It is possible that the wind effect will change as a Pilot tracks towards an NDB, and so regular adjustments to the Heading may be required. This is often the case as an aeroplane descends using the NDB as the tracking aid, due to variations in wind velocity and True Air Speed.

(c) With **Incorrect Drift Correction** made by the Pilot, the aeroplane will move off the desired track, i.e. the QDM (Magnetic Track to the NDB) will change. If a steady Heading is being flown, this will become obvious through a gradually changing Relative Bearing, with the ADF Needle **moving** left or right down the dial.

Suppose, for instance, the Pilot steers a Heading with a 5° Wind Correction Angle to the left to counteract the effects of a wind from the left. If the wind effect turns out to be less than expected, then the aeroplane will gradually move to the left of the desired Track to the NDB, and the QDM will gradually increase. Typical cockpit indications could be:

Time 0715	*Time 0725*
MH 091	MH 091
RB 005	RB 008
QDM 096	QDM 099 (QDM = MH + RB).

Fig. 11b-26. An Incorrect Wind Correction Angle Causes QDM to Change.

The head of the ADF Needle falling away to the right indicates that a turn right must be made to track to the NDB. Conversely, the head of the ADF Needle falling away to the left indicates that a left turn must be made to track to the NDB. Just how great each correcting turn should be depends upon the deviation from track.

NOTE: Be careful of terminology. **Drift** is the angle between Heading and the actual Track Made Good, which may not be the Desired Track. The perfect Wind Correction Angle will counteract any drift exactly, and the actual TMG will follow the Desired Track, which is usually the aim of tracking.

Fig.11b-27. Drift is the Angle Between Heading and TMG.

WHAT TO DO TO MAINTAIN TRACK

Flying Straight and Level usually consists of many tiny climbs and descents in an attempt by the Pilot to maintain the desired altitude perfectly. Similarly, it is almost impossible to maintain a perfect track, and so many small turns will usually have to be made by the Pilot in an attempt to do so by correcting any deviations from track.

Re-intercepting a track, having deviated from it, involves the same procedure as the initial intercept of a new track, except that the angles will be smaller provided the Pilot is vigilant and does not allow large deviations to occur. Realising that the aeroplane is diverging from the direct track to the NDB, the Pilot has several options. He may either:

(a) track direct from the present position (along a new track); or

(b) regain the original track.

(a) **To track direct to the NDB** from the present position (even though it is not on the originally desired track) turn slightly right (say 3° in this case), and track direct to the NDB from the present position. In most NDB tracking, this technique is used only when very close to the station (say 1 or 2 nm from the NDB), when there is insufficient distance remaining to regain track.

Fig.11b-28. Flying a New Track to the NDB.

Needle Head Falling Right;
Turn Right.

(b) **To regain the original track,** turn further right initially (say 5° onto MH 096), re-intercept the original track by allowing the wind to blow the aeroplane back onto it and, once the track is regained, turn left and steer a Heading with a different Wind Correction Angle (say WCA 3° left instead of 5° left), i.e. MH 093 instead of MH 091. This is a very moderate correction, something you would expect to see from an experienced Instrument Pilot who would have noticed any deviation from track fairly quickly.

Fig. 11b-29. Regain the Desired Track.

Attempting to maintain the Desired Track (i.e. remaining on the one QDM) is the normal navigational technique when at some distance from the NDB. If, when maintaining a steady Magnetic Heading, the ADF Needle near the top of the dial indicates a constant Relative Bearing, then the aeroplane is tracking directly to the NDB, and no correction to Heading is necessary.

If MH + RB = Desired QDM constantly, then ADF Tracking is Good.

Just how great each correcting turn should be depends upon the deviation from track. A simple method is to **double the error** . If the aeroplane has deviated 10° left indicated by the RBI moving 10° right, then alter Heading by 20° to the right. (If you alter Heading by only 10° to the right, the result will probably be a further deviation to the left, a further correction to the right, with this being repeated again and again, resulting in a curved *homing* to the NDB.)

Having regained track, turn left by only half the correcting turn of 20°, i.e. turn left 10° to intercept and maintain Track. This leaves you with a WCA different to the original one (remembering that the original WCA caused you to deviate from track). The new WCA should provide reasonable tracking. If not, make further minor corrections to Heading!

Fig.11b-30. Regaining Track by 'Doubling the Error', and maintaining Track thereafter.

'BRACKETTING' TRACK

In practice, an absolutely perfect direct track is difficult to achieve. The actual Track Made Good by the Pilot will probably consist of a number of minor corrections such as that described above, a technique known as *bracketting* the Track, i.e. making regular corrections, left or right as required, to maintain or regain the Desired Track.

The aim of bracketting is to find the precise WCA needed to maintain track. If, for instance, a WCA of 10° right is found to be too great and the aeroplane diverges to the right of track, and a WCA of only 5° right is too little and the wind blows the aeroplane to the left of track, then try something in between, say WCA 8° right.

A precise Instrument Pilot will monitor the tracking of the aeroplane on a regular basis, and make corrections earlier rather than later, the result being a number of small corrections rather than just one big correction. However, if a big correction is required as may be the case in strong winds, he will make it. Be positive in your actions!

Fig. 11b-31. 'Bracketting' the Track.

Head of Needle falling Right – Turn Right;
Head of Needle falling Left – Turn Left.

WHAT TO DO IF UNCERTAIN OF WIND EFFECT

If the wind direction and strength is not obvious, then the best technique is to initially **steer Track as Heading** (i.e. make no allowance for drift). The effect of the wind will become obvious as the ADF Needle moves to the left or right. Observe the results, and then make Heading adjustments to bracket Track.

Fig.11b-32. If Uncertain of Wind, Initially Steer Track as Heading.

TRACKING OVERHEAD THE NDB

The ADF needle will become more and more sensitive as the NDB station is approached. Minor displacements left or right of track will cause larger and larger changes in Relative Bearing and QDM, i.e. the ADF Needle becomes *agitated* as the NDB is approached. For a very precise track to be achieved, the Pilot must be prepared to increase his scan rate as the NDB is approached, and to make corrections more frequently.

Fig.11b-33. Approaching the NDB, the ADF Needle Becomes More Sensitive.

Close to the station and just prior to passing overhead, however, the ADF Needle becomes very sensitive. The Pilot, at this point, can relax a little and steer a steady heading until the aeroplane passes overhead the NDB, indicated by the ADF needle moving towards the bottom of the dial and settling down.

Having passed overhead the NDB, tracking **from** the NDB should be checked and suitable adjustments made to Heading. If the track outbound is different to that inbound, then a suitable heading change estimated to make good the new desired track could be made as soon as the ADF needle falls past the 090 or 270 position on its way to the bottom of the dial.

Fig.11b-34. Do Not Overcorrect When Close to the Station.

The ADF needle becoming extremely active and then falling rapidly to the bottom of the dial indicates that the aeroplane has passed directly overhead the NDB.

The ADF needle moving gradually to one side and slowly falling to the bottom of the dial indicates that the aeroplane is passing to one side of the beacon – the rate at which the needle falls being an indication of the aeroplane's proximity to the NDB. If it falls very slowly, then possibly the tracking by the Pilot could have been better. Time overhead (or abeam) the NDB can be taken as the needle falls through the approximate 090 or 270 position.

Fig.11b-35. Good ADF Tracking; Reasonable Tracking; Poor Tracking.

TRACKING AWAY FROM AN NDB

When tracking away from an NDB, the Head of the ADF Needle will lie towards the bottom of the dial.

1. Tracking Away from an NDB with No Crosswind Effect

If the Pilot tracks overhead the NDB and then steers Track as Heading, the aeroplane will track directly away from the NDB with the Head of the ADF Needle steady on 180, and the Tail of the ADF Needle steady at the top of the dial on 000.

Fig.11b-36. Tracking Away From an NDB with No Crosswind Effect.

The aeroplane illustrated above has a QDR of 040 (Magnetic Track from the station to the aeroplane), and a QDM of 220 (Magnetic Track from the aeroplane to the station).

2. Tracking Away from an NDB with a Crosswind

Suppose that the Desired Track outbound from an NDB is 040°M, and the Pilot estimates that a WCA of 5° to the right is necessary to counteract a wind from the right. To achieve this, he steers MH 045, and hopes to see the Tail of the ADF Needle stay on − 005 (i.e. 355). The Magnetic Track away from the station (QDR) is found from:

QDR = MH +/− deflection of the Tail of the Needle.

In this case, MH 045 − 005 tail = QDR 040, and the chosen WCA and Magnetic Heading to steer are correct.

Fig.11b-37. Tracking Away From an NDB, with a WCA of 5° Into Wind.

If the estimated WCA is incorrect, then the actual Track Made Good by the aeroplane will differ from that desired. If, in the above case, the wind is stronger than expected, the aeroplane's actual TMG may be 033°M, and to the left of the Desired Track of 040°M.

Fig.11b-38. Tracking Away From an NDB with an Incorrect Wind Correction Angle.

Whereas inaccurate tracking **to** an NDB is indicated by the ADF Needle falling, incorrect tracking **away** from an NDB can occur with the ADF Needle indicating a steady reading. Having passed overhead the NDB, an aeroplane can track away from it in any of 360 directions. The Pilot must always ensure that he is flying away from the NDB along the correct track, and the easiest means to do this is to calculate QDR or QDM using the **DI** and the **RBI** .

REGAINING TRACK AWAY FROM AN NDB IN A CROSSWIND

If an incorrect Wind Correction angle is flown, then the aeroplane will of course be blown off track. The vigilant Pilot/Navigator will observe the incorrect TMG, probably by visualising QDR (from the NDB) or QDM (to the NDB) whilst a constant Magnetic Heading is flown.

Example 13: In the situation illustrated below, the Pilot is flying Track as Heading, i.e. initially making no allowance for drift. If the head of the ADF Needle moves right from 180 into the negative quadrant, then the aeroplane must be turned right to regain track.

Fig.11b-39. Turning Right to 'Trail the Tail' or 'Pull the Tail Around'.

NOTE: It is generally easier to work off the top of the dial, since that is where the aeroplane is going, rather than off the bottom of the dial. The right turn necessary to regain track, turning right towards the Head of the Needle and therefore away from the Tail of the Needle, can be thought of as *pulling the tail of the ADF Needle around* or *trailing the tail*. Some Instructors, however, prefer to say that if the Head of the Needle is moving left, then turn left (and vice versa), even though the Head of the Needle is at the bottom of the dial. Your instructor will advise his preferred method.

In the case illustrated above, the aeroplane has been blown to the left of track. The off-track QDR is given by:

MH 040 − 015 tail = QDR 025;
which is left of the desired QDR 040.

To regain track, the Pilot has turned right by 30° (double the error) from MH 040 to MH 070, which causes a simultaneous change in the Relative Bearing of the NDB, the ADF Needle Tail moving from − 015 (345) to − 045 (315). (The Head of the Needle, indicating Relative Bearing, will move from 165 to 135, but this is not a calculation for the Pilot to make, only an observation.)

The Relative Bearing will naturally change as the aeroplane is turned but, once the aeroplane is flown on its steady intercept heading of MH 070, the tail of the needle will be gradually pulled around.

The Pilot will continue with the intercept Heading until the aeroplane approaches the Desired Track, QDR 040. This is indicated to the Pilot by MH 070 and the tail of the needle moving up towards − 030 (since QDR 040 = MH 070 − 030 tail). For a 30° intercept of 040°M outbound, the Pilot is steering +30 (040 + 30 = MH 070), waiting for the Tail of the Needle to rise to − 030.

Flying Track plus 30, waiting for minus 30 on the Needle.

As the Desired Outbound Track is approached, the Pilot turns left to maintain QDR 040. Estimating a WCA of 10° into wind to be sufficient, the Pilot steers MH 050 and checks regularly that the needle tail stays on − 010.

Example 14: If, on the other hand, the head of the ADF Needle moves left from 180 into the positive quadrant, then the aeroplane must be turned left to regain track. Looking at the top of the ADF Dial and the Tail of the Needle, turn left and 'trail the tail'.

In the case illustrated next, the aeroplane has been blown to the right of track. The off-track QDR is given by:

MH 040 + 015 tail = QDR 055;
which is right of the desired QDR 040.

To regain track, the Pilot has turned left by 30° from MH 040 to MH 010, which causes a simultaneous change in the Relative Bearing of the NDB, the ADF Needle Tail moving from 015 to 045.

ANGLES
NOT TO
SCALE

W/V

Maintaining
TR 040
on MH 030

Turn Right to
maintain Track

On QDR 040 again
(QDM 220)

Tail of Needle movement

"TRAIL THE TAIL";
Turn Left to regain Track

QDR 055
(QDM 235)

NDB

*Fig.11b-40. Turning Left to
'Trail the Tail' or 'Pull the Tail Around'.*

The Relative Bearing will naturally change as the aeroplane is turned but, once the aeroplane is flown on its steady intercept heading of MH 010, the tail of the needle will be gradually pulled around. For a 30° intercept of 040°M outbound, the Pilot is steering − 30 (040 − 30 = MH 010), waiting for the Tail of the Needle to rise to +030.

Flying Track minus 30, waiting for plus 30 on the Needle.

The Pilot will continue with the intercept Heading until the aeroplane approaches the Desired Track, QDR 040. This is indicated to the Pilot by MH 010 and the tail of the needle moving up towards 030 (since QDR 040 = MH 010 + 030 tail).

As the Desired Track outbound is approached, the Pilot turns right to maintain QDR 040. Estimating a WCA of 10° into-wind to be sufficient, the Pilot steers MH 030 and checks regularly that the needle tail stays on +010.

211

THE NDB APPROACH

The NDB/ADF combination is very useful for tracking, and use is made of this in the Instrument Approach to Land known as the *NDB Approach* or *NDB Let-Down,* such as that at *Lyneham,* illustrated below. The top section of the chart shows a **plan view** for *tracking* purposes, and the bottom section shows a **profile view** for *vertical navigation* (i.e. descent).

Fig. 11b-41. Plan and Profile of the Lyneham NDB Approach for Runway 25.
(Jeppesen chart)

Prior to being used for tracking, the NDB must have been *selected, identified* and checked that it is indeed *'ADFing'*. Flying towards Lyneham at the end of a cross-country flight, the pilot can track to the NDB (using his ADF) at an altitude no lower than the Minimum Safe Altitude (MSA) for that sector (shown as Sector Safe Altitude, SSA, on Aerad charts). From the Southwest, the MSA is 3000 ft AMSL.

From overhead the NDB, the pilot may track outbound on 090°M, and descend to 3000 ft on QNH *(2533 ft on QFE)*, the height difference in these being due to the Threshold Elevation of 467 ft. Normal outbound tracking procedures are used, with the ADF needle being very sensitive at first, and becoming less sensitive as the aeroplane flies further away from the NDB. It is good airmanship to monitor the *IDENT* of the NDB periodically.

At 8 nm outbound from the NDB, a left turn is commenced to intercept the inbound track of 255°M. During the turn, the aircraft is permitted to descend to 2500 ft on QNH *(2033 ft on QFE)*.

When established on the inbound track of 255°M (within +/–5°), the aircraft may be descended to the Minimum Descent Altitude (MDA, on QNH), or the Minimum Descent Height (MDH, on QFE). Reference to MDA and MDH combined is often written as MDA(H). (Calculating these minima is discussed in Chapter 19.) The absolute minimum height for an NDB Approach by an IMC-Rated Pilot is 600 ft on QFE (i.e. AAL), but it could be significantly higher, depending on obstacles in the vicinity.

If the pilot becomes *visual* at or above the MDA(H), he may descend further for a landing. If he does **not** become visual at the MDA(H), then he may continue tracking to the NDB at the MDA(H) in the hope of becoming visual, but otherwise must make a *Missed Approach* at the NDB by climbing away on the outbound track of 245°M, to at least the published Missed Approach altitude of 2000 ft on QNH. The options then are to return for another approach in the hope that conditions have improved, or to divert to another aerodrome at a safe cruise level.

Fig.11b-42. Flying the Lyneham NDB Approach using an RBI.

□ Now complete **Exercises 11b – The RBI.**

11c

THE RADIO MAGNETIC
INDICATOR (RMI)

The RMI, compared with the RBI, significantly reduces Pilot Workload.

The *Radio Magnetic Indicator* combines the Relative Bearing Indicator and Direction Indicator (also known as Heading Indicator) into the one instrument, with the ADF Card being aligned automatically with Magnetic North. This considerably reduces the workload on the pilot by reducing the amount of *visualisation* and *mental arithmetic* required. Even the Manually Rotatable Card (the *poor man's RMI*, which allows the pilot to align the ADF Card **manually** with Magnetic North) lightens the workload, since it also reduces the amount of visualisation and mental arithmetic required.

The discussion that follows applies to both the RMI and the Manually Rotatable Card ADF, except that whereas:
- the RMI is continuously and automatically aligned with Magnetic North;
- the Manually Rotatable Card must be re-aligned with the DI by hand following every Heading change (and of course the DI must be re-aligned with the Magnetic Compass by hand every 10 minutes or so).

Fig.11c-1. The RMI is automatically aligned with Magnetic North.

Fig.11c-2.
The Manually
Rotatable ADF Card.

ORIENTATION USING THE RMI

An RMI gives a graphic picture of where the aeroplane is:
- the Head of the RMI Needle displays QDM (Magnetic Track *to* the NDB); and
- the Tail of the RMI Needle displays QDR (Magnetic Track *from* the NDB).

Example 1: Orientate an aeroplane with MH 320 and RMI 050. Determine the QDM, QDR and QTE (True Track from the NDB). The Magnetic Variation is 7°W.

NOTE: 'RMI 050' means QDM 050°M to the NDB (whereas 'RBI 030' or 'ADF 030' means a Relative Bearing of 030 to the NDB, i.e. relative to the nose of the aeroplane and its Heading).

QDM is 050, QDR is 230.

Variation West, Magnetic Best; so True Track to the NDB is given by:
QTE = QDR 230 – 7°W Var'n = QTE 223.

Fig.11c-3. Orientation with an RMI is quite straightforward.

QTE is really only of value for plotting a Position Line on a Visual Chart, and so is rarely used in Instrument Flying.

THE INITIAL INTERCEPTION OF TRACK

INTERCEPTING AN INBOUND TRACK USING THE RMI

A common use for the RMI, after the Pilot has used it to orientate himself with respect to the NDB, is to **track** to the NDB. The RMI makes it easy for a Pilot to visualise:
- where he is;
- where he wants to go; and
- how to get there.

Example 2: An aeroplane has MH 340 and RMI 030. The Pilot is requested to intercept a Track of 090 TO the NDB.

Step 1. Orientating the aeroplane is made easy by the RMI. The QDM (Magnetic Track to the NDB) in the present position is 030. If the Pilot now imagines a model aeroplane attached to the Tail of the Needle, and on the actual Heading (which in this case is MH 340), then he has a very good picture of the situation.

The Desired Track to the NDB, 090°M TO, is ahead of the present position of the aeroplane. If the Pilot visualises the Desired Track on the RMI, with the model aeroplane on the Tail of the Needle tracking as desired, it becomes quite clear what turns are required to intercept the desired Track.

Fig.11c-4. Visualising Track on an RMI.

Step 2. To intercept the Track 090 TO the NDB, the aeroplane should be turned onto a suitable intercept heading, such as one of those illustrated below.

Fig. 11c-5. Intercepting Track at 90°, 60°, or 45°.

Step 3. Maintain the chosen intercept heading and periodically observe the RMI Needle as it falls towards the desired inbound track of 090°M.

Step 4. As the 090 Track is approached, indicated by the RMI Needle approaching 090, turn right to take up the Desired Track to the NDB, allowing for any estimated crosswind effect on tracking. In this case, a WCA of 10° right has been used. With MH 100, and the RMI steady on 090, the aeroplane now tracks 090 TO the NDB.

Example 3: An aeroplane is given a Radar Vector by ATC to steer a Heading of 010°M, and then to make an intercept 055°M Inbound to an NDB.

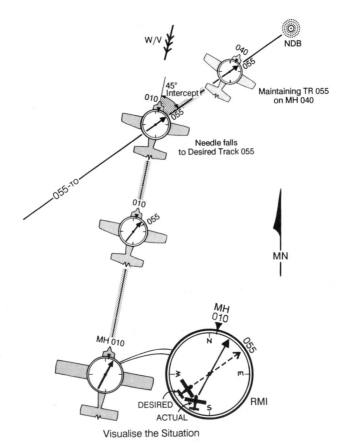

Visualise the Situation

Fig.11c-6. Intercepting 055°M Inbound from Radar Vector 010.

Visualising the situation confirms that Radar Vector 010 will intercept the 055 TO Track, and it will in fact be a 45° intercept (055 − 010 = 45). The RMI Needle falls towards 055 approaching the Desired Track Inbound, and the Pilot should commence a turn shortly before reaching it to avoid overshooting it. This is known as *leading-in* (which is really *anticipating*), and the amount of lead-in can be judged by the **rate** at which the Needle is falling, and the distance required for the aeroplane to turn onto a suitable Heading to track inbound. Another means of achieving a smooth intercept is to reduce the closing angle as the Desired Track is approached, say from 45° to 30° to 15° and, finally, to zero as it is intercepted.

In this case, the Pilot has chosen to track inbound with a WCA of 15° left to counteract drift caused by a strong northerly wind. Correct tracking to the NDB will be confirmed by the RMI Needle staying on 055.

INTERCEPTING AN OUTBOUND TRACK USING THE RMI

Example 4: The Pilot is given a Radar Vector of 340 to intercept 280 Outbound from an NDB.

Step 1. Orientate the aeroplane.

Step 2. Consider the intercept, 60° in this case (340 – 280 = 60). Visualise the situation. Again, the model aeroplane imagined on the Tail of the Needle helps.

Fig.11c-7. Visualise the Situation.

Step 3. Monitor the intercept by steering a steady MH 340 and periodically checking the Tail of the RMI Needle rising to 280.

Step 4. As the Desired Track 280 Outbound (or QDR 280) is approached, and as the Tail of the Needle approaches 280, the Pilot turns left to pick it up, in this case allowing no Wind Correction Angle, since he expects no crosswind effect.

Fig.11c-8. Intercepting 280 Outbound off Radar Vector 340.

MAINTAINING TRACK

1. Tracking Towards an NDB, with No Crosswind Effect

With no crosswind, a direct track inbound can be achieved by heading the aeroplane directly at the NDB. The Magnetic Heading will, in this case, be the same as the Desired Track, and the RMI Needle will be on the nose indicating the Track.

Fig.11c-9. Tracking Inbound on 250°M Using an RMI, with No Crosswind.

If there is no crosswind to blow the aeroplane off track, then everything will remain constant as in the case illustrated above — the Magnetic Heading 250 and the RMI 250 will remain constant. This will be the situation in:
- nil wind conditions;
- a direct headwind; or
- a direct tailwind.

2. Tracking Inbound with a Crosswind

(a) With **No Correction for Drift** made by the Pilot, and the aeroplane headed straight at the NDB with the RMI Needle initially on the nose, any crosswind will cause the aeroplane to be blown off track.

Time 0715	*Time 0725*
MH 250	MH 250
RMI 250 (QDM)	RMI 255 (QDM)

In the case illustrated below, the wind, with a northerly component, has blown the aeroplane to the left of track. This is indicated by the Head of the RMI Needle starting to move down the right of the dial. To return to track, the aeroplane must be turned towards the right, i.e. towards the direction in which the Head of the Needle is moving.

If the Pilot turns left to put the NDB on the nose again, i.e. MH = RMI 255, then after a short period the aeroplane will again be blown to the left of track, and the RMI Needle will move to the right of the nose. Another turn to the right will be required.

In this way the path to the NDB will be curved, with the aeroplane finally approaching the NDB heading roughly into-wind, and a longer distance will be travelled compared to the direct track from the original position. This is known as **Homing** (keeping the NDB on the nose). It is not a very tidy procedure. Professional Pilots rarely use it!

Fig.11c-10. Homing to the NDB.

(b) With **Correct Drift Correction** made by the Pilot — a far better procedure than Homing — the aeroplane tracks direct to an NDB by heading into-wind and laying off a Wind Correction Angle (WCA) to counteract drift. If 15° right is indeed the correct WCA, then the aeroplane will track 250°M direct to the NDB by steering MH 265.

Fig.11c-11. Tracking Direct to the NDB.

Different Winds Require Different Wind Correction Angles. An aeroplane is on Track when the RMI indicates Track. This is illustrated in the figure below. In each situation, the aeroplane is on the Desired Track of 355°M, but using a different Wind Correction Angle to counteract the drift under different wind conditions.

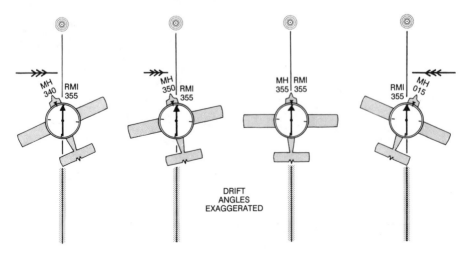

DRIFT
ANGLES
EXAGGERATED

Fig.11c-12. Laying Off Drift to achieve the Desired Track.

If the precise wind effect is not known, then use a "best guess" WCA estimated from the available information as an initial WCA. For the same crosswind, slower aeroplanes will need to allow a greater WCA than faster aeroplanes.

It is possible that the wind effect will change as a Pilot tracks towards an NDB, and so regular alterations of Heading may be required. This is often the case as an aeroplane descends using the NDB as the tracking aid.

(c) With **Incorrect Drift Correction** made by the Pilot the aeroplane will move off the desired track, i.e. the QDM (Magnetic Track to the NDB) will change. This will become obvious through a gradually changing RMI reading (since the RMI indicates QDM).

Suppose, for instance, the Pilot steers a Heading with a 5° Wind Correction Angle to the right to counteract the effects of a wind from the right. If the wind effect turns out to be greater than expected, the aeroplane will gradually deviate to the left of the Desired Track to the NDB, and the RMI reading (QDM) will gradually increase. Typical cockpit indications could be:

Time 0715	*Time 0725*
MH 020	MH 020
RMI 015 (QDM)	RMI 018 (QDM)

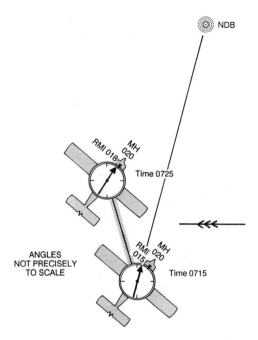

Fig.11c-13. An Incorrect Wind Correction Angle causes RMI Reading (QDM) to Change.

The head of the RMI Needle falling away to the right indicates that a turn right must be made to track to the NDB. Conversely, the head of the RMI Needle falling away to the left indicates that a left turn must be made to track to the NDB. Just how great each correcting turn should be depends upon the deviation from track.

WHAT TO DO TO MAINTAIN TRACK

Re-intercepting a track, once having deviated from it, uses the same procedure as the initial intercept of a new track, except that the angles will be smaller, provided the Pilot is vigilant and does not allow large deviations to occur. Realising that the aeroplane is diverging from the direct track to the NDB, the Pilot has several options. He may either:
(a) track direct to the NDB from the present position even though it is slightly off the original Track; or
(b) regain the original Track.

Method (a). Turn slightly right (say 5° in this case), and track direct to the NDB from the present position, even though it is not on the originally desired Track. In most NDB tracking this technique is used only when very close to the station (say 1 or 2 nm).

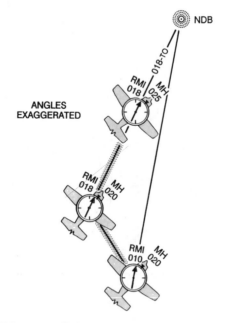

Fig.11c-14. Flying a New Track to the NDB.

Needle Head falling Right;
Turn Right.

Method (b). Turn further right initially (say 10° onto MH 030), and re-intercept the original Track, indicated by the RMI Needle moving down to read 015 again. Once Track is regained, turn left (say by half the correcting turn of 10°) onto MH 025. This is a very moderate correction, something you would expect to see from an experienced Instrument Pilot. (See Fig. 11c-15 opposite.)

Attempting to maintain the Desired Track (i.e. remaining on the one QDM) is the normal navigational technique when at some distance from the NDB. If the RMI remains on a steady reading, then the aeroplane is tracking directly to the NDB.

Just how great each correcting turn should be depends upon the displacement from track and the distance from the station. A simple method is to initially **alter Heading by double the error**. If the aeroplane has deviated 10° left (indicated by the RMI moving 10° right), then alter Heading by 20° to the right. (If you alter Heading by only 10° to the right, the result will probably be a further deviation to the left, a further correction to the right, resulting in a curved *homing* to the NDB.)

Having regained track, turn left by only half the correcting turn of 20°, i.e. turn left 10° to intercept and maintain Track. This leaves you with a WCA different to the original one (that caused you to deviate from track), and one that should provide reasonable tracking. If not, make further corrections to Heading!

Fig.11c-15. Regain the Desired Track.

BRACKETTING TRACK

In practice, an absolutely perfect direct track is difficult to achieve. The actual Track Made Good by the Pilot will probably consist of a number of minor corrections such as those described above, a technique known as **bracketting** the Track, i.e. making regular corrections, left or right as required, to maintain or regain the Desired Track.

The aim of bracketting is to find the precise WCA needed to maintain track. If, for instance, a WCA of 10° right is found to be too great and the aeroplane diverges to the right of track, and a WCA of only 5° right is too little and the wind blows the aeroplane to the left of track, then try something in between, say WCA 8° right.

A precise Instrument Pilot will monitor the tracking of the aeroplane on a regular basis and make corrections earlier rather than later, the result being a number of small corrections rather than just one big correction.

NDB

Turn Right 5° onto MH 005 to maintain Track

Turn Left 10° onto MH 360 to allow Wind to drift the aeroplane back onto Track

Deviating Right of Track; Wind must have changed

Turn Left 10° onto MH 010 to maintain Track

Turn Right 20° onto MH 020 to rejoin Track

Insufficient WCA; Aeroplane has blown Left of Track

Fig. 11c-16. 'Bracketting' the Track.

Head of Needle falling Right – Turn Right;
Head of Needle falling Left – Turn Left.

What to do if Uncertain of Wind Effect

If the wind direction and strength is not obvious, then a useful technique is to initially steer the Track to the station as Heading (i.e. make no allowance for drift), observe the results, and then make Heading adjustments to bracket Track. This is illustrated in *Fig.11c-16.*

TRACKING OVERHEAD THE NDB

The RMI Needle will become more and more sensitive as the NDB station is approached, minor movements left or right of track causing larger and larger changes in the RMI reading; i.e. the RMI Needle becomes *agitated* as the NDB is approached. For a very precise track to be achieved, the Pilot must be prepared to increase his scan rate and respond more frequently.

Fig.11c-17. Approaching the NDB, the RMI Needle becomes More Sensitive.

Close to the station and just prior to passing overhead, however, the Pilot can relax a little and steer a steady heading until the RMI needle moves towards the bottom of the dial and settles down, at which time tracking from the NDB should be checked and suitable adjustments made to Heading. If the track outbound is different to that inbound, then a suitable heading change estimated to make good the new desired track could be made as soon as the RMI needle falls past the mid-position on its way to the bottom of the dial.

Fig.11c-18. Do Not Overcorrect when close to the Station.

The RMI needle becoming extremely active and then falling rapidly to the bottom of the dial indicates that the aeroplane has passed directly overhead the NDB. The RMI needle moving gradually to one side and slowly falling to the bottom of the dial indicates that the aeroplane is passing to one side of the beacon, the rate at which the needle falls being an indication of the aeroplane's proximity to the NDB. If it falls very slowly, then possibly the tracking by the Pilot could have been better. Time overhead (or abeam) the NDB can be taken as the needle falls through the approximate mid-position.

Fig. 11c-19. Good ADF Tracking; Reasonable Tracking; Poor Tracking.

TRACKING AWAY FROM AN NDB

When tracking away from an NDB, the Head of the RMI Needle will lie towards the bottom of the dial, and the Tail of the RMI Needle will be towards the top of the dial.

1. Tracking Away From an NDB with No Crosswind Effect

If the Pilot tracks overhead the NDB and then steers Track as Heading, the aeroplane will track directly away from the NDB with the Head of the RMI Needle steady at the bottom of the dial, and the Tail of the RMI Needle steady at the top of the dial under the MH Lubber Line.

Fig.11c-20. Tracking Away from an NDB with No Crosswind Effect.

The aeroplane illustrated above has a QDR of 090 (Magnetic Track from the station to the aeroplane) indicated by the Tail of the RMI Needle, and a QDM of 270 (Magnetic Track from the aeroplane to the station) indicated by the Head of the RMI Needle. Since it is **Track Outbound** that is being considered here, the position of the **Tail** of the Needle is of more use to the Pilot.

2. Tracking Away From an NDB with a Crosswind

Suppose that the Desired Track outbound from an NDB is 340°M, and the Pilot estimates that a WCA of 12° to the right is necessary to counteract a wind from the right. To achieve this, he steers MH 352, and hopes to see the Tail of the RMI Needle stay on 340, the Desired Outbound Track.

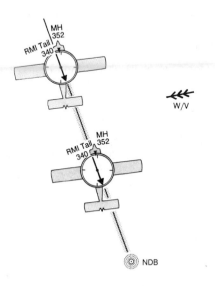

Fig.11c-21. Tracking Away From an NDB with a WCA of 12° Into Wind.

In the case illustrated above, the chosen WCA and MH are correct, and the Desired Track of 340°M Outbound is maintained.

If the estimated WCA is incorrect, then the actual Track Made Good by the aeroplane will differ from that desired. If, in the above case, the wind is stronger than expected, the aeroplane's actual TMG may be 335°M, and to the left of the Desired Track of 340°M.

Fig.11c-22. Tracking Away From an NDB with an Incorrect Wind Correction Angle.

Whereas inaccurate tracking **to** an NDB is indicated by the ADF Needle falling, incorrect tracking **away** from an NDB can occur with the RMI Needle indicating a steady reading – but the aeroplane may be on the **wrong QDR**. Having passed overhead the NDB, an aeroplane can track away from it in any of 360 directions. The Pilot must always ensure that he is flying away from the NDB along the correct track, and the easiest means to do this is to **observe the QDR on the Tail of the RMI Needle**.

REGAINING TRACK AWAY FROM AN NDB IN A CROSSWIND

If an incorrect Wind Correction Angle is flown, then the aeroplane will of course be blown off track. The vigilant Pilot/Navigator will observe the incorrect TMG (actual Track Made Good), probably by noting that the Tail of the RMI Needle is indicating something other than the Desired Outbound Track.

NOTE: It is generally easier to work off the top of the dial, since that is where the aeroplane is going, rather than off the bottom of the dial. The left turn necessary to regain track (i.e. turning left towards the Head of the Needle and therefore away from the Tail of the Needle) can be thought of as *Pulling the Tail of the RMI Needle around* or *Trailing the Tail*. Some Instructors, however, prefer to use the Head of the Needle – in this case, the Head of the Needle (now at the bottom of the dial) moves left, indicating that a correcting turn to the left is required. Your Instructor will advise his preferred method.

Example 5: In the situation illustrated below, the Pilot is flying Track as Heading, i.e. initially making no allowance for drift. If the Tail of the RMI Needle moves right, then the aeroplane must be turned left to regain Track.

Fig.11c-23. Turning Left to 'Trail the Tail' or 'Pull the Tail Around'.

In the case illustrated above, the aeroplane has been blown to the right of the Desired Track QDR 035, onto QDR 043 indicated by the Tail of the RMI Needle.

To regain track, the Pilot has turned left by 16° (double the error) from MH 035 to MH 019. As the aeroplane is flown on its steady intercept heading of MH 019, the Tail of the Needle will be gradually pulled around.

The Pilot will continue with the intercept Heading until the aeroplane approaches the Desired Track, QDR 035. This is indicated to the Pilot by the Tail of the RMI Needle moving up the dial towards 035.

As the Desired Track outbound is approached, the Pilot turns right to maintain the RMI Tail on 035, i.e. QDR 035. Estimating a WCA of 8° into wind to be sufficient, the Pilot steers MH 027 and checks regularly that the Tail of the RMI Needle stays on 035.

Similarly, if the Tail of the RMI Needle is left of where it should be, then the Desired Track is out to the right, and a right turn should be made to *Trail the Tail.*

Fig.11c-24. Turn Right to 'Trail the Tail'.

NOTE: If using the Head of the Needle is the preferred technique, then the need for a left turn is indicated by the Head of the Needle moving to the left of the Datum QDM 215.

THE NDB APPROACH

The NDB Approach discussed at the end of the previous chapter is made simpler for a Pilot with an RMI to use for his NDB tracking, rather than an RBI. The actual NDB Let-Down procedure for the Pilot to follow is identical for all ADF presentations.

Fig.11c-25. Tracking using an RMI during an NDB Approach.

☐ Now try **Exercises 11c – The RMI.**

232

12

THE VOR

The VOR (pronounced 'Vee-Oh-Are') is a Very High Frequency radio navigation aid that is extensively used in Instrument Flying. Its full name is the Very High Frequency Omni-Directional Radio Range, commonly abbreviated to the **VHF O**mni **R**ange, **VOR**, or **Omni**.

Each VOR ground station transmits on a specific VHF frequency between 108.00 and 117.95 MegaHertz (MHz), which is a lower frequency band than that used for VHF Communications. A separate VHF-NAV radio is required for navigation purposes, but is usually combined with the VHF-COM in a NAV/COM set.

Fig.12-1. VOR Equipment in the Cockpit.

The VOR was developed in the United States of America during the late 1940s, and was adopted by the International Civil Aviation Organisation (ICAO) as the standard short-range radio navigation aid in 1960. When introduced, it offered an immediate improvement over previously existing aids such as the ADF/NDB combination, most of which operated in lower frequency bands than the VOR and suffered significant limitations, such as Night Effect, Mountain Reflections, Interference from electrical storms, etc.

Principal advantages of the VOR include:

- a reduced susceptibility to electrical and atmospheric interference (including thunderstorms);
- the elimination of Night Effect, since VHF signals are line-of-sight and not reflected by the ionosphere (as are NDB signals in the LF/MF band).

The **reliability and accuracy of VOR signals** allows the VOR to be used with confidence in any weather conditions, by day or by night, for purposes such as:
- **orientation** and position fixing (Where am I?);
- **tracking** to or from a VOR ground station;
- **holding** (for delaying or manoeuvring action); and
- **instrument approaches** to land.

Many VORs are coupled with a DME (Distance Measuring Equipment providing a measure of distance from the station in nautical miles), so that selection of the VOR on the VHF-NAV set in the cockpit also selects the DME, thereby providing both tracking and distance information.

HOW THE VOR WORKS

The VOR ground station transmits two VHF radio signals:
1. the **Reference Phase**, which is *omni-directional* (i.e. the same in all directions); and
2. the **Variable Phase**, which rotates uniformly at a rate of 1800 rev/min, with its **phase** varying at a constant rate throughout the 360°.

The aerial of the VOR airborne receiver picks up the signals, whose **phase difference** (the difference between the wave peaks) is measured, this difference depending upon the bearing of the aeroplane from the ground station. In this manner, the VOR can determine the **magnetic bearing** of the aeroplane from the VOR ground station.

Fig. 12-2a. Typical Examples
of VOR Aerials.

Fig.12-2b. A VOR Ground Station
(Brookmans Park, near London).

The two signals transmitted by the VOR ground station are:
- in-phase on Magnetic North, which is the reference for VOR signals;
- 90° out of phase at Magnetic East 090°M;
- 180° out of phase at Magnetic South 180°M;
- 270° out of phase at Magnetic West 270°M; and
- 360° out of phase (i.e. back in-phase) at Magnetic North 360°M, or 000°M.

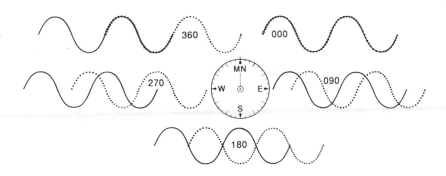

Fig.12-3. The VOR Transmits Two VHF Signals with a Phase Difference
between them.

Every 10 seconds or so a Morse Code *IDENT* signal is transmitted, allowing the Pilot to positively identify the VOR. Some VORs may also carry voice transmissions with a relevant Automatic Terminal Information Service (ATIS).

The VOR is a Very High Frequency aid operating in the frequency band 108.0 MHz to 117.95 MHz. It allows high quality *line-of-sight* reception due to there being relatively little interference from atmospheric noise in this band. Reception may be affected by the terrain surrounding the ground station, the height of the VOR beacon, the altitude of the aeroplane and its distance from the station.

THE RANGE OF A VOR

The approximate maximum range of a VHF signal is given by the formula (which is not necessary for you to remember):
VHF Range in nm = the square root of (1.5 x altitude in feet)

Example 1: At 7000 ft AMSL, approximate VHF range
$$= \text{square root of } (1.5 \times 7000)$$
$$= \text{square root of } (10,000)$$
$$= 100 \text{ nm.}$$

Different VORs may operate on the same frequency, but they should be well separated geographically so that there is no interference between their VHF line-of-sight signals. The higher the aeroplane's altitude, however, the greater the possibility of interference. The Aeronautical Information Publication specifies a Designated Operational Coverage (DOC) for each VOR above which interference is possible. Within the DOC coverage, VOR reception should be reliable. *Detling VOR,* for instance, has a DOC of 60 nm/50,000 ft (AIP COM 2).

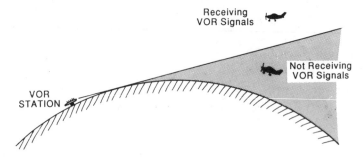

Fig. 12-4. VHF Line-of-Sight Signals.

Tracking – the Main Use of the VOR

The VOR can be used by a pilot to indicate the **desired track** and the aeroplane's **angular deviation** from that track. For a desired track of 015°M, the pilot would expect to steer a Heading of approximately 015°M, plus or minus a Wind Correction Angle (WCA). By selecting an Omni Bearing of 015 under the Course Index of the VOR Cockpit Display, the pilot can obtain tracking information, as illustrated in the next figures (12-5 & 12-6).

Aeroplane to the
Right of Track —
Desired Track is
to the Left

Aeroplane to the
Left of Track —
Desired track is
to the Right

Aeroplane
On Track

Right of
Track —
Track to
the Left

Left of Track —
Track is to
the Right

On Track

Fig.12-5. The VOR is used
to Indicate Track.

Fig.12-6. The VOR Cockpit Display is NOT Heading Sensitive.

The VOR Cockpit Display is not Heading-sensitive, which means that the display will **not** change as a result of the aeroplane changing Heading. Fig.12-6 shows the same aeroplane as Fig.12-5, except that a Wind Correction Angle of 10° Right is being used by the Pilot to counteract a wind from the right, and so the aeroplane's Magnetic Heading is now MH 025 (rather than MH 015 previously).

Points to note are:

- the VOR Indication depends on the **angular deviation** of the aeroplane relative to the Selected Track;
- the VOR Indication will **not** change with any Heading change of the aeroplane.

237

Change VORs at the Approximate Mid-Point between them

It is usual, when tracking en route from one VOR to another, to select the next VOR when the aeroplane is approximately halfway between them. This will allow the use of the stronger signal, although intervening mountains which might shield the signal of a VOR may affect a Pilot's decision in this regard.

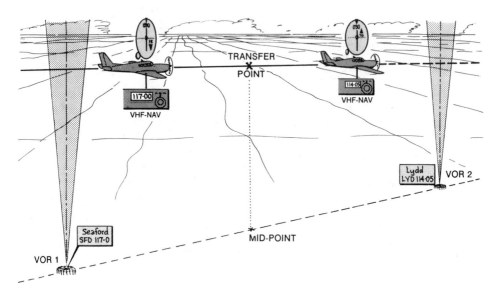

Fig.12-7. Tracking Between Two VORs.

A VOR RADIAL

As its name **Omni** suggests, a VOR ground transmitter radiates signals in **all** directions. Its most important feature, however, is that the signal in any particular direction differs slightly from its neighbours. These individual directional signals can be thought of as **tracks** or **position lines** radiating out from the VOR ground station, in much the same way as spokes from the hub of a wheel.

By convention, 360 different tracks away from the VOR are used, each separated from the next by 1°, and each with its direction related to **Magnetic North**. Each of these 360 VOR tracks or position lines is called a **Radial**.

A Radial is the Magnetic Bearing Outbound *FROM* a VOR.

NOTE: A specific VOR Radial is the same as **QDR**. For instance, the 293 radial is QDR 293, which is a track of 293° Magnetic away **from** the VOR ground station.

Fig.12-8.
A Radial is a
Magnetic Bearing
FROM the VOR
(i.e. QDR).

VORs ON AERONAUTICAL CHARTS

Most aeronautical charts show the position, frequency and Morse Code identification *(IDENT)* of each VOR ground station. Information on a particular VOR may be found in the UK Aeronautical Information Publication (AIP COM), and any changes to this information will be referred to in NOTAMs (to which a pilot may refer prior to flight).

A VOR ground station may be represented in various ways on a chart – the common representations being illustrated below. Since Magnetic North is the reference direction for VOR radials, a Magnetic North arrowhead usually emanates from the VOR symbol, with a compass rose heavily marked each 30°, and the radials shown in 10° intervals on the rose. This is generally adequate for in-flight estimation of track to an accuracy of +/–2°, however, when flight planning, it is advisable to be more accurate.

At the Flight Planning stage, the pilot should use a protractor or plotter for precise measurement of track, although in some cases this may not be necessary because some much-used tracks are published on Radio Navigation Charts (RNCs) in degrees Magnetic. If the pilot measures the Track in degrees True (°T), then Magnetic Variation needs to be applied to convert to degrees Magnetic *("Variation West, Magnetic Best")*.

Fig.12-9. A VOR and its Radials represented on Different Charts.

It is usual for Instrument-Rated Pilots to use the Radio Navigation Charts (published by *Aerad* and *Jeppesen),* and IMC-Rated Pilots to use the CAA 1:500,000 ($1/2$ million) ICAO Topographical Charts, already well known from visual navigation.

Further Information on VORs

The UK Aeronautical Information Publication carries information regarding radio navigation aids in its *COM* Section. For example, the AIP extract for *Goodwood,* shown below, includes:

- its frequency, 114.75 MHz (also found on the charts);
- its callsign, or identification, 'GWC' (also found on the charts) which, in Morse Code, is *"dah-dah-dit dit-dah-dah dah-dit-dah-dit";*
- its hours of service (24 hours a day, Summer and Winter);
- its location in Latitude and Longitude (if you cannot find it on the chart); and
- *Remarks* that:
  - the VOR is an Approach Aid to CHICHESTER/Goodwood aerodrome (and there will therefore be an Instrument Approach Chart available for it from Jeppesen, Aerad and the CAA); and
  - it has a Designated Operational Coverage (DOC) of 80 nm up to 50,000 ft AMSL, above which there may be interference from distant VORs using the same frequency.

RADIO COMMUNICATION AND NAVIGATION FACILITIES

STATION	SERVICE	CALL SIGN OR IDENT	EM	TRANSMITS		RECEIVES	
				kHz	MHz	kHz	MHz
1	2	3	4	5	6	7	8
Goodwood	VOR	GWC	A9W	–	114.750	–	–

INFORMATION ONLY Not for Navigational Purposes

HOURS OF SERVICE		CO-ORDINATES	LOCATION		OPERATING AUTHORITY AND REMARKS
WINTER PERIOD	SUMMER PERIOD		MAG	NM	
9	10	11	12	13	14
H24	H24	N5051.28 W00045.31	–	–	NATS. Approach Aid to CHICHESTER/Goodwood. DOC 80 nm/50000 ft. Aerial Hgt 113 ft.

Fig.12-10. UK AIP COM 2 Extract for Goodwood VOR.

Also, the beginning pages of AIP COM advise a pilot not to use any VOR if it cannot be identified by its Morse Code *IDENT.* It may be that the VOR is radiating signals on test, in which case the IDENT is suppressed or the Morse letters 'TST' (for *test)* are transmitted, to indicate that the facility is not to be used for navigation.

Those VORs which have a DME (Distance Measuring Equipment) associated with them may be described as VOR/DMEs. The DME is automatically tuned when the pilot selects the VOR frequency on the VHF-NAV radio.

RADIO COMMUNICATION AND NAVIGATION FACILITIES

STATION	SERVICE	CALL SIGN OR IDENT	EM	TRANSMITS		RECEIVES		HOURS OF
				kHz	MHz	kHz	MHz	WINTER PERIOD
1	2	3	4	5	6	7	8	9
Guernsey	VOR	GUR	A9W	–	109.400	–	–	H24
	DME		P0N					

	SERVICE	CO-ORDINATES	LOCATION		OPERATING AUTHORITY AND REMARKS
	SUMMER PERIOD		MAG	NM	
	10	11	12	13	14
	H24	N4926.28 W00236.15	–	–	States of Guernsey Approach Aid to Guernsey DOC 60 nm/50000 ft. (80 nm/50000 ft in Sector 022° to 067° MAG). DME Ch 31X. Aerial Hgt 347 ft amsl.

Excerpted from *EUR/2* Radio Navigation Chart by permission of BRITISH AIRWAYS *AERAD*

Fig.12-11. AIP COM 2 Extract for Guernsey, and from the Aerad RNC.

The VOR, being a VHF radio navigation aid, is line-of-sight, and so its signals may be stopped or distorted by high mountains in some locations. AIP COM should contain a warning for the pilot, as is the case shown below, where Inverness VOR has reduced coverage in the sector between 154°M and 194°M from the VOR ground station.

STATION	SERVICE	CALL SIGN OR IDENT	EM	TRANSMITS		RECEIVES		HOURS OF
				kHz	MHz	kHz	MHz	WINTER PERIOD
1	2	3	4	5	6	7	8	9
Inverness	VOR	INS (Reduced coverage in Sector R154°-R194°. Flag alarms may occur in this sector when aircraft are 30 nm or more from the VOR and flying at or below 7000 ft).	A9W	–	109.200	–	–	H24

Fig.12-12. AIP COM 2 Extract for Inverness.

THE VOR COCKPIT INSTRUMENT

There are various types of VOR Cockpit Display, however they are all reasonably similar in terms of operation. The VOR Cockpit Display is often referred to as the **O**mni **B**earing **I**ndicator, or **OBI**. It displays the Omni Bearing selected by the Pilot on the Course Card using the **O**mni **B**earing **S**elector (OBS), a small knob which is geared to the card.

- If the aeroplane is on the selected radial, then the VOR Needle, known as the **Course Deviation Indicator** or **CDI**, will be centred. If the aeroplane is not on the Selected Track, then the CDI will not be centred.
- Whether the selected track would take the aeroplane to or from the VOR ground station is indicated by the **TO/FROM** flags.

Fig. 12-13. The VOR Cockpit Display (OBI) for Aeroplanes on the 030 Radial.

The OBI is only to be used for navigation if:
- the red *OFF* warning flag is hidden from view;
- the correct Morse Code *IDENT* is heard.

When a VOR is operating normally, the radials are transmitted to an accuracy of at least +/–2°.

NOTE: *Course* is an American term with the same meaning as *Track*. Since most aviation radio equipment is manufactured by US companies, American terminology is used. In the UK, 'Course' sometimes refers to *Heading*, however it will **not** be used in this sense in the *Air Pilot's Manual*.

COURSE DEVIATION

The **C**ourse **D**eviation **I**ndicator (or **CDI**) in the VOR Cockpit Instrument indicates **off-track deviation** in terms of **angular deviation from the Selected Track**. At all times, **the reference when using the VOR is the Selected Track** under the Course Index. (This is a totally different principle to that of the ADF Needle which simply points at an NDB ground station and indicates its relative bearing.)

The amount of angular deviation from the Selected Track is referred to in terms of *dots,* there being 5 dots either side of the central position. The inner dot on both sides is often represented by a circle passing through them. **Each dot is equivalent to 2° Track Deviation.**

- If the aeroplane is on the selected track, the CDI is centred.
- If the aeroplane is 2° off the selected track, the CDI is displaced 1 dot from the centre (i.e. on the circumference of the inner circle).
- If the aeroplane is 4° off the selected track, the CDI is displaced 2 dots.
- If the aeroplane is **10° or more** off the selected track, the CDI is fully deflected at 5 dots, i.e. full scale deflection of the VOR at 5 dots indicates a course deviation of 10° *or more.*

A 1 dot Deviation of the CDI on the VOR Cockpit Display represents 2°.
Full Scale Deflection represents 10° or More.

Fig.12-14. Each of these Aeroplanes is Displaced 6° from the 070 Radial.

Since the CDI indicates **angular** deviation, the actual **distance** off track for a given CDI indication will be smaller the closer the aeroplane is to the ground station. In a manner of speaking, the aeroplane is *funnelled* in towards the VOR ground station.

TO or FROM

The 090 Radial, which is QDR 090 (a Magnetic Bearing away FROM the station) of 090°M, is the same Position Line as QDM 270 TO the station. If an aeroplane is on this Position Line, then the CDI will be centred when **either** 090 **or** 270 is selected with the OBS. Any ambiguity in the mind of the Pilot regarding the position of the aeroplane relative to the VOR ground station is resolved with the TO/FROM indicators.

The *TO* or *FROM* flags or arrows indicate to the Pilot whether the selected Omni Bearing will take him TO the VOR ground station, or away FROM it. In the case illustrated below, the Pilot could centre the CDI by selecting either 090 or 270 (reciprocals) with the OBS. A Track of 090°M would take the aeroplane FROM the VOR, whereas a Track of 270°M would lead it TO the VOR.

Fig.12-15. Using the TO/FROM Flag.

Example 2: Illustrate two indications on the Omni Bearing Indicator that would inform the Pilot that the aeroplane is on the 235 radial.

The 235 radial is either;
• 235°M FROM the VOR; or
• 055°M TO the VOR;
so, with the CDI centred, the VOR Cockpit Display could indicate either 235-FROM or 055-TO.

Fig.12-16. Indications that the Aeroplane is on the 235 Radial.

At all times, the reference when using the OBI is the Track selected under the Course Index. It determines:
- CDI deflection; and
- whether the TO or the FROM flag shows.

DIFFERENT PRESENTATIONS OF THE OMNI BEARING

There are various presentations of VOR information. In all cases, full scale deflection is 10° either side of the Selected Omni Bearing (i.e. a total arc of 20°), with five dots either side of centre. In many VOR Cockpit Displays the two inner dots are joined by the circumference of a circle.

The Course Deviation Indicator (CDI) may also differ between instruments. It may move laterally as a whole, or it may hinge at the top and swing laterally.

Similarly, the means of displaying the Selected Omni Bearing may differ between instruments. It may be shown under a Course Index, or it may be shown in a window. In some equipment, the TO and the FROM flags may be displayed in the one window, in others they may have separate windows.

In instruments where the VOR Cockpit Display also doubles as the ILS (Instrument Landing System) Display, which is the usual case, vertical dots may be marked to indicate Glide Slope (GS) Deviation (using a second Needle which lies or is hinged horizontally so that it can move up or down). When being used for the VOR (and not the ILS), the Glide Slope Cross Bar (or Needle) may be biased out of view, and there may be a **red GS warning flag** showing.

PREPARING THE VOR FOR USE

A Radio Navigation Aid is of little value if the Pilot does not use it correctly. Prior to using the VOR, a Pilot must:
- ensure electrical power is available, and switch the VHF-NAV *ON*;
- select the desired frequency (e.g. 114.3 MHz for Aberdeen VOR as found on Navigation Charts or in AIP-COM);
- identify the VOR (dit-dah dah-dit-dit dah-dit, which is *ADN* in Morse Code as shown on the Navigation Charts for AberDeeN);
- check that the *OFF* flag is not showing (i.e. the signal is usable, otherwise the OFF flag would be visible).

ORIENTATION USING THE VOR

ORIENTATION – Using the VOR to Obtain a Position Line

Orientation is a term that means 'to determine one's approximate position'. The first step in orientation is to establish a Position Line (PL) along which the aircraft is known to be at a particular moment.

To obtain a Position Line using the VOR display, the pilot should:
- rotate the OBS (Omni Bearing Selector) until the CDI (Course Deviation Indicator) is centred; and
- note whether the *TO* or the *FROM* flag is showing.

Example 3: A pilot rotates the OBS until the CDI is centred – this occurs with 334 under the Course Index and the *TO* flag showing. Illustrate the situation.

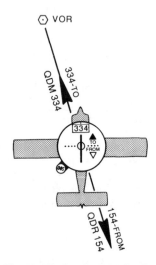

Could another OBI (Omni Bearing Indicator) reading be obtained with the Course Deviation Indicator centred?

In the aircraft's location, the CDI will be centred with either:
- *334-TO;* or
- *154-FROM.*

Fig.12-17. On the 154 Radial.

Using Two PLs to Fix Position

One Position Line alone does not allow a pilot to positively fix the position of the aircraft overhead a particular point; it only provides a line somewhere along which the aircraft lies.

It requires two or more Position Lines to positively fix the position of an aircraft. Also, to be of any real value for position fixing, the two PLs need to intersect at an angle of at least 45° – any cut less than this decreases the accuracy of the fix.

Radio Position Lines can be provided by any convenient radio navigation aid, including VORs, NDBs and DMEs, as illustrated in the next figure.

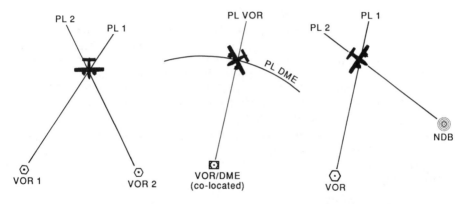

Fig. 12-18a. Fixing Position requires Two Position Lines with a Good Cut.

Fixing Position using Two VORs

Some aeroplanes are fitted with two independent VHF-NAV systems, enabling two different VORs to be tuned at the same time, and thus two PLs from two different VOR ground stations can be obtained simultaneously. In an aeroplane fitted with only one VHF-NAV set, a pilot can, if he so desires, obtain two PLs using the one VHF-NAV by retuning it from one VOR to another.

Example 4: An aeroplane fitted with two VHF-NAVs is tracking 134°M from Prestwick to Manchester via Dean Cross, and obtains the following indications:
VOR 1: Dean Cross 115.2 is selected, and the CDI centres with *134-TO.*
VOR 2: Talla 113.8 is selected, and the CDI centres with *220-FROM.*

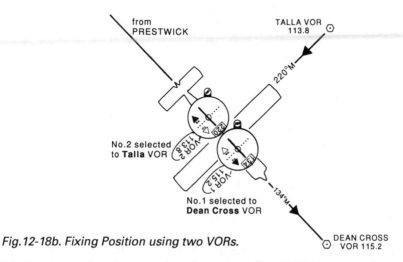

Fig. 12-18b. Fixing Position using two VORs.

This illustrates that the aeroplane is on track (i.e. 134°M between Prestwick and Dean Cross) and passing the Talla 220 radial. The two Position Lines cut at a good angle, and the pilot has a fairly positive indication of where the aeroplane is.

Fixing Position using a VOR and a DME

Probably the most common form of en route position fixing between aids is the VOR/DME fix, based on a ground station where the DME (Distance Measuring Equipment) is co-located with the VOR ground station. The VOR can provide a straight position line showing the radial that the aeroplane is on, and the DME can provide a circular position line showing the distance that the aeroplane is from the ground station. The intersection of the lines is the position of the aeroplane.

Example 5: An aircraft tracking north from Brecon (ident BCN, freq. 117.45 MHz) has the cockpit indications of:

- BCN VOR *008-FROM;* and
- BCN DME *31 nm.*

Where is the aircraft?

As can be seen from the next figure, the aircraft is at the *RADNO* position, an in-flight position determined purely by radio navaids.

Fig. 12-19. Fixing Position using a Co-Located VOR/DME.

Fixing Position Overhead a VOR

As an aircraft approaches overhead a VOR, the CDI will become more and more agitated and confused as the +/–10° funnel either side of track becomes narrower and narrower.

As the aircraft passes through the **'Zone of Confusion'** over the VOR ground station, the CDI may flick from side to side, before settling down again as the aircraft moves away from the station. The *TO/FROM* flag will also change from *TO* to *FROM* (or vice versa), and the red-coloured *OFF* flag may flicker in and out of view because of the temporarily unusable signal.

The Zone of Confusion can extend in an arc of 70° overhead the station, so it may take a minute or so for the aircraft to pass through it before the CDI and the *FROM* flag settle down, and the *OFF* flag totally disappears.

Fig.12-20a. Fixing Position Overhead a VOR.

Fixing Position Passing Abeam a VOR

A common means of checking flight progress is to note the time passing **abeam** (i.e. to one side of) a nearby VOR ground station. The most straight-forward procedure is to:

- select and identify the VOR; and
- under the Course Index, set the radial perpendicular (i.e. at 90°) to your Track.

Example 6: An aircraft is tracking 350°M, and will pass approximately 20 nm abeam a VOR ground station out to its right. The VOR radial perpendicular to Track is the 260 radial, and so *260* should be set with the OBS. The CDI will be fully deflected to one side if the aircraft is well away from the abeam position, and will gradually move from full deflection one side to full deflection on the other side as the aircraft passes through the +/−10° arc either side of the selected radial. The aircraft is *at* the abeam position when the CDI is centralised.

The abeam position can also be identified by setting the QDM *TO* the VOR under the Course Index (rather than the QDR or Radial *FROM* the VOR), in which case the movement of the CDI will be from the opposite side.

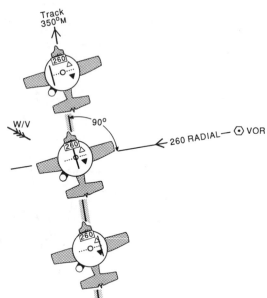

*Fig. 12-20b.
Passing abeam
a VOR.*

The 1-in-60 Rule, frequently used in navigation, states that 1 nm off-track in 60 nm subtends an angle of 1°. In rough terms, this means that, as the aircraft flies at right angles through the 10° from when the CDI first starts to move to when it is centred, it will travel approximately 10 nm abeam the VOR when it is located 60 nm from the VOR ground station (or 5 nm at 30 nm, etc.). At say GS 120 kt (i.e. 2 nm/min), passing through a 10° arc abeam the VOR will take 5 minutes at 60 nm, or 2.5 minutes at 30 nm.

Crossing a Known Radial from an Off-Track VOR

It is a simple procedure to identify passing a known radial from an off-track VOR and, indeed, some en route Reporting Points are based on this.

Example 7: *UPTON* Reporting Point en route on the track between *Ottringham* and *Wallasey* VORs is specified by the 330 radial from *Gamston* VOR.

- With two VOR displays in the cockpit, it would be normal procedure to track using VOR 1 on Ottringham (and later Wallasey), and check *UPTON* using VOR 2 tuned to Gamston.

- With only one VOR set fitted in the aircraft, it would be normal procedure to leave it on the main tracking aid (Ottringham) until almost at *UPTON* (say two minutes before ETA), and then select Gamston and the 330 radial. Having crossed this radial, the VOR could be selected to a tracking aid (Ottringham or Wallasey).

Fig. 12-21. Crossing a Known Radial.

If a 1:500,000 Aeronautical Chart is being used (rather than a Radio Navigation Chart), the pilot can construct his own checkpoints along Track using nearby off-track VORs. In the case illustrated below, the pilot has chosen to check position crossing the 105, 075 and 045 radials from an off-track VOR. By measuring the distance between these planned fixes en route and noting the time of reaching them, the pilot can calculate the Ground Speed and revise his estimates for positions further along Track.

Fig. 12-22. Using an Off-Track VOR to Monitor Progress.

THE VOR DISPLAY IS NOT HEADING SENSITIVE

The VOR indicates the position of the aeroplane with respect to the selected VOR track, and the actual VOR Display in the cockpit will be the same irrespective of the aeroplane's Heading. Each of the aeroplanes below will have the same VOR Display, provided the same track is set under the Course Index with the OBS.

Fig.12-23. The VOR Cockpit Display is NOT Heading Sensitive.

The CDI position will *not* change as the aeroplane changes Heading.

ORIENTATION WITHOUT ALTERING THE OBS

It is possible, without altering the Omni Bearing Selector, to determine which quadrant the aeroplane is in with respect to the Selected Track. In the case illustrated below, the selected Omni Bearing is 340.

(a) The CDI is deflected left, which indicates that, when looking in direction 340, the aeroplane is out to the right (of the line 340-160); and

(b) The *FROM* flag indicates that tracking 340 would take the aeroplane FROM the VOR ground station, i.e. the aeroplane is ahead of the line 250-070 when looking in the direction 340.

Fig.12-24. Using the CDI and the TO/FROM Flag for Orientation without moving the Omni Bearing Selector.

This puts the aeroplane in the quadrant:

• away from the CDI; and

• away from the TO/FROM flag.

i.e. between 340 and 070 radials (omni bearings from the VOR ground station).

Fig.12-25. The Aeroplane is in the Quadrant Away From the CDI and TO/FROM Flag.

NOTE: No information is available from the VOR Cockpit Display regarding aeroplane Heading. Heading Information in °M must be obtained from the Direction Indicator.

Example 8: With 085 under the Course Index, the OBI reads CDI deflected right with the TO flag showing. Position the aeroplane with respect to the VOR.

Fig.12-26. The Aeroplane is Between the 355 and 265 Radials.

This method is just a quick means of determining the **approximate** position of the aeroplane with respect to the VOR ground station.

TRACKING USING THE VOR

TRACKING TO A VOR

To track TO a VOR:

- select the VOR frequency;
- identify the station (Morse Code *IDENT*);
- check that the red *OFF* warning flag is **not** displayed; and
- select the **Omni Bearing** of the Desired Track with the OBS.

Orientate the aeroplane with respect to the Desired Track, and then take up a suitable intercept heading using the Direction Indicator (aligned with the Magnetic Compass). If the aeroplane is heading approximately in the direction of the Desired Track, the centre circle will represent the aeroplane, and the CDI the Desired Track; to intercept Track in this case, the Pilot would turn towards the CDI.

This is using the OBI as a **Command Instrument,** i.e. *commanding* the Pilot to turn towards the CDI to regain Track. Be aware, however, that this only applies when the aeroplane's Heading is roughly in the same direction as the selected Omni Bearing.

On intercepting Track, the Pilot steers a suitable Heading to maintain it, bearing in mind wind direction and strength. **If the Desired Track is maintained, the CDI will remain centred.**

Example 9: In the case illustrated below, with the Desired Track 030 set in the OBI, the CDI is out to the right. Since the aeroplane's initial Heading agrees approximately with the Track of 030, the Pilot concludes that the Track is out to the right of the aeroplane. The CDI out to the right **commands** him to turn right to regain track and centre the CDI.

The Pilot has taken up a Heading of 050°M to intercept a Track of **030 TO** the VOR, which will give him a 20° intercept. This is satisfactory if the aeroplane is close to the Track. If the aeroplane is well away from Track, then a 60° or 90° intercept might be more appropriate. This would be MH 090 or MH 120.

VOR ⊙

MH

Desired Track 030-TO
maintained by steering
HDG 010, (i.e. 20°
Right Drift)

MH

Back On Track;
Set up a suitable HDG
to maintain Desired TR,
say HDG 010

MH

Turn further Left to
re-intercept Track,
steer Heading 350 say,
(i.e. Turn **towards** CDI)

MH

Wind blows Aircraft Right
of Track, (i.e. Track is to
Left of Aircraft)

MH

Steer 050°M
to intercept
030-TO

MH

On Track 030-TO,
Steer Heading 030 say

030-TO
210 RADIAL

Fig. 12-27. Using the VOR Indicator as a Command Instrument.

DETERMINING DRIFT ANGLE WHEN TRACKING ON THE VOR

When tracking inbound on 360 TO a VOR with 360 set under the Course Index, MH 360 will allow the aeroplane to maintain Track provided there is no crosswind component.

If, however, there is a westerly wind blowing, then the aeroplane will be blown to the right of Track unless a Wind Correction Angle (WCA) is applied and the aeroplane steered on a Heading slightly into wind. This is MH 352 in the case illustrated.

If, on the other hand, there is an easterly wind blowing, the aeroplane will be blown to the left of Track, unless a Wind Correction Angle (WCA) is applied and the aeroplane steered on a Heading slightly into wind, such as MH 005 in the case illustrated.

DRIFT ANGLES EXAGGERATED

Fig.12-28a. Tracking Inbound and Allowing for Drift.

Just how great the WCA need be is determined in flight by trial and error (although any pre-flight calculations using the Navigation Computer when flight planning may suggest a starting figure for WCA). If the chosen WCA is not correct, and the aeroplane gradually departs from Track causing the CDI to move from its central position, then Heading should be altered, the Track regained (CDI centred), and then a new Magnetic Heading flown with an improved estimate of WCA. This process of achieving a suitable WCA is known as *bracketting*.

Of course, in the real world the wind frequently changes in both strength and direction, and so the Magnetic Heading required to maintain Track will also change from time to time. This becomes obvious by gradual movements of the CDI away from its central position, which the Pilot will notice in his regular scan of the radio navigation instruments, and which he will correct by changes in Magnetic Heading.

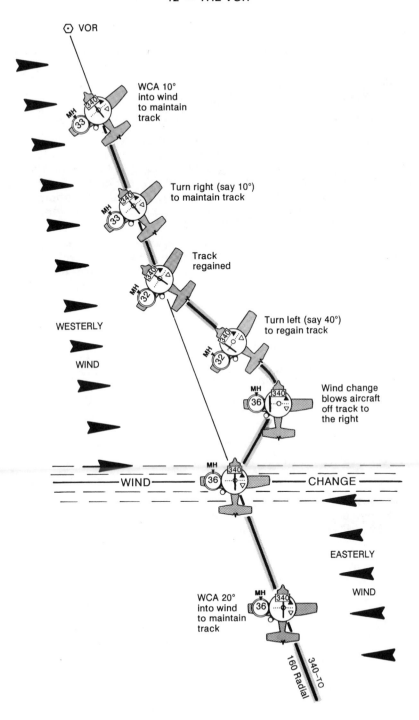

⊙ VOR

WCA 10°
into wind
to maintain
track

MH
33

Turn right (say 10°)
to maintain track

MH
33

Track
regained

MH
32

Turn left (say 40°)
to regain track

MH
32

WESTERLY

WIND

Wind change
blows aircraft
off track to
the right

MH
36

WIND —— CHANGE ——

MH
36

EASTERLY

WIND

WCA 20°
into wind
to maintain
track

MH
36

160 Radial   340-TO

Fig.12-28b. Tracking Inbound through a Wind Change.

TRACKING *FROM* A VOR

To track FROM a VOR (assuming the VOR has not already been selected and identified):

- select the VOR frequency;
- identify the station (morse code *IDENT*);
- check that the red *OFF* warning flag is **not** displayed; and
- wind in the **Omni Bearing** of the Desired Track with the OBS.

Orientate the aeroplane with respect to the Desired Track, and then take up a suitable intercept heading using the Direction Indicator (aligned with the Magnetic Compass). If the aeroplane is heading approximately in the direction of the Desired Track, the centre circle will represent the aeroplane, and the CDI the Desired Track.

To intercept Track in this case, the Pilot would turn towards the CDI. This is using the OBI as a **Command Instrument**, i.e. *commanding* the Pilot to turn towards the CDI to regain Track. Be aware, however, that this only applies when the Heading is roughly in the same direction as the selected Omni Bearing.

On intercepting Track, the Pilot steers a suitable Heading to maintain it, keeping in mind the wind direction and strength. If the Desired Track is maintained, the CDI will remain centred.

Example 10: In the case illustrated opposite, with the Desired Track 140 set in the OBI, the CDI is out to the right. Since the aeroplane's initial Heading agrees approximately with the Track of 140, the Pilot concludes that the Track is out to the right of the aeroplane (or, in this case, straight ahead and to the right).

The Pilot has taken up a Heading of 220°M to intercept a Track of **140 FROM** the VOR, which will give him an 80° intercept. This is satisfactory if the aeroplane is well away from the Track. If the aeroplane is close to Track, then a 60° or 30° intercept might be more applicable which, in this case, would be MH 200 or MH 170.

Fig.12-29. Using the VOR Indicator as a Command Instrument.

Use the VOR Cockpit Display as a Command Instrument whenever possible

With the Desired Track set in the OBI, and the aeroplane headed at least roughly in the same direction as the Selected Track, the Omni Bearing Indicator will act as a *Command Instrument*. By flying **towards** the deflected CDI, the Pilot can centre it, and thereby regain Track. For example:

- tracking *060 TO* the VOR, set 060 under the Course Index;
- tracking *030 FROM* the VOR, set 030 under the Course Index.

Fig.12-30. Use the OBI as a Command Instrument.

A Minor Complication (easily solved)

A minor complication can arise when the aeroplane is steered on a Heading approximating the **reciprocal** of the Omni Bearing selected on the OBI. It causes the VOR Cockpit Display to be **no longer a command instrument**.

Example 11: Suppose a Pilot has been tracking *140 FROM* a VOR, with 140 selected in the OBI and by steering MH 140. The aeroplane has drifted left of Track, and so the CDI will be deflected to the right of centre. To regain the *140 FROM* Track, the Pilot must turn towards the needle, in this case towards the right, i.e. Heading and OBI selection are similar, so it is used as a command instrument.

Suppose now that he wishes to return to the VOR ground station on the **reciprocal** Track, which is *320 TO* the VOR, and so turns through approximately 180° onto MH 320 without altering the 140 set under the Course Index. The Omni Bearing Indicator, because it is **not Heading sensitive**, indicates exactly as it did before the turn, with the CDI as seen by the Pilot out to the right of centre.

To regain Track on this reciprocal Heading, the Pilot would turn, not towards the CDI, but away from it. Turning towards the CDI on this reciprocal Heading to the Selected Track would take the Pilot further away from the Selected Track, i.e. it is no longer a Command Instrument, which is a pity!

This inconvenience can be easily removed, and the OBI returned to being a Command Instrument, by selecting the new Desired Track under the Course Index, i.e. 320, which approximates the Heading being flown. The immediate effect will be for:

• the *TO* flag to appear, replacing the *FROM* flag, and

• the CDI to swing across to the other side.

The CDI will now be out to the left, and a turn towards it will bring the aeroplane back towards the Selected Track. The OBI is once again a Command Instrument, easier to understand, and easier to fly.

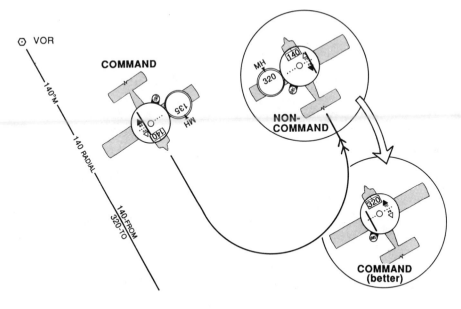

Fig. 12-31. For Ease of Operation, Use the OBI as a Command Instrument.

To keep the OBI as a Command Instrument when flying on a VOR (so that the Pilot can regain Track by flying *towards* the CDI), set the Desired Track in the direction nearest to the Heading to be flown.

A good example of this is the *(Goodwood)* CHICHESTER *VOR 32* Instrument Approach, which uses a Base Turn let-down:

- outbound on *160-FROM,* where the pilot should set 160 with the OBS; and
- inbound on *325-TO,* where the pilot should set 325 with the OBS.

The 15° between the 2-minute outbound leg and the inbound leg of the descent in still air allows sufficient arc for a Rate-1 turn or less to align the aeroplane very nicely for the final descent inbound to the VOR.

Fig. 12-32. Using the OBI as a 'Command Instrument' during a VOR Base Turn.

Slower aircraft carrying out a Rate-1 turn will have a smaller turning radius than faster aircraft (for which the Approach Plates are designed), and so may tend to undershoot the inbound track (unless there is a very strong tailwind in the turn). To avoid undershooting the inbound leg, the aeroplane should be rolled out of the Rate-1 base turn onto a suitable heading to allow for a reasonable intercept of the inbound leg (say a 60°, 45° or 30° intercept).

A lot depends upon the wind strength and direction on the day. For instance, a strong tailwind during the base turn will cause the aeroplane to intercept the inbound leg more quickly than in nil wind or headwind conditions.

NOTE: The Instrument Landing System (ILS) uses the same Cockpit Instrument as the VOR. Whereas the pilot can select any VOR Track, there is only one ILS Track. This is discussed in detail in the ILS Chapter (13), but the main points are:

- when flying inbound on the ILS Track (known as the Localizer), the Cockpit Display is a Command Instrument (i.e. fly towards the CDI to centre it and regain Track); but

- when flying from overhead the aerodrome back towards where the ILS procedure commences, i.e. flying *outbound* on the Localizer, course-sensing is reversed and the Cockpit Indicator is no longer a Command Instrument. More of this later in the Chapter on the ILS!

INTERCEPTING A TRACK USING THE VOR

Visualising Where You Are, and Where You Want to Go

A pilot needs to know:
- Where am I?;
- Where do I want to go?; and
- How do I get there?

The easiest method of orienting the aircraft using the VOR is to rotate the OBS until the CDI centres. This can occur on one of two Headings (reciprocals of each other); choose the one with the Omni Bearing that most resembles the aircraft's Magnetic Heading. If the aircraft is heading towards the VOR ground station, then the *TO* flag will show; if it is heading away from the VOR, then the *FROM* flag will show.

Select the Desired Track in °M using the Omni Bearing Selector (OBS). Determine which way to turn to intercept the Desired Track, and then take up a suitable Intercept Heading.

INTERCEPTING AN OUTBOUND TRACK

The VOR is just as useful tracking away from a VOR ground station as tracking towards it, and it is much easier to use than the NDB/ADF combination.

The next example illustrates the normal method of doing this.

Example 12: An aeroplane is tracking inbound on the 170 radial to a VOR (i.e. *350-TO*). ATC instructs the pilot to take up a Heading to intercept the 090 radial outbound (i.e. *090-FROM*).

Orientation is not a problem in this example since the pilot already knows where he is (the usual situation). The better method tracking inbound on the 170 radial (which is the same as QDR 170, making the inbound QDM 350) is to have 350 set in the OBI Course Index, since the aeroplane is tracking 350 *TO* the VOR. This ensures that the Indicator is a Command Instrument (i.e. fly towards the CDI Needle to regain the Selected Track).

The pilot visualises the situation:
• tracking northwards towards the VOR;
• the Desired Track, *090-FROM,* lying ahead to the right.

To intercept the *090-FROM* Track, the pilot:
• sets 090 under the Course Index;
• takes up a suitable Intercept Heading (MH 030 for a 60° intercept); and
• maintains MH 030 until the CDI moves from full-scale deflection towards the centre. To avoid overshooting the Track, the pilot would anticipate the interception, and 'lead-in' by commencing a turn just prior to intercepting Track.

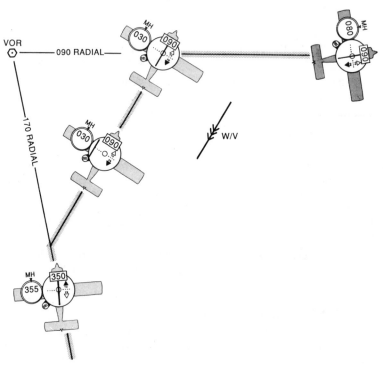

Fig. 12-33. Intercepting a Track Outbound from a VOR.

INTERCEPTING AN INBOUND TRACK

Example 13: ATC instructs a pilot to track inbound on the 010 radial to a particular VOR.

The pilot:
- selects and identifies the VOR; then
- orientates himself with respect to it (perhaps by centring the CDI suitably);
- sets the Desired Track under the Course Index – *Inbound on the 010 radial* (QDR) is *190-TO* (QDM) – and determines the position of this track;
- takes up a suitable Intercept Heading, and waits for the CDI to centre.

In the case illustrated below:
- the CDI centres on *050-FROM* (it would also centre on *230-TO*);
- the pilot has chosen a 90° intercept, steering MH 280 to intercept *190-TO*; and
- as the CDI starts to move (within 10° of the selected track), the pilot leads in to smoothly join track, and allows a Wind Correction Angle of 5°.

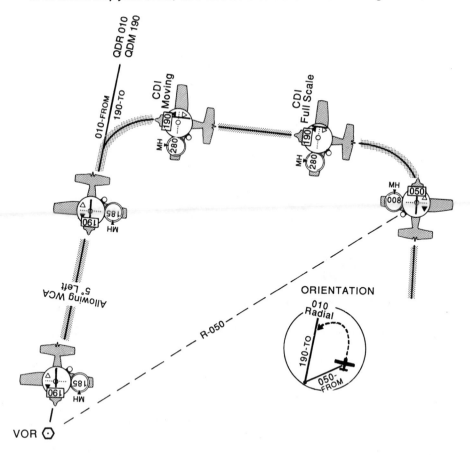

Fig.12-34. Intercepting an Inbound Track to a VOR.

OTHER PRESENTATIONS OF THE VOR

There are various presentations of the VOR Cockpit Display (as discussed earlier) with which a Pilot should be familiar. In some aircraft, it is also possible to use an RMI Needle to point to the VOR ground station as if it were an NDB. This can, on occasions, be very useful.

THE RADIO MAGNETIC INDICATOR (RMI)

The Radio Magnetic Indicator (RMI) combines a Direction Indicator and a Relative Bearing Indicator into the one instrument. The RMI Compass Card is continually aligned with Magnetic North, and the RMI Needles point at the ground stations to which they are tuned. These ground stations, on many RMIs, may be **either an NDB or a VOR**, the selection of either ADF or VOR being made with small switches at the base of the RMI.

Fig. 12-35.
RMI Needle 1 indicating the NDB;
RMI Needle 2 indicating the VOR.

In the case illustrated above, the Pilot has selected RMI Needle 1 to the ADF, hence:
- the Head of Needle 1 indicates Magnetic Bearing **To** the NDB (QDM); and
- the Tail of Needle 1 indicates Magnetic Bearing **From** the NDB (QDR).

RMI Needle 2 has been selected to the VOR, hence:
- the Head of Needle 2 indicates Magnetic Bearing **To** the VOR (QDM); and
- the Tail of Needle 2 indicates Magnetic Bearing **From** the VOR (radial or QDR).

Using the RMI with one needle selected to a VOR allows the VOR to be used as if it were an NDB for orientation and tracking purposes. Refer to the Section on the RMI and the NDB.

Orientation with VOR selected to one needle on the RMI

This makes orientation with the VOR very easy, and it does not involve altering the OBS (Omni Bearing Selector). In the case illustrated, RMI Needle 2 indicates that the QDM (Magnetic Bearing **to** the VOR) is 043 (hence the aeroplane is on the 223 radial).

Fig. 12-36.
The RMI Indicates
043 to the VOR.

Note that there is no need to alter the OBS to determine this, as would be necessary if an RMI were not fitted. Without an RMI, the Pilot would have had to alter the OBS until the CDI centred at either '043-TO' or '223-FROM'.

INTERCEPTING A TRACK WITH THE RMI SELECTED TO A VOR

If the Pilot wishes to intercept the 090 Inbound Track to the VOR, then he would (since he has already orientated the aeroplane using the RMI):
• set 090 under the Course Index with the OBS (already done); and
• take up a suitable Intercept Heading.

If the Pilot is uncertain of his orientation, he can use the ADF technique of imagining:
• the aeroplane on the Tail of the Needle in its current situation; and
• the aeroplane on the Tail of the Needle where he wants to go (i.e. 090 TO).

Fig. 12-37.
Determining 'Where To Go?'
using the RMI.

On MH 010, it would be an 80° intercept. If the Pilot wanted a 60° intercept, he would turn onto MH 030. Tracking on MH 030, the RMI Needle will gradually fall towards 090. Once the aeroplane is within 10° of the Selected Track on the OBI, the CDI will start to move.

THE HORIZONTAL SITUATION INDICATOR (HSI)

The HSI is a more sophisticated instrument that combines a Direction Indicator and the VOR Cockpit Display to give a very easily understood pictorial display of the aircraft's 'situation' relative to the selected VOR radial.

Figure 12-38 shows an HSI in an aircraft heading 340°M and about to intercept 320 to the VOR (the 140 radial).

The HSI always acts as a Command Instrument when tuned to a VOR.

*Fig.12-38.
A Horizontal Situation Indicator.*

THE VOR INSTRUMENT APPROACH

The VOR is used as the tracking aid when carrying out a VOR Approach such as the *Sumburgh Rwy 27* approach (Aerad chart shown opposite). The top part of the chart is a plan view for tracking, and the bottom part of the chart is a profile view for vertical navigation (descent).

The pilot tracks to the VOR at or above the Sector Safe Altitude (SSA) (referred to as Minimum Safe Altitude, MSA, on *Jeppesen* charts) and then takes up the outbound track of 096°M (i.e. the 096 Radial or QDR 096), maintaining it using the VOR. This is most easily achieved by having 096 selected with the OBS. Descent may be carried out to 1520 ft on QNH, *1500 ft on QFE.*

At 6 DME, a left turn may be commenced to intercept 264°M inbound to the VOR, most easily intercepted and maintained if 264 is selected with the OBS. (264°M inbound may be referred to as the 084 radial.) From 5 DME, descent may be commenced to the calculated Minimum Descent Altitude on QNH, or Minimum Descent Height on QFE – often abbreviated as *MDA(H).*

Calculation of your particular MDA(H) is covered in detail in Chapter 19 but, for any VOR Let-Down carried out by an IMC-Rated Pilot, it will not be less than an **absolute minimum of 600 ft AAL,** and could be considerably higher if there are obstacles in the approach area.

If the pilot becomes visual at or above MDA(H), then further descent for a landing is permissible. If the pilot does not become visual, then he may continue tracking to the Missed Approach Point (MAPt) not below the MDA(H) in the hope of becoming visual. At the MAPt a Missed Approach should be commenced (at the VOR, without DME; or at 1.5 DME, with DME) – climb straight ahead on track 264°M to 2000 ft on QNH, then turn left to return to the VOR.

❑ Now complete **Exercises 12 – The VOR.**

Fig. 12-39. The VOR/DME Approach for Sumburgh Runway 27.
(Aerad chart)

13

THE INSTRUMENT LANDING SYSTEM (ILS)

The Instrument Landing System is known as the **ILS** (pronounced "Eye-Ell-Ess"). It enables a suitably equipped aeroplane to make a **Precision Approach to a particular runway** – a *precision approach* being one in which slope guidance, as well as tracking guidance, is given. Each ILS is known by the runway it serves – for example, *the Liverpool ILS Rwy 27.*

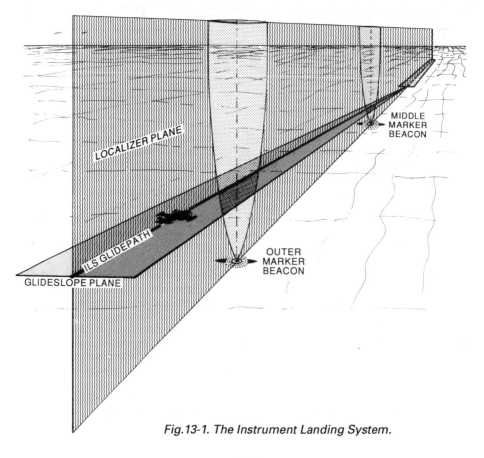

Fig.13-1. The Instrument Landing System.

The Instrument Landing System has three main elements:

1. The *Localizer (LLZ)*, which provides tracking guidance along the extended centreline of the runway (i.e. guidance in azimuth left or right of the extended centreline).

2. The *Glideslope*, which provides vertical guidance towards the runway touchdown point, usually at a slope of approximately 3° to the horizontal, or 1:20 (i.e. vertical guidance above or below the glideslope).

3. *Marker Beacons*, which provide accurate range fixes along the approach (usually an Outer Marker and a Middle Marker).

On some ILS approaches, **Locator Beacons** may be substituted for the Marker Beacon(s) and, on others, a **DME distance** may be substituted for the Outer Marker. These can be used in place of Marker Beacons to provide the pilot with an accurate fix along the approach.

The ideal flightpath on an ILS Approach, where the Localizer plane and the Glideslope plane intersect, is referred to as the **Glidepath.** The word *glide* is really a misnomer carried over from earlier days, since modern aircraft make *powered approaches* down the Glidepath, rather than glide approaches. However, the term is still used.

Since ILS approaches will often be made in conditions of poor visibility or at night, there is always **associated visual information** that can be used once the pilot becomes 'visual'. This may include approach lights leading towards the runway, runway lights, touchdown lights, and centreline lights.

There may also be a *VASIS (Visual Approach Slope Indicator System)* to provide slope guidance during the visual stage of the approach. This, and other visual information, will assist the pilot to maintain a stable descent path down to the runway surface and complete the flare and landing.

Lighting is considered in detail in the section on *Night Flying,* although it is, of course, valuable in daylight hours also, especially in poor weather conditions.

The ILS is selected in the cockpit on the **VHF-NAV** radio. Its Cockpit Display is usually the same instrument as for the VOR except that, as well as the 'vertical' Localizer Needle that moves left and right for track guidance, there is a second needle that comes into view. It is 'horizontal', and is able to move up and down to represent the position of a glideslope relative to the aircraft.

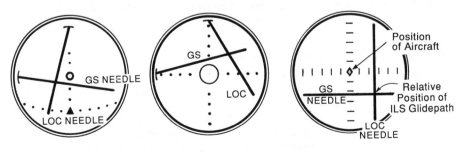

Fig. 13-2. The ILS Cockpit Display.

THE LOCALIZER

The Localizer provides directional guidance along the extended centre-line of the landing runway. Its transmitting aerial, which may be 20 metres wide and 3 metres high, is positioned at the far end of the runway (i.e. the stopping end), and typically 300 metres beyond the end so as not to be an obstacle to aeroplanes taking off.

Fig. 13-3. Localizer Transmitting Aerials.

The Localizer transmits on a frequency in the VHF band between 108.10 and 111.95 MHz, the specific frequency being published on Charts.

THE LOCALIZER GROUND EQUIPMENT

The Localizer aerial at the far end of the runway transmits **two overlapping lobes** of radio energy on the Localizer's carrier frequency (e.g. 110.10 MHz at Birmingham). The lobe on the left hand side of the approach path is modulated at 90 Hz (traditionally known as the *YELLOW* sector), and the lobe on the right hand side of the approach path is modulated at 150 Hz (the *BLUE* sector). The two lobes overlap to provide a path 5° wide in line with the extended centreline of the runway, i.e. 2.5° either side of the extended centreline.

Fig. 13-4. The Localizer's Radiation Pattern.

The main function of the Localizer is to provide guidance in azimuth to an aeroplane on final approach to a particular runway. The signal transmitted out along the approach path is sometimes called the Localizer *Front Beam*. It is calibrated (and flight-checked) out to 10 nm from the runway threshold (as is the Glideslope), and protected from interference from other stations out to 25 nm. Usable localizer signals may be received out to 25 nm within ±10° of the localizer front-course line, and out to 17 nm when in the area 10° to 35° either side of the front-course line.

A few Localizers also transmit a *Back Beam*. This can be used for tracking – for instance when continuing overhead the runway and straight ahead following a *Missed Approach*. In the UK, the Back Beam is usually suppressed.

Fig. 13-5. A Localizer with both a 'Front Beam' and a 'Back Beam'.

The **Back Beam** of a Localizer does **not** have an associated Glideslope for an approach in the opposite direction (although **false** Glideslope signals might exist), nor is it maintained to the same accuracy as the Front Beam. Do not confuse the Back Beam of a Localizer with an ILS for the reciprocal runway, which will be a totally different installation with its own transmitting aerials.

Fig. 13-6. Two Different ILSs serving Opposite Runways.

THE LOCALIZER AIRBORNE EQUIPMENT

The Localizer transmits on a frequency in the VHF band between 108.10 and 111.95 MHz. The specific frequency is published on the relevant Instrument Approach Chart. The Pilot can select this frequency on the VHF-NAV radio, and must **identify** the Localizer by its morse code *IDENT* before using it. It will begin with the letter 'I' (i.e. *'dit-dit'*) and will usually, but not always, consist of a three letter group.

Identifying the Localizer serves to identify the ILS (including the glideslope). The Birmingham Runway 33 ILS, for instance, has an *IDENT* of 'IBM' (i.e. *'dit-dit dah-dit-dit-dit dah-dah'*). The ILS in the opposite direction, on Runway 15, has an *IDENT* 'IBIR' (i.e. *'dit-dit dah-dit-dit-dit dit-dit dit-dah-dit'*). **Correct identification is vital** before an ILS (or any radio aid for that matter) is used.

For the Localizer to be usable, it must be identified, and there should be no red *OFF Flag* covering the vertical needle. If the *OFF Flag* is visible, then the signal being received at the aeroplane is not sufficiently strong, and so the CDI (Course Deviation Indicator) indications will be unreliable.

The aeroplane's VHF-NAV receiver, when tuned to a Localizer frequency, compares the strengths of the two signals (150 Hz and 90 Hz) it receives, and produces a voltage that energises the Localizer Needle in the cockpit. If the 150 Hz signal is stronger (which will occur if the aeroplane on approach is out to the right), then a voltage is fed to the Localizer Needle that moves it to the left. This indicates that the Localizer centreline is to the left of the aeroplane on approach. On some instruments, the needle will point to a blue marking, as a further indication that the aeroplane is to the right of centreline and in the Blue sector.

If the signals are of equal strength, then the Localizer Needle is centred, providing an *ON TRACK* indication. If the 90 Hz signal predominates, then the voltage fed to the Localizer Needle moves it to the right, indicating that the aeroplane is in the Yellow sector and, on approach, will need to move to the right to get back on centreline.

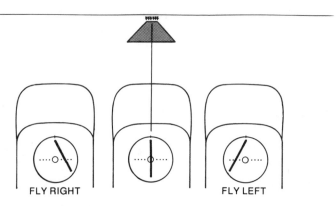

FLY RIGHT   FLY LEFT

Fig. 13-7. An Aeroplane on Approach.

Full scale deflection will occur when the aeroplane is displaced 2.5° or more from the centreline. This means that the VHF-NAV Display (with its five dots either side of centre) is *four times more sensitive* when it is tuned to a Localizer (i.e. 0.5° per dot), compared to when it is tuned to a VOR (2° per dot, to provide an indication 10° either side of the selected VOR radial). Usable Localizer signals may be obtained up to +/–35° from course centreline (giving **full-scale deflection** beyond +/–2.5°). Outside this signal area, the *OFF Flag* will come into view.

The Localizer course is a **single** fixed beam, unlike the VOR which gives the Pilot a choice of 360 radials using the Omni Bearing Selector (OBS). With an ILS or Localizer selected on the VHF-NAV, however, the OBS has absolutely no significance, and changing it will have no effect on the indications of the CDI Needle. It is good operating procedure, however, to dial in the inbound track of the Localizer (using the OBS) simply as a reminder.

The Localizer Cockpit Indicator does **not** give any heading information, but only **position** information. It displays how many degrees the aeroplane is displaced from the Localizer track, and in which sector (Blue or Yellow).

Fig.13-8. The CDI indicates Angular Displacement from the Localizer, and does NOT give Heading Information.

If the Localizer signal fails, then the whole ILS approach becomes unauthorised (including the Glideslope), and an ILS approach in such a situation is **not permitted**.

FLYING THE LOCALIZER

The ILS Cockpit Instrument is a **performance instrument**. It should be included in the selective radial scan when information from it is desired. Having gained that information (which, in this case, is the position and/ or movement of the Localizer Needle), the eyes should return to the **Attitude Indicator**. Any corrections to Heading to regain or maintain the Localizer track can then be made with a small coordinated turn on the AI. The Direction Indicator can be checked for Heading, and the ILS Cockpit Indicator can be checked again for position and/or movement of the Localizer Needle.

The aim is to fly a Heading that will maintain the aeroplane on centreline. If a crosswind exists, a Wind Correction Angle will be required, and the aeroplane Heading will differ slightly from the published Inbound Track of the Localizer. The wind will probably back and weaken in strength as the aeroplane descends, and there will be gusts and lulls, so continual adjustments to Heading can be expected. The Localizer beam narrows as the runway is approached, a bit like a 'funnel', and so the corrections should become smaller and smaller (hopefully). This is the same bracketting technique used for tracking on the NDB or VOR, except that the Localizer is far more sensitive (four times as sensitive as the VOR).

For an aeroplane on approach, the Localizer Needle indicates which way the aeroplane should move to regain the centreline. If the Localizer Needle is to the right, then the aeroplane should be moved right. On approach, the CDI acts as a **Command Instrument**, i.e. to regain centreline, **fly towards the Needle**.

Fig.13-9. Typical Heading Corrections for a Deviation Right of Centreline.

It is usual to make many such heading corrections on the one approach to regain and maintain the Localizer centreline. This is to be expected, since the wind effect almost certainly will vary along the approach. Because the CDI Needle displays *angular* displacement from the centreline, it will become more and more sensitive as the runway is approached, and so **the heading corrections should become finer and finer.** Aim to *capture the Localizer* early on the approach, so that small deviations are corrected before they have a chance to become large devations.

NOTE: A typical Heading Bug on a DI has an angular width of about 12°, i.e. 6° either side of centre. If such a Heading Bug is used as a Heading Datum on the DI, then most heading changes to maintain the Localizer can be contained within its angular width.

The Localizer is usable out to about 25 nm from the runway, however it is not usually intercepted until within approximately 10 nm of the aerodrome at 3000 ft AAL or less.

When **tracking outbound on a Localizer**, which may occur when positioning the aeroplane for an ILS, the CDI Needle will still indicate which sector the aeroplane is in (Blue or Yellow), and will display the angular displacement from centreline as if the aeroplane were on approach. This means that, when flying outbound, to regain centreline the aeroplane must be turned **away** from the CDI Needle, i.e. it is acting as a **non-command instrument** when the aeroplane is **flying outbound**.

Fig.13-10. Tracking Outbound on a Localizer.

Additional tracking guidance is always useful (especially when tracking outbound on a Localizer using a non-command instrument), and in many ILSs this additional guidance can be obtained from a Locator NDB.

NOTE: Some advanced instruments combine a Compass Card with the CDI to form a *Horizontal Situation Indicator (HSI)*, which simplifies tracking outbound on the Localiser. The HSI is not considered in detail in this manual.

With the HSI, the Course Arrow is aligned with the Localizer Inbound Course, and rotates along with the Compass Card as the aircraft turns; therefore the Deviation Bar can be used as a *Command Instrument* when the aeroplane is both inbound and outbound.

Fig.13-11. The HSI.

THE GLIDESLOPE

The most suitable approach to a runway for large modern aircraft is a glideslope of approximately 3° to the horizontal (a gradient of 1 in 20, or 5%) which intersects the runway approximately 300 metres in from the threshold. The 3° slope provides a loss of approximately 300 ft in height for every 1 nm travelled, which gives a reasonable *rate of descent* for most aeroplanes at typical approach speeds – 600 ft/min at 120 kt Ground Speed, for instance, and 450 ft/min at 90 kt Ground Speed. With a slope of 300 ft per nautical mile, you can expect the Glideslope to be:

• 3000 ft AAL at approximately 10 nm to touchdown;
• 2100 ft AAL at approximately 7 nm; and
• 1500 ft AAL at approximately 5 nm.

Fig. 13-12. The Glideslope loses Height at about 300 ft per Nautical Mile.

The approximate height on slope can be checked by multiplying the distance from the runway in nautical miles by 300. For example, at 3 DME the aeroplane should be at 900 ft QFE.

THE GLIDESLOPE GROUND EQUIPMENT

The Glideslope transmitting aerial is usually situated about 300 metres in from the runway threshold to ensure that any aeroplane flying the glideslope will have adequate wheel clearance over the threshold and any objects and/or terrain on approach. The Threshold Crossing Height (TCH) of the Glideslope is published on the ILS Chart. The main wheels on some larger aircraft follow a much lower flightpath than the glideslope receiving antenna, which could be located near the nose of the aeroplane or somewhere else significantly higher than the wheels.

The aim when flying a Glideslope is not to touch down on the 'piano keys', but to touch down in the *Touch Down Zone* near where the Glideslope intersects the runway. On some runways, the Glide Slope Transmitting Aerial may be further in than 300 metres if there are high and restricting obstacles on the approach path.

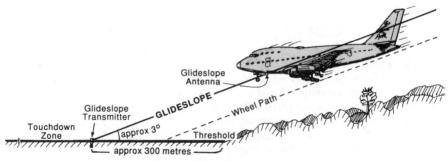

Fig.13-13. The typical Glideslope Transmitting Aerial is approximately 300 metres in from the Runway Threshold.

As well as being some 300 metres in from the threshold, the **Glideslope Transmitting Aerial** is usually situated some 100–200 metres to the side of the runway to avoid being an obstacle to aircraft operating on the runway, and to reduce interference with the Glideslope signal to these aircraft. The Glideslope is transmitted on an Ultra High Frequency (UHF) carrier wave using a similar principle to the Localizer transmission (that of two over-lapping lobes), but the transmission pattern is slightly more complex.

A large 90 Hz lobe overlaps a 150 Hz lobe in the vertical plane. The actual Glideslope, formed where the two signals are equal, is typically at 3° to the horizontal, but some Glideslopes may be shallower, at 2.5°, and others may be steeper at 3.5°. It may not seem much of an approach angle, but a 4° approach angle is extremely steep, very noticeable in the cockpit and possibly difficult to maintain in some jet transports.

*Fig.13-14.
The Glideslope*

The area of overlap of the two signals is about 1.4°, i.e. the useful signals extend 0.7° above and below the precise glideslope. The Glidepath is calibrated out to 10 nm, although signals can be received at greater distances. The approximate 3° glideslope is protected in the range: 1.35° to 5.25° above the horizontal, and is accurate within +/–8° of the localizer centreline.

Unfortunately, due to ground reflection of some of the transmissions, there may be more than one overlapping of the lobes, giving rise to one or more false glideslopes at different angles to the horizontal, and well above the true glideslope. The false glideslopes may occur at multiples of the true glideslope angle (typically 3°), i.e. at 6°, 9°, 12° and 15°. A pilot should be aware that one or more false glideslopes may exist, and not be surprised when a false on-slope indication is given in the cockpit, for instance above 12,000 ft AAL when only 10 nm from the aerodrome, or when manoeuvring around the aerodrome to intercept the ILS.

The Glideslope Needle in the cockpit may oscillate as the aeroplane meets one of the false glideslopes, or it may exhibit other abnormal indications such as reverse sensing, but it will be fairly obvious that the signal is a false one. If the Localizer transmits a *Back Beam,* then there will probably be false glideslope signals in that area, which can cause the Glideslope *OFF Flag* to flicker in and out of view. Be prepared to recognise a false glideslope signal for what it is, and then disregard it.

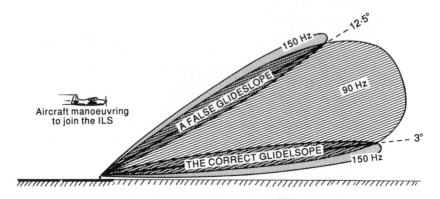

Fig. 13-15. Beware of False Glideslopes.

The problem of false glideslopes is easily solved if the pilot has in mind the height/distance relationship of the real Glideslope (300 ft/nm). Also, and most importantly, there will be **no false glideslope below the true Glideslope** – any false glideslopes will be above it, and will be at approximately 6° (or more) to the horizontal. For this reason it is recommended to **intercept the Glideslope from below.** For instance, it may be preferable to fly in from 10 nm at 2500 ft AAL to intercept the Glideslope at about 7 nm-to-run, than to carry out a very steep descent from above the Glideslope in an attempt to intercept it.

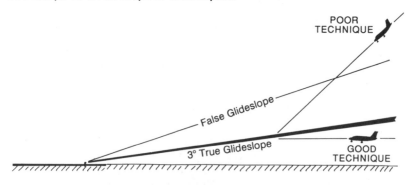

Fig. 13-16. Ideally, intercept the Glideslope from Below.

13 – THE INSTRUMENT LANDING SYSTEM (ILS)

The electronic Glideslope of the ILS is accurate from approximately 10 nm, but descent on the Glideslope should not be commenced until the aeroplane has first intercepted the Localizer. In the **Leeds Bradford ILS/ DME Rwy 32,** the published procedure starts overhead the runway at 4000 ft AMSL on QNH *(3340 ft AAL on QFE)* and proceeds outbound on 156°M (or 165°M for the faster aeroplanes with the larger turning radii) on descent to 3000 ft AMSL *(2340 ft AAL)* at 9.0 DME *LF* (the identifier for the Rwy 32 DME, selected automatically with the Rwy 32 ILS, and which is the zero point for the approach – the runway threshold).

During the turn inbound, the published path is beneath the Glideslope, and so the Localizer inbound track of 324° can be intercepted before descent on the Glideslope is commenced, when it is intercepted from below after 9.0 DME inbound.

Fig.13-17. Plan and Profile of the Leeds Bradford ILS/DME Rwy 32.

THE AIRBORNE GLIDESLOPE EQUIPMENT

The position of the Glideslope relative to the aircraft is indicated by the 'horizontal' needle of the VHF-NAV Cockpit Display. To be certain that the Glideslope signal is usable, the red *OFF Flag* should be biased out of view. The vertical glideslope scale on the usual Cockpit Indicator consists of 5 dots above and below the central position, although the first dots *UP* and *DOWN* may be joint in a circle.

Fig. 13-18.
Different types of
Glideslope Cockpit Display.

A particular glideslope transmission frequency is always **paired** with the same Localizer frequency, so that the pilot **automatically** selects the associated Glideslope when he selects the Localizer on the VHF-NAV. For instance, a frequency of 329.300 MHz in the Ultra High Frequency band for the Glideslope is always paired with a Localizer frequency of 108.900 MHz. For instance, by selecting the *Edinburgh Rwy 25 Localizer* frequency, which is published on charts as 108.900 MHz, the pilot automatically selects its paired Glideslope frequency without even knowing what it is.

The Glideslope Receiver in the aircraft compares the relative strength of the two signals, producing a voltage that positions the Glideslope Needle. If the 90 Hz signal is stronger because the aeroplane is above the Glideslope, then the Glideslope Needle moves down. This indicates that the aeroplane must *FLY DOWN* to recapture the Glideslope. It is the aircraft which moves to the Glideslope (and not vice versa).

Conversely, if the aircraft is below the Glideslope, the needle will move up – known as a *FLY-UP* indication. This does not mean that the aircraft must actually climb to recapture the Glideslope. Flying level, or even just reducing the Rate of Descent, as the aircraft flies towards the runway may be sufficient.

Fig. 13-19. The Glideslope Needle indicates
where the Glideslope is with respect to the Aircraft.

282

A full-scale *FLY-UP* indication means that the aircraft is at 0.7° or more below the Glideslope. Deviation from the Glideslope is referred to in terms of 'dots' rather than degrees, there being 5 dots up and 5 dots down on the instrument.

It is recommended that the aircraft be kept right on Glideslope (to the best of your ability), and **not exceed more than one-half full-scale *FLY-UP* deviation below slope** to retain adequate obstacle clearance towards the end of the approach. This would put the aeroplane 0.3° or 0.4° below slope, which is significant since the slope is only 3° thick. As a general rule, make a strong effort to stay right on Glideslope throughout the approach.

Conversely, a **full-scale *FLY-DOWN* indication** means that the aircraft is 0.7° or more above the slope. Full-scale deflections once the ILS approach has been commenced are not acceptable, since the deviation from slope is at least 0.7°, but it could be anything! There is no indication on the Cockpit Display of just how far the aircraft is above or below slope when the Glideslope Needle is fully deflected.

The 1.4° of overlap (0.7° above and below the perfect slope) is equivalent to about 140 ft in 1 nm (using the familiar 1:60 rule and the approximation that 1 nm = 6000 ft), which means that the vertical thickness of the overlapping Glideslope beam is:
- 1400 ft at 10 nm (from full-scale *UP* to full-scale *DOWN*);
- 700 ft at 5 nm;
- 420 ft at 3 nm;
- 280 ft at 2 nm;
- 140 ft at 1 nm; and
- a few feet thick at the funway threshold.

The Glideslope signal is only approved for navigational use down to the lowest authorised Decision Height (DH) for that particular ILS, and any reference to glideslope indications below that height **must** be supplemented by visual reference to the runway environment.

A *Category-1 ILS* is approved down to DH 200 ft, a *Category-2 ILS* is approved down to DH 100 ft, a *Category-3 ILS* is approved down to DH 0 ft – all of which are well below the Decision Heights allowed for an IMC-Rated Pilot carrying out an ILS approach (an absolute minimum of 500 ft AAL, or higher).

If the Glideslope fails, but not the Localizer, then the pilot is still permitted to carry out a (non-precision) Localizer Approach, using the Localizer for guidance in azimuth, and using range markers (such as the Marker Beacons, DME distances or a Locator) for descent to suitable heights which will be marked on the profile part of the Approach Chart.

Referring back to the *Leeds Bradford ILS/DME Rwy 32* profile (page 281) a Localizer checkpoint can be seen when crossing the Outer Marker (OM), 3.9 DME, at 1960 ft AMSL *(1300 ft AAL)*. Because of the lack of glideslope guidance, the Decision Height (DH) for an IMC-Rated Pilot on a Localizer Approach will be 600 ft AAL or higher (compared to the DH for the full ILS approach of 500 ft AAL or higher).

FLYING THE GLIDESLOPE

Flying the Glideslope is very similar to flying straight and level except of course, that the aim is to keep the aeroplane on a **constant descent plane,** rather than on a level plane at constant altitude. In level flight, the Altimeter is checked regularly to ensure height is being maintained; during an ILS, the Glideslope Needle is checked regularly to ensure that the desired slope is being maintained.

The ILS Cockpit Instrument is a **performance instrument.** It should be included in the selective radial scan when information from it is desired. Having gained that information (which, in this case, is the position and/or movement of the Glideslope Needle), the eyes should return to the **Attitude Indicator.** Any corrections to regain or maintain the Glideslope can then be made with a small Pitch Attitude change on the AI. The ILS Cockpit Indicator can be checked again for position and/or movement of the Glideslope Needle.

A process similar to bracketting track is used to regain and then maintain the Glideslope, instead in this case it is Pitch Attitude that is altered slightly rather than Heading.

If, for instance, the aeroplane goes below slope whilst a particular Pitch Attitude is held, then it should be raised slightly and held until the Glideslope is regained. Once back on slope, the Pitch Attitude can be lowered slightly (but not quite as low as before) so that the glideslope is maintained.

There is also a target airspeed to be achieved on an ILS approach and, as in level flight, it can be controlled with power. With Pitch Attitude changes to regain and maintain glideslope, small airspeed changes will occur. Fluctuations of +/−5 kt are normally acceptable, but any trend beyond this should be corrected by a power alteration (typically 1 inch of Manifold Pressure or 100 rpm is sufficient, although greater power changes may be required in strong and gusty wind conditions or in windshear).

Maintaining glideslope and airspeed is one sign of a good Instrument Pilot. **Flightpath** and **airspeed** (in other words the **performance** of the aeroplane) are controlled by **attitude** and **power** on an ILS approach. If you have a good scan and quick response, then small deviations from the Glideslope will be corrected immediately, and not develop into large deviations which might require a power adjustment as well.

Flying the Glideslope involves **energy transfer.** If the aeroplane is slightly below slope and slightly fast, then the excess speed can be converted to height (or to a reduced Rate of Descent) by raising the Pitch Attitude on the AI, and *flying up* to regain slope. Conversely, if the aeroplane is above slope, the Pitch Attitude on the AI can be lowered slightly, and the aeroplane *flown down* to regain slope, possibly with a small speed increase.

• Hold the Glideslope with Pitch Attitude on the AI.
• Hold the desired Airspeed with Power.

Fig.13-20. Hold Glideslope with Elevator (Attitude Indicator), and Airspeed with Throttle.

Since it displays angular displacement, the Glideslope Needle will become more accurate and more sensitive as the aeroplane flies closer to the runway. Therefore, corrections on the Attitude Indicator to hold glideslope should become finer and finer as the runway is approached.

MARKER BEACONS

ILS Marker Beacons transmit a **vertical** elliptical pattern, often described as 'fan-shaped', which can be received by an aircraft as it passes overhead. Because the radio energy is transmitted upwards, it is not possible to track to a Marker Beacon (unlike an NDB or Locator whose energy is transmitted in all directions).

A typical ILS has two Markers along the Localizer to provide *range* check points. They are:
• the Outer Marker (OM) at approximately 5 nm; and
• the Middle Marker (MM) at 3500 ft (0.6 nm).

Fig.13-21. The Outer Marker and the Middle Marker.

Both Markers operate on the same VHF frequency of 75 MHz, but each is amplitude-modulated differently to provide aural Morse-code identification.

The **airborne equipment** of the glideslope consists of a Marker Receiver which indicates passage over a Marker by a light flashing in the cockpit and an aural morse code *IDENT*. The *IDENT* can be **heard** through the headset or cockpit speaker, and the light (one of three colour-coded lights on the Instrument Panel) can be **seen** flashing. The pilot does not have to make any specific selection to receive the Marker Beacons.

The **Outer Marker (OM)** is located between 3 and 7 nm from the runway threshold, usually at about 4 or 5 nm. The aeroplane, if it is on glideslope, should therefore be at approximately 1200–1500 ft AAL as it passes over-head the OM. The precise height crossing the OM (both *AMSL* and *AAL)* is specified on the profile diagram of the particular ILS, and the pilot should check this on the Altimeter as the aircraft passes over the OM. The cockpit indications of passage over the Outer Marker are:

- an aural series of low-pitched (400 Hz) dashes transmitted at two per second (i.e. *"-dah-dah-dah-dah-dah-dah-dah-"*); and
- a flashing **blue** light synchronised with the aural 'dah-dahs'.

The **Middle Marker (MM)** is located approximately 3500 ft (0.6 nm) from the runway threshold, where the Glideslope is approximately 200 ft AAL. This is near the Decision Height and Missed Approach Point for fully Instrument-Rated Pilots, but much lower than the more conservative Decision Height required for IMC-Rated Pilots (which is 500 ft AAL or higher). The Middle Marker crossing height may or may not be specified on the charts, since at this stage in the approach the pilot should be visual.

The cockpit indications of passage over the Middle Marker are:

- an aural series of medium-pitched (1300 Hz) dots and dashes trans-mitted at six per second (i.e. *"-dah-dit-dah-dit-dah-dit-dah-dit-"*); and
- a flashing **orange** light synchronised with the aural 'dah-dits'.

dah-dah-dah-dah-dah-dah-dah-

WHITE BLUE YELLOW

dit-dah-dit-dah-dit-dah-di-dah-

WHITE BLUE YELLOW

Fig. 13-22. Cockpit Indications
of the Outer Marker;

Cockpit Indications of
the Middle Marker.

The signals will increase in strength fairly quickly as the aeroplane nears the Marker Beacon, be very strong for a number of seconds, and then fade away as the aircraft moves further along the approach. Some airborne receivers have a *HIGH/LOW* sensivity switch – *LOW* sensitivity giving a much narrower vertical pattern. For Instrument Approaches, the sensitiv-ity switch is set to *HIGH*. Because the aircraft will be at a low level during the Instrument Approach, the Marker Beacon signal will only be heard and seen for a few seconds.

A typical ILS with two Marker Beacons on the Localizer track is **Belfast/ Aldergrove Rwy 17 ILS.**

The published glideslope (GS) crossing height at the OM is 1870 ft AMSL on QNH, or *1660 ft AAL on QFE.* This is what the Altimeter will read in **ISA conditions** if exactly on slope. In air significantly colder than ISA, however, the Altimeter will read slightly higher due to density error. Conversely, in air significantly warmer than ISA, the Altimeter will read slightly lower than the published figure.

Fig.13-23. Belfast/Aldergrove ILS Rwy 17 Profile.

Points of interest on this ILS profile chart at Belfast/Aldergrove are:
- the **inbound track** of the Localizer is 171°M;
- GS **crossing height at the OM** is 1870'*(1660')* with 5 nm to run;
- MM is (4.9 – 0.5 =) 4.4 nm beyond the OM, at 0.8 nm from the zero point (the runway threshold);
- GS crossing height at MM is 510'*(300');*
- ILS Glideslope **Threshold Crossing Height** (TCH) is 50 ft;
- Runway 17 **threshold elevation** is 206 ft AMSL (the 8 mb referring to the pressure difference between QNH and QFE);
- in this procedure, the *BEL* VOR, which is located on the airport, can be selected to provide useful DME information.

Airport elevation, 267 ft AMSL (the highest point on any runway), is shown at the top of the Aerad chart for the approach *(not shown in excerpt above).*

A few ILSs have **Inner Markers** situated very close to the threshold, indicated by high-pitched (3000 Hz) dots at six per second *("-dit-dit-dit-dit-dit-dit-"),* and a synchronised flashing white light. These have little significance to IMC-Rated Pilots.

Airways Fan Markers along Airways and **Z Markers** over LF Radio Range sites are no longer used in the UK, although they may be encountered elsewhere. They have a high-pitched (3000 Hz) *IDENT* and cause a **white** marker light (labelled A or FM/Z) to flash.

NOTE: A Locator beacon (NDB) is often co-located with the ILS Outer Marker – quite common in the UK – and labelled *'LOM' – Locator Outer Marker.* The advantage of the Locator is that it can be used for tracking purposes when positioning the aircraft to commence an ILS, or it can be used for holding.

OTHER MEANS OF CHECKING GLIDESLOPE

Not all ILS installations have an Outer Marker and/or Middle Marker. **Blackpool ILS DME Rwy 28,** for instance, does *not* have an Outer Marker. The Glideslope, however, can be checked at different DME distances:

- 2000 ft on QNH (or *1970 ft* on QFE) at 6.0 DME;
- 1680′ *(1650′)* at 5.0 DME;
- 1360′ *(1330′)* at 4.0 DME; as well as
- 370′ *(340′)* at the Middle Marker – although, by this stage in the approach, the IMC-Rated Pilot will have already reached his Decision Height and either continued the approach visually or made a Missed Approach.

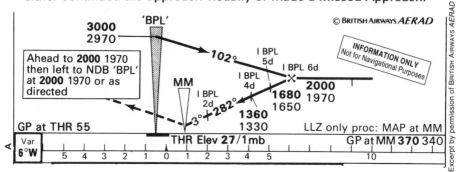

Fig. 13-24. Blackpool ILS DME Rwy 28.

A DME which is *frequency-paired* with an ILS will be **automatically** selected on many VHF-NAV receivers when the ILS frequency is selected. The DME is arranged to give a zero-range indication at the threshold of the ILS runway. **Precise** range will only be indicated by the DME when the aeroplane is in line with the runway on the approach path.

FLYING A TYPICAL ILS

The relevant **Instrument Approach Chart** should be checked for currency, and studied well before commencing the approach. Even though the chart can be referred to during the actual approach, it is helpful to build up an overall view of where the aeroplane is and what path it will follow. As an example, the published **Manchester ILS Rwy 06** chart (in plan and profile) follows, accompanied by an illustration (fig. 13-28) of how the approach will be flown.

The appropriate **Decision Height** to be used should be calculated. In this case the Decision Height is the **greater** of:

- published DH 200 + 50 altimeter correction + 200 IMC-Rating allowance = 450 ft QFE; or
- the IMC-Rating **absolute minimum** for any ILS, which is 500 ft QFE;

that is, 500 ft QFE (or, since the Threshold Elevation is 211 ft, 711 ft QNH).

The **Missed Approach** procedure should be reviewed, and **alternative action** planned if there is any doubt that a successful landing can be made. Low cloud fluctuating about the Decision Height, poor visibility, heavy rain, or anything that might prejudice your arrival, should lead you to consider suitable Alternate Aerodromes.

There is always a (remote) possibility that an essential ground aid required for the landing will become unserviceable (caused by a lightning strike or flooding during a storm, for instance).

The fuel situation should be thought about, and the **minimum fuel on board required for diversion** calculated. Allow for reserves. *Is there fuel enough for more than one approach before diverting? How much fuel is available for Holding? Is the weather at the Alternate still suitable for a visual approach, etc.?*

Prepare for the approach well before reaching the aerodrome, so that, once there, you can devote your complete attention to flying the approach.

Track to the aerodrome following the normal route and using the normal en route tracking aids, not descending below the relevant Sector Safe Altitude (SSA) or Minimum Sector Altitude (MSA) published on the charts. **All Radio Aids must be Morse-code identified before being used.** ATC may assist with *Radar Vectors*, which can save distance and time, and will provide adequate obstacle clearance. All clearances, headings, altitudes and pressure settings passed by ATC should be read back.

If a **Holding Pattern** has to be entered, then plan to use the correct entry procedure based on the aircraft's Heading when it reaches the Holding Fix. Vertical separation between aircraft in the one Holding Pattern should be 1000 ft or greater.

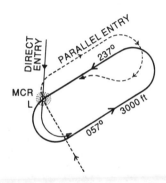

Stacking aircraft in Holding Patterns until a *slot* in the ILS becomes available is common during busy periods at major airports. As each aircraft leaves the bottom of the stack and proceeds into the ILS, the others in the stack can be cleared down one at a time.

Fig. 13-25. Holding Pattern Entry.

Some instrument approach procedures show a **DME Arc,** which may be flown to position the aircraft for the approach. One advantage of this procedure is that there will usually be less manoeuvring involved to reach the Final Approach Fix, often saving time and being more comfortable for passengers.

Fig. 13-26. A DME Arc.

In the illustration that follows, the aeroplane has flown en route to the VOR at the aerodrome, and then turned to track out to the Locator Outer Marker, where it will commence the ILS procedure.

Integrate the normal operational requirements into the approach so that the whole thing flows smoothly, without undue haste or panic. Radio calls, pre-landing checks, configuration and airspeed changes – the sorts of things that occur on all approaches – still must be attended to. Having prepared for the approach early in order to reduce the workload later on, you should now be able to sit back (more or less) and calmly follow the procedure, attending briefly to other duties as required.

Fig. 13-27. Plan and Profile of the Manchester Runway 06 ILS.

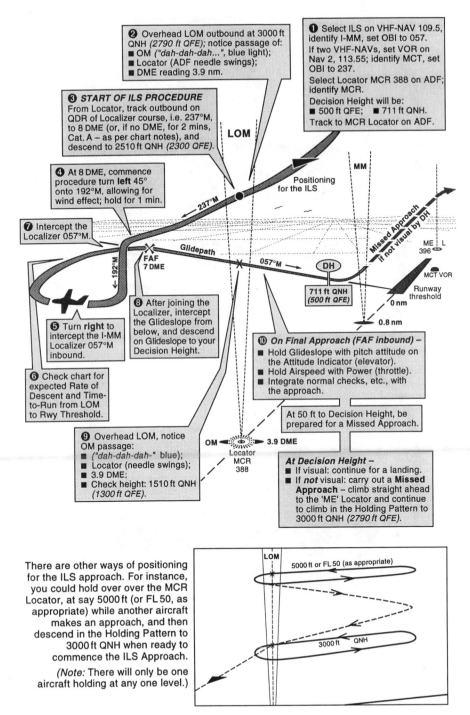

❶ Select ILS on VHF-NAV 109.5, identify I-MM, set OBI to 057.
If two VHF-NAVs, set VOR on Nav 2, 113.55; identify MCT, set OBI to 237.
Select Locator MCR 388 on ADF; identify MCR.
Decision Height will be:
■ 500 ft QFE; ■ 711 ft QNH.
Track to MCR Locator on ADF.

❷ Overhead LOM outbound at 3000 ft QNH *(2790 ft QFE)*; notice passage of:
■ OM *("dah-dah-dah...",* blue light);
■ Locator (ADF needle swings);
■ DME reading 3.9 nm.

❸ START OF ILS PROCEDURE
From Locator, track outbound on QDR of Localizer course, i.e. 237°M, to 8 DME (or, if no DME, for 2 mins, Cat. A – as per chart notes), and descend to 2510 ft QNH *(2300 QFE).*

❹ At 8 DME, commence procedure turn **left** 45° onto 192°M, allowing for wind effect; hold for 1 min.

❼ Intercept the Localizer 057°M.

Positioning for the ILS

❺ Turn right to intercept the I-MM Localizer 057°M inbound.

❽ After joining the Localizer, intercept the Glideslope from below, and descend on Glideslope to your Decision Height.

❻ Check chart for expected Rate of Descent and Time-to-Run from LOM to Rwy Threshold.

FAF 7 DME Glidepath 057°M **DH**

711 ft QNH *(500 ft QFE)*

Missed Approach if not visual by DH

ME L 396

MCT VOR

Runway threshold

0 nm

0.8 nm

❿ On Final Approach (FAF inbound) –
■ Hold Glideslope with pitch attitude on the Attitude Indicator (elevator).
■ Hold Airspeed with Power (throttle).
■ Integrate normal checks, etc., with the approach.

At 50 ft to Decision Height, be prepared for a Missed Approach.

❾ Overhead LOM, notice OM passage:
■ *("dah-dah-dah-"* blue);
■ Locator (needle swings);
■ 3.9 DME;
■ Check height: 1510 ft QNH *(1300 ft QFE).*

OM ◄ 3.9 DME
Locator MCR 388

At Decision Height –
■ If visual: continue for a landing.
■ If *not* visual: carry out a **Missed Approach** – climb straight ahead to the 'ME' Locator and continue to climb in the Holding Pattern to 3000 ft QNH *(2790 ft QFE).*

There are other ways of positioning for the ILS approach. For instance, you could hold over over the MCR Locator, at say 5000 ft (or FL 50, as appropriate) while another aircraft makes an approach, and then descend in the Holding Pattern to 3000 ft QNH when ready to commence the ILS Approach.

(Note: There will only be one aircraft holding at any one level.)

LOM 5000 ft or FL 50 (as appropriate)

3000 ft QNH

Fig. 13-28. Manoeuvring for the Manchester ILS Rwy 06.

Fig.13-29. Flying the ILS on Final Approach.

☐ Now do **Exercises 13 – The ILS**.

14

VHF DIRECTION FINDING (VDF)

THE PRINCIPLE OF VHF DIRECTION FINDING

Some aerodromes are equipped with radio aerials which can sense the **direction** of VHF-COM signals (i.e. normal voice signals) received from an aeroplane.

This information is presented to the Air Traffic Controller (usually the Approach Controller) as a radial line on a Cathode Ray Tube similar to a radar screen or, with the most modern VDF equipment, as a very accurate digital readout of bearing.

The Controller can then advise the Pilot of his bearing relative to the aerodrome. This is known as *Very High Frequency Direction Finding*, and is often abbreviated to *VHF D/F* or *VDF*.

An advantage of VDF is that no specific airborne equipment is required other than a VHF-COM, i.e. a normal VHF communications radio.

A typical VDF air/ground exchange would be a Pilot requesting ATC to provide his QDM (magnetic bearing to the ground station), followed by the Controller advising it. For example:

> Pilot: *Golf Mike Whiskey – Request QDM.*
>
> ATC: *Golf Mike Whiskey – QDM 090.*

Fig.14-1. QDM is Magnetic Bearing to the VDF Ground Station.

By steering the QDM, the Pilot is able to *home* to the ground station, i.e. head towards it.

293

Ground stations that are equipped to provide VDF are designated by the term *Homer*, e.g. Shoreham Homer, which operates on the VHF communications frequency of 123.15 MHz.

Whereas no special equipment is required in the aeroplane for VDF other than a VHF-COM radio, it does require a special installation at the ground station. Two typical designs for VDF aerials at aerodromes are the H-type aerial (a double-H dipole aerial in technical terms), or the Doppler-type VDF aerial.

Fig.14-2. Ground Equipment for VHF Direction Finding.

VDF ground equipment from years ago was known as a *Manual Homer*, and used an ADF-type null-seeking aerial which the Operator had to rotate manually to determine the direction of the aeroplane. It also required long transmissions from the aeroplane while the Operator sought the null position.

Modern equipment is fully automatic, with the Ground Operator having the direction of the aeroplane displayed to him automatically following only a short VHF-COM transmission from the Pilot.

THE INFORMATION AVAILABLE FROM VDF

Bearings that a Pilot may request from a VDF Operator are:

- QDM: *magnetic* bearing *TO* the station;
- QDR: *magnetic* bearing *FROM* the station (i.e. the reciprocal of the QDM);
- QTE: *true* bearing *from* the station.

Fig.14-3. QDM;   QDR;   QTE.

QDR, the magnetic bearing from the station, is useful for orientation (where am I?). QDR is similar information to a VOR radial. QTE, the true bearing from the station, is useful if you want to plot a Position Line from the VDF ground station to the aeroplane on a map (against True North). However it is QDM, the magnetic bearing to the station, that is the most commonly used and requested VDF bearing.

The **quality** of the bearings obtained by VDF is classified by the VDF Ground Operator to the Pilot as:

- Class A: accurate to within +/−2°;
- Class B: accurate to within +/−5°;
- Class C: accurate to within +/−10°.
- Class D: CAP 46 also lists some Class D VDF Stations with an accuracy poorer than even +/−10°.

Most modern equipment is generally accurate to +/−1°, although accuracy may be decreased by:

- VDF site errors such as reflection from nearby uneven ground, buildings, aircraft or vehicles; and
- VHF propagation errors caused by irregular propagation over differing terrain, especially if the aeroplane is at long range from the VDF ground station.

QDM is the most commonly requested bearing. It is the heading to steer direct to the VDF station provided no crosswind exists. In a crosswind, however, a Wind Correction Angle (WCA) into-wind must be used to counteract the drift if a reasonably straight track is to be achieved, rather than a curved (and inefficient) homing.

At typical light aircraft speeds, it is reasonable for the Pilot to request a QDM each half-minute or so to check tracking, and to modify heading if necessary.

Fig.14-4. Steering QDM to a VDF Ground Station
in Nil-Crosswind Conditions is Satisfactory.

If QDM is steered as Heading in crosswind conditions, then the aeroplane will drift downwind, and its QDM will gradually change. The next QDM passed by the Ground Operator will be different from the first.

In the case illustrated below, an original QDM 080 has become QDM 075, and so the Pilot would turn slightly left from a Heading of 080°M to a Heading of 075°M (the new QDM) to continue homing to the station.

There would be further changes to QDM advised by the Operator as the aeroplane continued on, the end result being a curved path with the aeroplane arriving overhead the ground station heading roughly into-wind – not a particularly professional arrival!

Fig.14-5. An Inefficient Homing to a VDF Ground Station.

A more efficient arrival can be achieved by allowing for wind effect, i.e. *tracking* using a Wind Correction Angle into-wind to counteract drift, rather than *homing* to the station by flying a continually changing QDM as heading.

TRACKING

TRACKING TOWARDS A VDF GROUND STATION USING QDM INFORMATION

To achieve a desired track to a VDF ground station, the Pilot should try to maintain a **Datum QDM** which is the same as the **desired track**. For instance, to maintain a track of 080°M to the VDF ground station, the Pilot should fly a Heading so that QDM 080 is consistently maintained.

Whilst the VDF Ground Operator can advise QDM, he will not advise Heading to steer to counter any crosswind effect; this the Pilot must determine if a direct track to the VDF station is to be achieved. If his selected WCA is perfectly correct, then the Ground Operator will advise, upon request for QDM, the **same QDM** as previously.

Fig. 14-6. Perfect Allowance for Drift.

The supply of QDMs by ATC may be thought of as a *'Talking RMI'*. The Pilot, by mentally placing the QDM onto the Direction Indicator, can form the same picture as that given to him by an RMI.

Fig. 14-7. The Stated QDM is like a Talking RMI.

If the stated QDM moves to the right of the Datum QDM, then the aeroplane has drifted to the left of the desired track, and should be turned right to re-intercept the desired track (i.e. to re-establish the Datum QDM). This is exactly the same response as for the head of an RMI needle moving to the right of the Datum QDM.

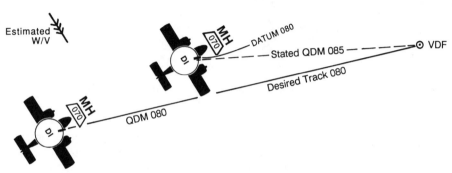

Fig. 14-8. Tracking Towards a VDF Ground Station;
if QDM moves Right of the Datum, turn Right.

In this case, whilst flying on a Magnetic Heading of 070, the actual QDM has moved to the right of the Datum QDM 080, indicated by ATC stating QDM 085. To regain the desired track, the Pilot should turn right and increase Heading (to say MH 090), and then request QDMs until the desired QDM 080 is reached. At this time, a more suitable Heading to maintain QDM 080 would be flown, say MH 075.

Fig.14-9. If QDM moves Right of Datum, turn Right.

If the stated QDM moves to the left of the Datum QDM, then the aeroplane has drifted to the right of the desired track, and should be turned left to re-intercept the desired track (i.e. to re-establish the Datum QDM). This is exactly the same response as for the head of an RMI needle moving to the left of the Datum QDM.

Fig.14-10. Tracking Towards a VDF Ground Station;
if QDM moves Left of the Datum, turn Left.

In this case, the stated QDM has moved left of the Datum QDM 080 to 075. The Pilot should turn left and decrease Heading (to say MH 060), and request QDMs until the desired QDM 080 is reached. At this time, a more suitable Heading to maintain QDM 080 would be flown, say MH 065.

Fig.14-11. QDM moving Left of Datum, Turn Left.

In known wind conditions, the Pilot should use his *'best-guess WCA'* as a starting point in estimating a Magnetic Heading to maintain the Datum QDM, making modifications to heading if the *actual* or *stated* QDM gradually moves away from the Datum QDM.

In unknown wind conditions, when a Pilot is unable to estimate a suitable Wind Correction Angle to counter drift, a simple procedure is to steer the QDM as Heading, and see what develops. Suitable corrections can then be made as changes in the QDM become apparent.

When tracking **towards** the VDF station:

• turn right if actual QDM moves to the right of Datum;

• turn left if actual QDM moves to the left of Datum.

The aim is to establish a Wind Correction Angle that allows for drift and results in the desired track being maintained – indicated by the QDM remaining constant. The process of finding a suitable WCA by trial and error is known as *bracketting*. Typically, it will take a number of heading changes to establish the WCA required to maintain track.

Changes to heading will also be required if the wind effect changes, which is often the case. Like most instrument flying, VDF tracking will consist of a continuing series of small (and sometimes not so small) corrections.

Fig.14-12. Tracking Towards a VDF Ground Station.

TRACKING AWAY FROM A VDF GROUND STATION

When tracking *away from* a VDF ground station, the **Datum QDM** is the reciprocal of the outbound track. For instance, to maintain a track of 060°M away from the VDF ground station, the aeroplane should be flown so that Datum QDM 240 is maintained.

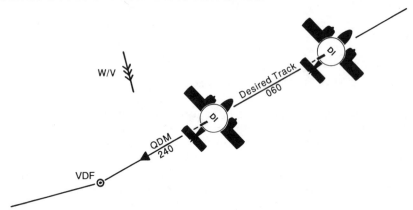

Fig.14-13. Tracking Away From a VDF Ground Station.

If the stated QDM moves to the rignt of the Datum QDM, then the aeroplane has drifted to the left of the desired track, and should be turned right to re-intercept the desired track (i.e. to re-establish the Datum QDM). This is exactly the same response as for the head of an RMI needle moving to the right of the Datum QDM.

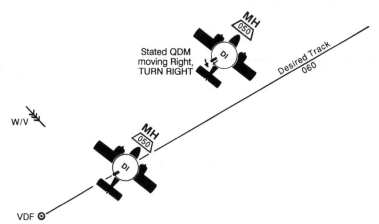

Fig.14-14. Tracking Away From a VDF Ground Station;
if QDM moves Right of the Datum, turn Right.

In this case, the Pilot would turn right and increase Heading (to say MH 060), which would allow the wind to blow the aeroplane back onto track, and request QDMs until the desired QDM 240 is reached. At this time, a more suitable Heading to maintain Datum QDM 240 would be flown, say MH 055.

If the stated QDM moves to the left of the Datum QDM, then the aeroplane has drifted to the right of the desired track, and should be turned left to re-intercept the desired track (i.e. to re-establish the Datum QDM). This is exactly the same response as for the head of an RMI needle moving to the left of the Datum QDM.

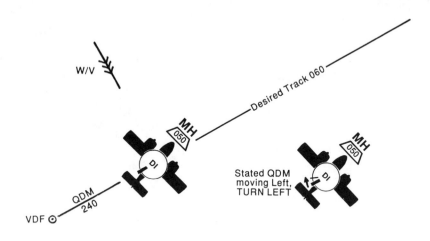

Fig.14-15. Tracking Away From a VDF Ground Station;
if QDM moves Left of the Datum, Turn Left.

In this case, since MH 050, allowing for an estimated 10° of drift, has taken the aeroplane to the right of track, the Pilot should turn left and decrease Heading (to say MH 040), and then request QDMs until the desired QDM 240 is reached. At this time, a more suitable Heading to maintain QDM 240 should be flown, say MH 045, allowing a WCA of 15° into wind.

In known wind conditions, the Pilot should use his *best-guess WCA* as a starting point in an attempt to maintain the Datum QDM, making modifications to heading if the actual QDM changes from the Datum.

In unknown wind conditions, when a Pilot is unable to estimate a suitable Wind Correction Angle to counter drift, a simple procedure is to steer the reciprocal of the QDM as Heading, and see what develops. Suitable corrections can then be made as changes in the QDM become apparent.

When tracking **away from** the VDF station:

• turn right if actual QDM moves to the right of Datum;

• turn left if actual QDM moves to the left of Datum.

Note that these are exactly the same rules as for tracking towards the VDF ground station.

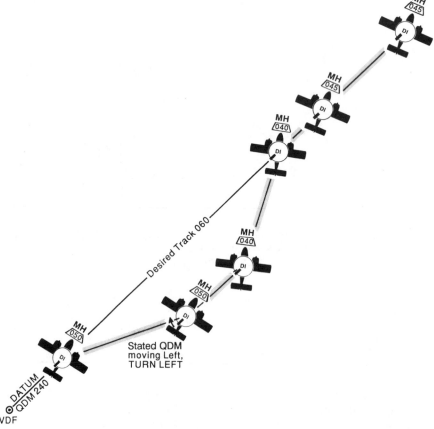

Fig.14-16. Tracking Away From a VDF Ground Station.

VDF TRACKING RULES

1. Determine Datum QDM for the desired track:
   • inbound: Datum QDM = desired track;
   • outbound: Datum QDM = reciprocal of desired track.
2. Use *best-guess WCA* to establish an initial heading in an attempt to maintain Datum QDM.
3. Both inbound and outbound from the VDF ground station:
   • if *stated QDM* moves left of Datum, turn left;
   • if *stated QDM* moves right of Datum, turn right;
   (i.e. treat the stated QDM on the DI as a *command instrument*).

302

FLYING OVERHEAD THE VDF GROUND STATION

As the aeroplane passes overhead (or near to overhead) the VDF ground station, the Ground Operator will be unable to determine the *direction* from which VHF-COM signals are received, even though the actual voice communications will be received normally. He will report this to the Pilot as *"No bearing"*.

If the outbound track differs significantly from the inbound track, then the Pilot will need to take up a suitable intercept heading until the Datum QDM for the outbound track is established, at which time normal tracking to maintain it should occur.

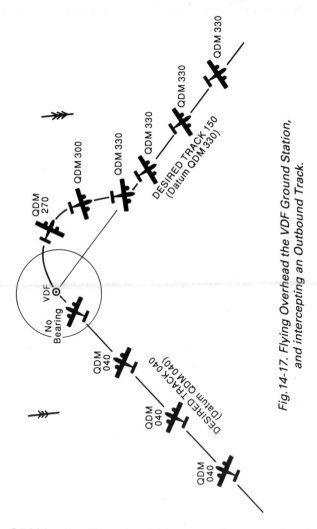

Fig. 14-17. Flying Overhead the VDF Ground Station, and intercepting an Outbound Track.

Requests for QDM by the Pilot should be more frequent the closer the aeroplane is to the ground station so that suitable adjustments to heading can be made.

APPROACHES

THE VDF INSTRUMENT APPROACH

VHF Direction Finding and the tracking procedures discussed above can be used by a pilot (in conjunction with the ground controller who will periodically pass the current QDM) to track to overhead the station.

It can also be used to carry out published let-down procedures at certain aerodromes, by tracking outbound from overhead the station, then turning and tracking inbound on the published QDM, and descending to not below a specified height until visual. VDF Let-Downs approved by the CAA are published by *Aerad* and *Jeppesen,* and are described in UK AIP RAC 4.

Fig. 14-18. A Typical VDF Instrument Approach.

The pilot flying cross-country may arrive overhead the VDF ground station by requesting QDMs from ATC, and altering Heading appropriately. At least the Minimum Safe Altitude (MSA) for the sector should be maintained until overhead, at which time the Ground Operator will advise, *"No bearing"*.

At least 10 nm prior to reaching the aerodrome, the pilot should have requested the weather conditions to enable a suitable approach to be planned, and the en route *(FREDA)* and icing checks should have been completed. The aeroplane should be slowed down to flap extension speed prior to reaching the station to allow for better manoeuvrability and immediate flap selection when descent is permissible.

When overhead the station, the pilot should take up a suitable heading to intercept the outbound track. Frequent QDMs will be required to allow an efficient interception of the Track close to the station. The Stopwatch should be started to enable accurate timing of the outbound leg, with allowance made for any strong wind effect.

For instance, with a 20-knot tailwind outbound, a reduction of 20 seconds per minute will result in a more appropriate track over the ground that does not extend too far from the station (i.e. a published 3-minute outbound leg could be reduced to 2 minutes), and does not require an exceptionally 'long haul' upwind back to the station.

Once the outbound track is intercepted, it can be maintained by flying a heading that allows for drift, e.g. 063°M +/– the estimated WCA (Wind Correction Angle). Periodic requests for QDM should be made to check on tracking accuracy. The desired QDM for the final approach on the *Coventry VDF procedure* (at left) is 225 (i.e. a magnetic bearing of 225° to the station), which will be used as the Datum. The aim is to establish a heading that allows this Datum QDM to be maintained.

If the Ground Operator advises a QDM that is moving to the left of the Datum, then turn left. If the advised QDM is moving to the right of the Datum, then turn right.

When within +/–5° of track, the aeroplane may be descended to 1570 ft on QNH, or 1300 ft on QFE (the difference being equal to the Runway Threshold Elevation of 265 ft, rounded off to the nearest 10 ft). Pre-landing checks should be carried out at some stage during the Intermediate Approach.

After 3 minutes flight time outbound (adjusted for wind effect), a left turn may be made to intercept QDM 225°M inbound to the station. A request for QDM halfway through the turn ideally will result in the 'mid-QDM' being advised. If not, the turn can be adjusted for an efficient intercept of the inbound QDM, which now becomes the Datum QDM. It may even be necessary to remove bank-angle temporarily part-way through the turn and fly wings-level for a short while to get closer to the inbound Track before completing the intercept turn.

Exactly the same tracking rules apply inbound as outbound. If the Ground Operator advises a QDM that is moving to the left of the Datum, then turn left. If the Ground Operator advises a QDM that is moving to the right of the Datum, then turn right.

When established inbound, the aeroplane is permitted to descend to the MDA (Minimum Descent Altitude) with QNH set on the altimeter, or MDH (Minimum Descent Height) with QFE set. For an IMC-Rated Pilot this will be no lower than an absolute minimum of 600 ft AAL, but it could be significantly higher at certain aerodromes with obstacles in the approach area. The calculation of MDA(H) for any particular approach is covered in Chapter 19 of this manual.

Once at the MDA(H), the aeroplane must not descend further unless the pilot becomes visual. If not visual at the MDA(H), he may proceed to the station at the MDA(H), and if still not visual make a *Missed Approach* by climbing straight ahead to 1270 ft (1000 ft QFE), then a climbing left turn on track 140°M, and follow the remainder of the published Missed Approach procedure.

THE QGH APPROACH

The QGH Approach is a VDF-type Approach where the Air Traffic Controller will provide, not QDM information as for a VDF let-down, but tracking guidance in the form of Headings-to-steer accompanied by descent instructions. Consequently, the QGH Approach is easier for a pilot than a VDF Approach, even though the same let-down path might be followed.

It is up to the pilot to request a QGH Approach if so desired, provided ATC has the capability to provide one at that particular aerodrome.

OTHER USES FOR VDF

Bearings obtained by VDF can be used for a number of common navigational purposes. For instance, a pilot may request a QDM from an abeam VDF station to verify that he is indeed flying abeam it.

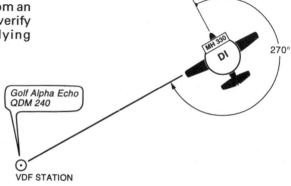

Fig. 14-19. QDM Abeam a Ground Station.

A position line given by a VDF bearing can be used together with another position line from say a VOR, NDB or even another VDF station to fix the position of the aeroplane.

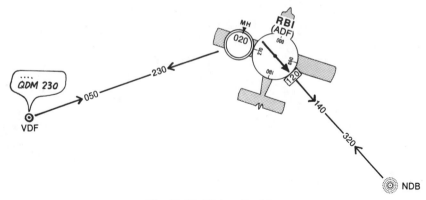

Fig.14-20. Fixing Position.

☐ Complete **Exercises 14 – VHF Direction Finding.**

Intentionally Blank

3

INSTRUMENT PROCEDURES

15

PREPARATION FOR FLIGHT

FLIGHT PLANNING

Planning for a flight on instruments is most important, especially since the safety advantages of visual flight may not be present during the flight. An Instrument Pilot flying in cloud or at night must be very conscious of **high terrain or obstacles** that cannot be seen, and ensure that a safe height above them is maintained.

He must be aware of the **danger of icing** (both airframe and carburettor icing) and take appropriate precautions, he must have an **alternate airfield** in mind in case a diversion becomes necessary, and he must have **sufficient fuel** to get there and still have a safety margin remaining in the tanks. The best time to organise these things is prior to flight.

Good flight planning is essential

Flight Planning procedures discussed in earlier volumes of *The Air Pilot's Manual* (especially Volume 3, Chapter 13) will have prepared you thoroughly. As a reminder of some of the vital points, a number of the exercises that follow will test your knowledge in these areas. Do not be afraid to review the relevant chapters. Always remember that **the Pilot-in-Command is responsible for the safety of the flight.**

Whether the submission of a Flight Plan is optional or compulsory for a particular flight is discussed in UK AIR RAC.

SOME ICING CONSIDERATIONS

Flying IFR often means flying in cloud or rain, i.e. in 'visible moisture'. If the temperature of the aeroplane is zero or below, then ice can form on the exposed parts of the airframe and on the propeller. Icing conditions are commonly defined as:
1. visible moisture; and
2. temperature at or below zero.

Many IFR aircraft are fitted with anti-icing and/or de-icing equipment – anti-icing equipment to prevent the formation of ice, de-icing equipment to remove ice that has already formed. Of course, there are some icing conditions that are so severe that even the best equipment cannot cope with them, and so you will find that most smaller IFR aircraft are certified only for slight to moderate icing conditions, and not for severe icing conditions. Often 'severe icing conditions' also means CBs, with associated severe turbulence and windshear – the sort of area in which no sensible pilot would fly. Light conditions might lead to 0.5″ of ice forming in 40 nm flight distance, whereas in moderate icing conditions the 0.5″ would form in about 20 nm.

If your IFR aeroplane is not fully equipped to handle icing conditions, then you should not enter an area where icing is possible. This does not mean that you should avoid cloud or other visible moisture altogether, but it does mean that you should avoid it if the temperature is zero or below. You can do this by ensuring that your IFR cruising level in cloud or visible moisture is lower than the freezing level (and do not forget to ensure that it is also above your safety altitude!)

Almost all IFR aircraft are fitted with pitot heaters to ensure that ice does not form over or in the pitot tube, and so cause faulty airspeed indications. Since the compass is usually swung (calibrated) with the pitot heaters on, you should always have them on in flight to ensure reasonably correct compass indications. This may or may not apply to windshield heaters, if fitted. The conditions under which your particular compass was swung will be specified on the deviation card in the cockpit.

There are two main types of anti-icing/de-icing equipment.

1. **De-icing fluid** which can be spread onto the leading edge of the wings, the tailplane and the propellers, preventing the formation of ice and removing any ice that has formed. It is usual to check this system during the pre-flight walk-around by switching it on and checking that the de-icing fluid bubbles out of the de-icing orifices on the leading edge. This ensures that the system is purged of air. (If not, ice could form over the outlets and the de-icing fluid would not be able to get at the ice because of an airlock.) You must ensure that only the correct type of de-icing fluid is used. Normally this system is engaged in anti-icing mode before you enter icing conditions. If ice does form, then you can switch to de-ice mode, which doubles the flow rate of the fluid.

2. **De-icing boots** which operate pneumatically – inflating and breaking up any ice that has formed, and then deflating. The ice meanwhile is blown away in the airstream. It is usual to check for punctures, possibly caused by stones thrown up by the propellers, during the pre-flight walk-around. A puncture wound, as well as degrading the inflation/deflation cycle, can also cause moisture to be drawn in and form ice within the boots. Normally this system is used for de-icing, being switched on after ice has formed, ¼" ice thickness being typical before they are used. If the de-icing boots are cycled too soon, the thin layer of ice crystals may be pushed out by the expanding boots but not broken up and dislodged. Further icing may form on this displaced layer, but the boots will be operating inside the layer, not touching it, and therefore unable to dislodge it. It is good airmanship to test the de-icing boots by cycling them before you enter icing conditions.

PRE-FLIGHT CONSIDERATIONS FOR AN IMC FLIGHT

Pre-flight considerations, which are all logical, include:
- Am I properly qualified (IMC Rating or Instrument Rating)?
- Is the aeroplane suitably equipped (serviceable radios, anti-icing equipment, lighting, etc.)?
- What is the weather? Are changes expected? Check aerodrome forecasts (TAFs) and en-route forecasts (e.g. area forecasts, such as provided by the AIRMET service and updated four times daily).
- Is the Departure Aerodrome suitable for my operation?
- Is the Destination Aerodrome suitable for my operation?

- Is an Alternate Aerodrome required (or more than one)?
- What routes are suitable in terms of terrain, weather and available en route Radio Navigation Facilities?
- Are there any important messages contained in NOTAMs, AICs or obtainable from a Briefing Office (e.g. seviceability of Radio Navigation Facilities, serviceability of aerodromes, changes to procedures if, for instance, a Purple Airway for a Royal Flight has been declared, etc.)?
- Is a Flight Plan required to be submitted (for instance, to enter Class D controlled airspace at a busy aerodrome)?
- Preparation of Charts (en route charts, approach charts, etc.).
- Compilation of a Flight Log (with tracks, distances, times, Minimum Safe Altitudes and cruising levels calculated).
- Compilation of a Fuel Log, with adequate fuel reserves.
- Preparation of the aircraft, and check of the Weight-and-Balance.
- Organising the cockpit for flight – keeping charts, torch, etc., handy.
- Briefing of passengers.

Calculation of a minimum **Safety Altitude** is important, since terrain and other obstacles may not be seen in IMC conditions. An IMC-Rated Pilot planning with a **visual chart,** such as the CAA 1/2 million series, may calculate a Safety Altitude based on 1000-foot vertical clearance from any obstacle within 5 nm of track. Published Maximum Elevation Figures (MEFs) for the latitude–longitude quadrangles en route are useful in determining a Safety Altitude. Adding a suitable buffer, e.g. 1000 ft, to the highest MEF en route can give a suitable Safety Altitude (or Safety Height). **Radio Navigation Charts** will specify Lowest Safe Altitudes for published routes.

Cruising levels should be chosen according to the IFR Cruising Level table – the Quadrantal Rule based on magnetic track (Rule 30). When flying over congested areas, attention should be paid to the Low Flying Rule (Rule 5).

Fuel Requirements should be calculated carefully, with consideration to arriving at a Diversion Airfield with **adequate fuel reserves** on board. Being tight on fuel significantly increases the *stress level* of a pilot if an unexpected diversion becomes necessary.

A review of **AIP RAC and COM Radio Failure Procedures** should be made from time to time by every IMC-Rated Pilot, to ensure competence.

FOLLOWING START-UP

After Start-Up and prior to Take-Off, all of the vital radio navigation equipment should be checked for correct functioning. This includes the VHF-COM, VHF-NAV, DME, ADF/RMI, Marker Lights and Transponder. The Altimeter should be checked for the correct subscale setting – check that QFE and QNH give a sensible value of airfield elevation between both readings.

During the taxi-out, the instruments should be checked:

Turning Left:	*Turning right:*
• DI/ RMI/Compass decreasing;	• DI/RMI/Compass increasing;
• ADF/RMI tracking;	• ADF/RMI tracking;
• Turn Coordinator shows left turn;	• Turn Coordinator shows right turn;
• Balance Ball shows skidding right;	• Balance Ball shows skidding left;
• AI steady.	• AI steady.

RADIO PROCEDURES

Communication between Air Traffic Service Units (ATSU) on the ground and an aeroplane is important, and is best achieved if correct radio procedures are used. Some typical Radiotelephony (RTF) calls follow, but you should refer to CAP 413 and UK AIP RAC 6-2 to 6-6 for a full discussion of these. Being prepared to handle the radio professionally using correct procedures will simplify any flight, but especially a flight in IMC conditions.

On initial RTF contact, the full callsign of the aircraft should be used, e.g. *"Golf Bravo Foxtrot Romeo Mike"* for the registration *G-BFRM* – the *G* indicating that it is a UK registration. Once communication has been established, however, the callsign may be shortened by the ATSU – for instance, to *"Golf Romeo Mike"* – in which case it is appropriate for the pilot also to use the abbreviated callsign.

As a general principle, all messages from an ATSU should be acknowledged by use of the aircraft callsign. Executive instructions should be acknowledged with an abbreviated read-back of the instructions and the callsign.

ATC: *"Golf Alpha Charlie – Aircraft Landing Runway 35 – Hold Position."*
Pilot: *"Holding – Golf Alpha Charlie."*

A full read-back should be made to instructions containing any of the following:
- Level instructions;
- Heading instructions;
- Speed instructions;
- Airways or Route Clearances;
- Runway in use;
- Clearance to enter, land on, take off, backtrack or cross an active runway;
- SSR operating instructions;
- Altimeter settings;
- VDF information; and
- Changes of radio frequency.

ATC: *"Gold Mike Echo – Descend to Two Thousand – QNH One Zero One Five."*
Pilot: *"Descend to Two Thousand – QNH One Zero One Five – Golf Mike Echo."*

ATC: *"Golf Zulu November – Contact London Control One Two Five Decimal Eight."*
Pilot: *"London One Two Five Decimal Eight – Golf Zulu November."*

En Route Position Reports should be passed in the form:
- Aircraft Callsign;
- Position and Time over that position;
- Altitude or Flight Level;
- Estimate Next Position and Time over it.

Pilot: *"Golf Charlie Delta*
Inverness at Three Five
Flight Level Seven Five
Estimate Aberdeen at Five Six."

NOTE: Position Reports are required in the circumstances listed in RAC 3.

Any request for **"Details"** from an ATSU should be passed in the form:
- Aircraft Callsign and Type;
- Position and Heading;
- Altitude or Flight Level; and
- Flight Conditions.

ATC: *"Golf Mike Whiskey – Pass your Details."*
Pilot: *"Golf Mike Whiskey, Cessna One Seven Two – One Six Miles North of Bodmin, Heading Zero Eight Zero – Three Thousand – VMC."*

Any request for **Route** (in addition to *Details)* from an ATSU should be passed in the form:
- Departure Aerodrome;
- Route, including an Estimate for a Position en route, and Destination;
- True Air Speed in knots;
- Any other relevant information.

ATC: *"Golf Mike Whiskey – Pass your Details and Route."*
Pilot: *"Golf Mike Whiskey, Cessna 172 – One Six Miles North of Bodmin, Heading 280 – Three Thousand – VMC – From Land's End, Estimating Okehampton Zero Four – To Exeter – One Three Five Knots."*

A *Non-Radar* Service is known as a **Procedural Service,** whereby separation between aircraft, for instance, is established by laid down time and/or distance separation standards. Details, Route, Position Reporting and Estimate over the next position are important, since the procedural separation will be based on these reports.

To make use of the **Lower Airspace Radar Service (LARS),** the pilot should, when **within approximately 40 nm** of a participating aerodrome, establish two-way RTF communication on the appropriate frequency. The response he receives will probably contain a request for 'details', which should be passed in the form detailed above.

Pilot: *"St. Mawgan – Golf Alpha Charlie X-ray Delta – Request Lower Airspace Radar Service."*

When in Operating in a Radar Environment, a pilot may request a:
- **Radar Information Service (RIS)** in which information regarding conflicting or nearby traffic is given (but no avoiding action in terms of heading changes is offered, this being left up to the pilot to initiate); or
- **Radar Advisory Service (RAS)** in which both traffic information and avoidance action is given by ATC to the pilot.

Be aware that the pilot is still responsible for ensuring terrain clearance.

To carry out a particular Instrument Approach, the pilot should request it.
"Exeter Approach – Golf Foxtrot Hotel India Lima – Request QGH Approach."

During a QDM Approach, the pilot may have to request QDMs.
Pilot: *"Exeter Tower – Golf Juliett Yankee – Request QDM."*
Tower: *"Golf Juliett Yankee – Exeter Tower – QDM 050 – Class Bravo."*

NOTE: *'Class Bravo'* indicates the bearing is accurate to within +/–5°.

See AIP RAC 6 for radio-failure procedures, and in our Appendix 3.

❏ Now complete **Exercises 15 – Preparation for Flight.**

16

INSTRUMENT DEPARTURES

A pilot should not take off unless certain that conditions at the departure aerodrome are suitable, and that conditions at the destination or alternate aerodrome(s) will allow a landing to be made. This is not to say that it is unsafe to operate in bad weather – it is strongly recommended, however, that a careful decision whether to operate or not is made, taking into account all the available relevant information, especially the weather information. The UK Private Pilot must dermine his own minima (and this is fully discussed in Chapter 19).

Bad weather can be said to exist if conditions are:
- cloud ceiling worse than 1000 ft AAL;
- in-flight visibility worse than 1800 metres; and
- Runway Visual Range (RVR)/aerodrome visibility worse than 1500 m.

The UK Aeronautical Information Publication recommends that, for non-public transport flights, the minimum weather conditions for take-off in a single-engined aeroplane should never be less than:
- **600 ft cloud ceiling;** and
- **1800 metres visibility.**

Following an unexpected engine failure in these minimum conditions, an experienced and current pilot of a relatively slow and manoeuvrable aircraft will have a reasonable chance of viewing a suitable forced landing field, and avoiding obstacles in an attempt to reach it. However, realistically speaking, the average IMC-Rated Pilot should only fly in conditions well in excess of these (such as 1500-foot cloud ceiling and 3 km flight visibility).

Prior to an instrument departure, ensure that your radio navaids and instruments are set suitably, with the aids identified (Morse Code). At a controlled airport you will need an ATC departure clearance specifying your route and altitude or flight level, and possibly a Transponder Code, and then you will need another ATC clearance to enter the runway and take off.

If you experience *radio failure,* you should taxi clear of the runway.

If you are airborne in uncontrolled airspace (Classes F and G) and **wish to enter controlled airspace,** you should ensure that ATC has your flight plan details (position, level, and proposed track), and then obtain an ATC clearance to enter. Rule 5 (the Low Flying Rule) should be complied with, and two-way radio communication is necessary. If you experience *radio failure* before entering the controlled airspace, then stay clear of it and land at the nearest suitable airport.

SETTING COURSE

Most departures on an instrument flight involve manoeuvring after take-off to intercept the departure track to or from a particular Radio Navigation Aid. It is good airmanship to have in mind, prior to take-off, the direction of turns required and the approximate time it will take to intercept the track.

The illustration below shows an aeroplane taking off and intercepting the 270°M track outbound from an NDB positioned near the aerodrome.

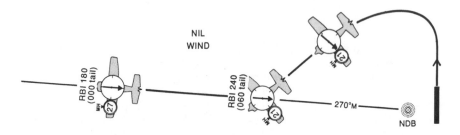

Fig. 16-1. Intercepting the Departure Track using an NDB.

In the illustration below, an aeroplane is taking off and intercepting the 030°M track to a VOR (i.e. the 210 radial), and then tracking outbound on the 090 radial.

Fig. 16-2. Intercepting the Departure Track using a VOR.

It is usual to have QNH set in the Altimeter subscale for departure on a cross-country flight so that the Altimeter indicates vertical distance AMSL. When cruising, the appropriate setting is:
- *Regional QNH* for cruising at or below the Transition Altitude (usually 3000 ft in the UK) when outside controlled airspace and not in the vicinity of an aerodrome; and
- *1013.2 mb* when cruising IFR at or above the Transition Level, preferably at a Quadrantal Level appropriate to the magnetic track.

NOTE: If departing an aerodrome located beneath a TMA, the QNH of an aerodrome beneath that TMA should be used for the period of flight beneath the TMA. The same applies to flight beneath any other controlled airspace. (Vertical navigation is discussed in detail in Volume 3 of the *Air Pilot's Manual.*)

STANDARD INSTRUMENT DEPARTURES

At some busy controlled aerodromes, certain Standard Instrument Departures (SIDs) are published. SIDs considerably simplify the issue of departure clearances by ATC. ATC simply names the SID without having to describe any further tracking details, because the pilot can obtain these in both diagrammatic and textual form from his SID Charts.

"PERTH THREE ALPHA" given by ATC to a pilot at Glasgow is a typical SID.

Fig.16-3. A Typical SID Chart.

SIDs are generally designed to separate departing traffic from arriving traffic, and to provide an efficient interception of the outbound track (bearing in mind that some of the airspace around these aerodromes may be heavily used), as well as avoiding noise-sensitive areas near some aerodromes. Radio transmissions are also considerably reduced, thereby reducing workload as well as freeing-up the particular communications frequency. SIDs are generally available only to Instrument-Rated Pilots (and not to IMC-Rated Pilots).

Not all Instrument Departures are complicated, as illustrated below for the *Lichfield SIDs* from Birmingham.

Fig. 16-4. AIP RAC Excerpt for the 'Lichfield' SIDs from Birmingham Airport.

EN ROUTE CHARTS

There are en route **Radio Navigation Charts** for IFR Pilots published by both *Aerad* and *Jeppesen,* on which certain IFR tracks are specified, along with a lot of other details. Study of these charts and their legends is necessary for an Instrument-Rated Pilot, and is recommended for an IMC-Rated Pilot. Sample Excerpts in colour are shown on the next page.

Fig.16-5. Sample Excerpts from Aerad (top) and Jeppesen Enroute Charts.
(Excerpted, with permission, from the Aerad EUR/3 and Jeppesen E(LO)1A Charts)

The IMC-Rated Pilot is generally able to plan his IMC flight using a visual chart such as the familiar CAA 1:500,000 series, measuring desired tracks and calculating Minimum Safe Altitudes (at least 1000 ft above the highest obstacle within 5 nm of track) in a similar manner to preparing for a visual cross-country flight – (see *The Air Pilot's Manual, Volume 3, Chapter 13*).

❏ Complete **Exercises 16 – Instrument Departures.**

17

HOLDING AND MANOEUVRING

Joining a Holding Pattern is an efficient and convenient means of delaying an aircraft in a prescribed pattern at a given location. Further progress of the flight ceases until the aeroplane is cleared to proceed.

The delaying action could be required for a number of reasons, such as waiting for an onwards en route clearance, or waiting until other aircraft have commenced an ILS approach and an approach *slot* has become available, or waiting until a storm has moved away from the intended aerodrome of landing.

A Holding Pattern is generally a *race-track* shape, and has five basic elements:

- the Holding Fix;
- the holding radial or bearing;
- the location of the holding radial or bearing relative to the 8 main points of the compass;
- the direction of turns; and
- the timing.

A typical Holding Pattern, as illustrated below, is a one-minute, right-hand pattern, south of the 250 VOR Radial, inbound 070. The Holding Fix is the VOR.

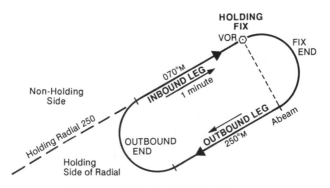

Fig.17-1. A Typical Holding Pattern.

Holding patterns are shown on charts in sufficient detail for a pilot to join and maintain one correctly. There may be other details superimposed on the chart, but, with experience, the details of the holding pattern are easily read. Most patterns are based on a Radio Navigation Aid (e.g. at *Southend* on the NDB, at *Glasgow* on the VOR), or on a combination of Radio Aids (e.g. Biggin Hill 243° inbound on the 063 VOR Radial with the Fix at 7 DME).

As well as the details listed above, they may also show the Minimum Holding Altitude (MHA), which is 1800 ft on QNH (and normally 2000 ft by ATC instruction) at *Biggin Hill (BIG)*, and 3500 ft on QNH at *Glasgow (GOW)*.

Do not be concerned with the technical-sounding descriptions given above – instrument flying has its own jargon which you will quickly learn.

Fig. 17-2. Examples of Holding Patterns on Instrument Approach Charts.

A complete one-minute Holding Pattern will, if flown perfectly, take four minutes. In nil wind conditions, the straight inbound and outbound legs will each take one minute, as will the Rate-One 180° turns at each end, making a total of four minutes. Normal timing commences from abeam the beacon outbound or from wings-level after rolling out of the turn (whichever is the latter).

In a two-minute Holding Pattern, the straight legs are increased to two minutes, the complete pattern then taking six minutes, and occupying more airspace.

Occasionally, the delay required during holding is less than four minutes, in which case **the timing of the outbound leg can be adjusted** for the aeroplane to arrive overhead the Fix at the desired time – for instance, at an Expected Approach Time (EAT) for an ILS Approach that has been nominated by ATC.

TRACKING IN HOLDING PATTERNS

The main tracking leg of a Holding Pattern is the inbound leg towards the specified aid – usually an NDB or a VOR. Normal tracking procedures are followed, i.e. allow for drift so that the desired track is maintained.

Monitor the tracking periodically on the ADF or VOR Cockpit Display, which act as navigation *performance* instruments. Most of your attention will be on the Attitude Flying Instruments (monitoring height, airspeed and direction), with an occasional scan of the Navigation Instruments (ADF, VOR, DME). Any adjustments to heading should be made with reference to the Attitude Indicator and the Direction Indicator.

During the turns and the outbound leg there is no direct tracking aid. Both the turns and the outbound leg of the Holding Pattern are modified according to the estimated wind effect, so that the Rate 1 turn to rejoin the inbound track will bring the aeroplane out right on track. Checking the instruments in the cockpit during this turn inbound will enable you to determine if you will overshoot or undershoot the inbound track, and enable you to take early corrective action.

CORRECTIONS FOR WIND IN HOLDING PATTERNS

The aim of a standard Holding Pattern is to achieve an approximate total time of *four minutes* around the pattern, with a fairly tidy turn from the outbound leg onto the inbound leg to the Fix.

In conditions of **nil wind**, the ground track of the Holding Pattern will be a straightforward *race-track* pattern, with the outbound timing commencing as the aeroplane passes abeam the Fix, and with the outbound leg (where there is no tracking aid) simply being the reciprocal of the inbound leg and flown for 1 minute.

If there is a strong **tailwind outbound**, however, then 1 minute outbound will carry the aeroplane much further than in still wind conditions, and it will be carried even further downwind during the turn inbound. With an airspeed of 90 kt, for instance, the Ground Speed will be 110 kt outbound with a 20 kt tailwind and only 70 kt inbound. It will be a long haul (well in excess of 1 minute) back to the Fix – unless some correction to the outbound timing is made.

A reasonable correction is to **reduce the 1 minute outbound by 1 second per knot of tailwind**. For instance, with a 20 knot tailwind outbound, reduce the timing to 40 seconds outbound before commencing the Rate 1 turn inbound.

Fig. 17-3. Adjust Outbound Timing to allow for Head/Tail Wind.

Conversely, in a strong **headwind outbound, add 1 second per knot**. The timing is commenced when abeam the Fix and on heading – another use for the **Stopwatch**.

In strong **crosswind** conditions, the aeroplane will tend to be carried downwind both on the straight legs and during the turns. The **inbound track** to the Fix is the easiest part of the pattern, since it has a direct tracking aid, and a suitable drift allowance for the inbound leg can be found by normal tracking corrections.

For the turns and the outbound leg, however, measures to counter the wind effect can only be estimated, since there is no direct tracking aid. One turn will be downwind, the outbound leg will have a crosswind, and the other turn will be into a headwind. Common sense and a little experience, however, will enable a Pilot to handle this effectively.

Example 1: In the pattern below, a strong tailwind on the Rate 1 turn outbound will increase its **ground radius**, i.e. the path it follows over the ground. If the aeroplane then flies the published outbound heading without any adjustment for wind, it will be carried even further downwind. The Rate 1 turn inbound, with its much smaller ground radius into-wind, will then place the aeroplane well short of the required inbound track, and the attempt to regain it will require a long haul back into-wind. The result is an unsatisfactory Holding Pattern but, with some thought, this may be remedied.

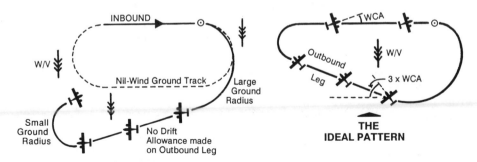

Fig.17-4. Apply 3 x WCA on the Outbound Leg.

On the outbound leg, simply applying a comparable drift allowance to that inbound will cause the aeroplane to parallel the inbound leg, however it will not overcome the problem of the different ground radii of the turns. To allow for this, it is recommended that, when a particular Wind Correction Angle is used on the inbound leg, you should **apply a triple Wind Correction Angle into wind on the outbound leg, to a maximum of 30°.**

For instance, if a 8° WCA to the left is used inbound, then a 24° right WCA should be applied outbound. This means that the Rate 1 turn outbound will be modified to 294° in this case. The Rate 1 turn onto the inbound leg at the far end of the Holding Pattern will then be much neater.

The triple drift allowance can be thought of as one drift allowance to allow for the wind effect during the outbound turn, plus a second to allow for the drift on the outbound leg, plus a third to allow for the wind effect during the turn onto the inbound leg. If the triple drift allowance (to a maximum of 30°) results in an outbound heading within 30° of the wind direction, then there will be little drift on the outbound leg itself, in which case the correction can be reduced to a double drift allowance, i.e. 2 x WCA, just to allow for the wind effect in the turns.

The success of the outbound leg drift allowance will be discovered when turning to rejoin the inbound leg. It is unlikely that it will have been perfect. If too great a correction was made, then the aeroplane will fly through the inbound track. If the correction was too small, then the turn inbound will have to be stopped early until the inbound track is regained. Aim to regain the inbound track without delay, and then make suitable adjustments to tracking and timing for the next run around the pattern.

Fig.17-5. Rejoining the Inbound Leg.

Summary of the Wind Corrections for a Holding Pattern.

1. Apply a triple Wind Correction Angle outbound, to a maximum of 30°. If the resulting outbound heading is within 30° of the wind direction, reduce it to a double WCA.

2. Reduce the outbound timing by 1 second per 1 kt of tailwind (and increase it by 1 sec/kt for a headwind component).

JOINING A HOLDING PATTERN

There will usually be some manoeuvring required to join a Holding Pattern, since an aeroplane may approach the Holding Fix from any direction and, surprisingly, this is often the most difficult manoeuvre to perform. Three types of **Sector Entry** have been devised, based upon the direction of the Inbound Holding Track and an imaginary line angled at 70° to the Inbound Holding Track. How the aeroplane joins the pattern depends on the aircraft's **Heading,** since this determines the Sector from which it is approaching.

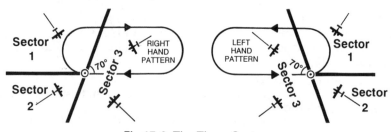

Fig.17-6. The Three Sectors.

A Sector 1 Entry is a **parallel entry**

- Fly to the Fix and **turn onto an outbound heading** to fly parallel to the inbound track. Do not backtrack on it – just fly parallel to it on the non-holding side for a period of 1 minute (plus or minus 1 sec/kt wind correction).
- Turn in the direction of the holding side through more than 180° to either intercept the inbound track or return to the Fix.
- On reaching the Fix, turn to follow the Holding Pattern.

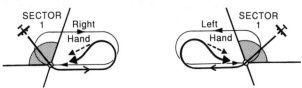

Fig.17-7. The Sector 1 Parallel Entry.

A Sector 2 Entry is a **teardrop** entry

- Fly to the Fix and **turn onto a heading to fly a 30° teardrop**, i.e. to make good a track within the pattern (on the holding side) at 30° to the reciprocal of the inbound leg for a period of 1 minute (+/– wind correction).
- Turn in the direction of the Holding Pattern to intercept the inbound track.
- Track to the Fix, and proceed with normal Holding Patterns.

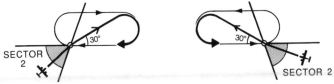

Fig.17-8. The Sector 2 Teardrop Entry.

A Sector 3 Entry is a **direct** entry

- Fly to the fix and **turn to follow the Holding Pattern.**

If a full 180° turn (or greater) is required to take up the outbound heading, then commence turning immediately you reach overhead the Fix. If, however, the turn onto the outbound leg is less than 180°, then hold heading for an appropriate time past the Fix before commencing the Rate 1 turn. For instance, if the turn is less than 180° by 45° (which at Rate 1 of 3°/sec would take 15 sec), maintain the original heading for 15 seconds before turning.

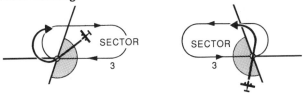

Fig.17-9. The Sector 3 Direct Entry.

Entering a Holding Pattern correctly and efficiently (if one has to be entered) is a sign of a good Instrument Pilot. Holding Patterns often precede an Instrument Approach, so a good Holding Pattern is a good start to the Let Down.

Using the ADF to enter and maintain a Holding Pattern based on an NDB

Many Holding Patterns use an NDB or Locator as the Fix. In the illustration below, typical ADF indications are shown as the Pilot initially tracks to the NDB, and then joins the Holding Pattern.

Fig.17-10. Making a Sector 1 Entry using the ADF.

Fig.17-11. Making a similar Sector 1 Entry using an RMI.

Using the VOR to Enter and Maintain a Holding Pattern

Some Holding Patterns use a VOR ground station as the Fix. In the illustration below, typical VOR cockpit indications are shown as the pilot initially tracks to the VOR, and then joins the Racetrack Pattern.

Fig.17-12. Making a Sector-2 Entry using the VOR.

PROCEDURE TURNS

Unless suitable fixes, or radar vectoring by ATC, permit a direct entry into an Instrument Approach Procedure, a positioning turn of some kind may be necessary. Course reversals can be made using *procedure turns* or *teardrop turns*. Positioning Turns can also be made by following the appropriate Sector Entry into the Racetrack Pattern.

THE 45°/180° PROCEDURE TURN

The 45° Procedure Turn consists of:
- an outbound track from the Fix;
- a turn of 45° away from the outbound track for 1 minute from the **start** of the turn (+/– wind correction in terms of both drift and time); and then
- a 180° turn in the opposite direction to intercept the inbound track.

Fig.17-13. The 45° Procedure Turn.

Left or *Right* in a description of the Procedure Turn refers to the direction of the initial turn.

THE 80°/260° PROCEDURE TURN

The 80° Procedure Turn is less common in the UK. It consists of:
- an outbound track away from the Fix;
- a turn of 80° away from the outbound track;
- followed almost immediately by a 260° turn in the opposite direction to intercept the inbound track.

Fig.17-14. The 80° Procedure Turn.

If the initial turn is into a strong headwind, then the 80° heading can be held for a brief time (e.g. an extra *one second per knot of headwind),* before the 260° turn is commenced.

If the initial turn puts a strong tailwind behind the aeroplane, then stop turning before 80° is reached, and gently roll immediately into the reversal turn.

THE BASE TURN

The Base Turn, used to reverse direction by more than 180°, is a teardrop pattern which consists of:
- a specified outbound track and timing or distance limit;
- followed by a turn to intercept the inbound track.

Fig.17-15. A Base Turn.

POSITIONING IN A RACETRACK PATTERN FOR AN INSTRUMENT APPROACH

Many instrument approaches commence at the Holding Fix, and simply by carrying out a sector entry to the Holding Pattern (even if a full pattern is not required) the aeroplane is in position to commence the approach. An aeroplane approaching the LBA NDB at Leeds Bradford from the East, for instance, could enter the Holding Pattern with a Sector-1 Parallel entry, and be ready immediately on reaching the Fix on the inbound leg of the pattern to commence the approach. If there is any delay in approval to commence the approach, however, the aeroplane can simply remain in the Holding Pattern.

Fig. 17-16. Positioning in a Holding Pattern.

Sometimes alternative procedures are marked on the Instrument Approach Chart. On the Norwich chart, for instance, there is a 45° Procedure Turn specified, but there is also an alternative, and simpler, procedure: *extend the outbound leg of the Holding Pattern to 2 minutes, and then turn left to intercept the Localizer.* Only one turn will be required, instead of three.

Fig. 17-17. Two Possibilities at Norwich.

❏ **Exercises 17 – Holding and Manoeuvring.**

18

INSTRUMENT APPROACHES

VERTICAL NAVIGATION

Correct vertical navigation is vital during instrument flight, when terrain, obstacles and other traffic may not be seen. Vertical navigation is based mainly on the indications of the Altimeter, therefore **winding-in the correct altimeter subscale setting is most important.** It is also important, that each new altimeter setting advised by ATC should be read back by the Pilot as confirmation.

The datum for vertical navigation is *Mean Sea Level,* and the subscale setting that allows the Altimeter to indicate **Altitude,** the vertical distance of the aircraft AMSL, is known as **QNH.**

PROCEDURES AT AERODROMES

Aerodrome Elevation is the vertical distance (in feet AMSL) of the highest point on the landing area of the aerodrome, and is published on all Instrument Approach Charts (usually near the top of the page) as *Elev* or *Apt. Elev* (i.e. Airport Elevation).

For visual manoeuvring at an aerodrome, it is usual in the UK to have **Aerodrome QFE** set in the subscale, so that the Altimeter indicates **Height above the aerodrome elevation.**

On straight-in Instrument Approaches to a particular runway that has a Threshold Elevation published (which may be the case if it is 7 ft or more below Aerodrome Elevation), the Altimeter may be set to **Threshold QFE** to indicate vertical distance above the Runway Threshold. For a 30 ft difference between Aerodrome and Threshold Elevations, QFE Threshold will be 1 mb greater than QFE Aerodrome.

Fig. 18-1. Aerodrome Elevation and Runway Threshold Elevation on an Instrument Approach Chart (Aerad).

Aircraft taking off for a cross-country flight will be given **Aerodrome QNH** prior to take-off so that the Altimeter will indicate Altitude (AMSL). For en-route cruising, the pilot will fly at a level based on:

- 1013.2 mb when cruising IFR at or above the Transition Level, and preferably at a Quadrantal Level; and
- Regional QNH when cruising at or below the Transition Altitude (usually 3000 ft in the UK) when outside controlled airspace and not in the vicinity of an aerodrome.

Arriving aircraft will initially be given **Aerodrome QNH,** and ATC reference to vertical position will be in terms of Altitude until the aircraft commences Final Approach. **Minimum Sector Altitudes (MSAs)** are published on Instrument Approach Charts and will provide at least 300 metres (1000 ft) vertical clearance within **25 nm** of the homing facility for the particular Instrument Approach.

If the aircraft remains at or above the relevant MSA, then it should be clear of terrain and obstacles as it tracks in to the aerodrome prior to making the approach. Some aerodromes have Instrument Approaches with an MSA that applies to all sectors (e.g. *East Midlands),* however most aerodromes have different MSAs for different sectors, depending upon the direction from which the aircraft is arriving and the terrain over which it has to pass (e.g. *Leeds Bradford ILS/DME Rwy 32,* and *Chichester VOR 32).*

- *Jeppesen* publishes MSAs in a circle at the top of its charts, with the sectors delineated by **magnetic** bearings from the homing facility;
- *Aerad* publishes the information slightly differently, as four *Sector Safe Altitude (SSA)* boxes, one in each corner of the plan section of the Instrument Approach Chart. An SSA of 2300 ft AMSL within 25 nm of the aerodrome will be published as **SSA 25 nm 2₃.**

Fig. 18-2. Typical MSAs on Jeppesen Charts (top), and SSAs on an Aerad Chart.

If Visual Manoeuvring (Circling) around the aerodrome is required, then *Aerodrome* **QFE** will be given; if a straight-in landing is possible, then *Runway Threshold* QFE may be given.

After a **Missed Approach,** vertical position will be referred to in terms of Altitude, and so QNH will be the more appropriate subscale setting at this stage (except at Military Aerodromes, which normally use a QFE procedure).

Fig. 18-3. Altimeter Subscale Settings in the Vicinity of an Aerodrome.

THE INSTRUMENT APPROACH

Having arrived in instrument conditions at the Homing Facility (which may be a Locator, VOR, etc.), the aircraft is then in a position to commence the Instrument Approach. Delaying action, if necessary can be taken by entering a Holding Pattern.

When an Instrument Approach is designed by an Aircraft Performance Specialist, the initial consideration is the Final Approach track to a minimum altitude (or minimum height). The procedure is then designed backwards from this desirable Final Approach Track through a number of segments, with the aim of providing a suitable flightpath between the en route phase of the flight and Final Approach.

Generally, the fewer the turns the less complicated the approach, and the better it is for the pilot and for ATC.

THE SEGMENTS OF AN INSTRUMENT APPROACH

The complete Instrument Approach Procedure may be divided into up to five separate segments that blend into each other. They are:
1. Arrival Segment;
2. Initial Approach Segment;
3. Intermediate Approach Segment;
4. Final Approach Segment; and
5. Missed Approach Segment.

IAF = Initial Approach Fix   FAF = Final Approach Fix
IF = Intermediate Fix   MAPt = Missed Approach Point

Fig.18-4. A Simple and Well-Designed Instrument Approach.

1. The **Arrival Segment** is the route followed from the en route phase of the flight to the Initial Approach Fix (IAF). It usually starts at an *En Route Fix* and ends at the *Initial Approach Fix (IAF)*, usually the first navigational facility associated with the procedure. The Arrival Segment may also be referred to as a *Feeder Route* or *Terminal Route.* An example of an Arrival Segment is shown below: the Feeder Route from the *LANAK* fix (at 20 DME on the 127° Glasgow VOR radial) toward the Glasgow (GOW) VOR, on a track of 307°M, probably at or above 4500 ft AMSL (since the procedure starts at 4500 ft AMSL); turning left at 2 DME from GOW VOR to track outbound on the Rwy 05 Localizer course.

Fig.18-5. Arrival Segment for the Glasgow ILS Rwy 05 Approach (Aerad chart).

There may be a number of Feeder Routes into the one Instrument Approach Procedure to cater for aircraft arriving from different directions, or there may be none. Many procedures do not require an Arrival Segment – for instance, if the en route tracking ends at the Initial Approach Fix.

2. In the **Initial Approach Segment,** the aircraft is manoeuvred to enter the Intermediate Segment. The Initial Approach Segment commences at the Initial Approach Fix (IAF), and may consist of a particular track, VOR radial, arc, procedure turn, holding pattern, radar vector – or any combination of these.

Arrival Segment too High to commence the Approach

Initial Approach Segment using a Holding Pattern to lose Height

FIX

Fig. 18-6. The Initial Approach Segment.

3. The **Intermediate Approach Segment** blends the Initial Approach Segment and the Final Approach Segement. It is the segment in which aircraft configuration, speed and positioning adjustments should be completed prior to entering the Final Approach Segment, by which time all cockpit Pre-Landing checks should normally be completed, with the aircraft established in a suitable condition for landing. Your Flying Instructor will explain the procedures to use for your particular aircraft.

The Intermediate Approach Segment ends at the Final Approach Fix (FAF), and may begin either:

- at a designated Intermediate Approach Fix (such as an NDB or Locator Outer Marker); or

- upon completion of a dead-reckoning track, or a reversal or racetrack procedure.

4. The **Final Approach Segement** of a Non-Precision Approach (such as an NDB Let-Down) begins at the *Final Approach Fix (FAF),* and is the segment in which the alignment and descent for landing are accomplished. It ends at the *Missed Approach Point (MAPt).* In some Instrument Approaches, the Final Approach Fix is the same as the Initial Approach Fix (e.g. the IAF may be the Locator Outer Marker, LOM, when flying outbound, and the FAF is the same LOM when flying inbound).

Final Approach may be made to a runway for a **straight-in landing,** or it may be made for a **circling approach** (i.e. *visual manoeuvring* for at least a partial circuit) to a runway with which the Final Approach of the Instrument Procedure is not aligned, provided of course that the pilot becomes visual at a suitable time.

The Final Approach Fix should be crossed at or above the specified height before Final descent is commenced. Where no *Final Approach Fix* is shown, the Final Approach Segment commeces at the completion of the procedure turn, with the aircraft within +/–5° of the *Final Approach Track (FAT),* whereupon Final Descent may be commenced.

Fig. 18-7. The Five Segments of a typical NDB Approach.

Step-Down Fixes, if published on the chart profile diagram, are limiting heights, and should be crossed at or above their minimum crossing heights.

Where a suitable DME exists, especially a DME located at the Runway Threshold, some descent slope *guidance* may be provided for Non-Precision Approaches in the form of a table of *altitude or height* versus *DME distance*. It is not mandatory to follow this information precisely – it is intended to assist pilots in carrying out Straight-In and Non-Precision Approaches.

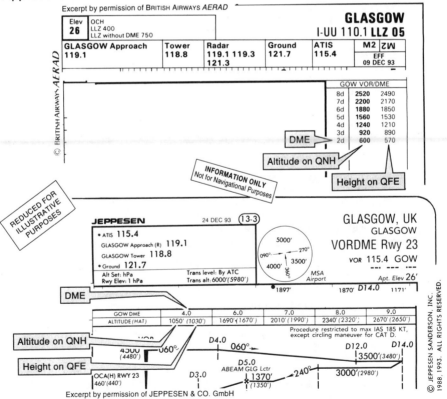

Fig. 18-8. Typical final Descent Guidance using the DME.

335

The **Final Approach Segment** for a Precision Approach is considered to commence at the *Final Approach Point (FAP)*, where the Intermediate Segment of the procedure intersects the Glidepath for the precision part of the ILS. It is marked on *Aerad* and *Jeppesen* charts with a 'Maltese' Cross. If this point coincides with a suitable fix (e.g. a LOM), it is called a **Final Approach Fix (FAF)**. The ILS approach is designed so that the aeroplane will intercept the Glideslope from below, generally by flying level until the slope is intercepted, to avoid the possibility of following one of the *false glideslopes* that may exist at steep angles such as at 6°, 9°, 12°, etc.

Fig.18-9. The Final Approach Segment of an ILS.

Final descent slope guidance on an ILS is provided by the electronic glideslope. Descent on the glidepath should not be initiated unless the aircraft is on track (within half-scale deflection of the Localizer). A fix or facility, usually the Outer Marker (OM) (but it could be a Locator (L) or a DME distance), is provided to allow the pilot to verify the *glidepath/altitude* relationship at one point on the precision approach. Descent below the **published crossing altitude** at the fix or facility should not occur before passing the fix or facility.

It is most important that a pilot does *not* descend below his minimum permitted altitude/height for a particular approach unless he has become 'visual' and can continue his approach to land visually, with the runway environment and nearby ground features in view.

The calculation of the minimum altitude/height should be done well before the instrument approach is even commenced, in a period when the workload is not as high – possibly as far back as on the cruise, or even pre-flight on the ground at the flight planning stage.

The starting point in calculating minima is the **OCA(H)** published on the Instrument Approach Chart, to which *significant additions* must be made. *OCH* is the Obstacle Clearance Height above the aerodrome level (and so is applicable when using QFE). *OCA* is the Obstacle Clearance Altitude above Mean Sea Level (and is applicable when the pilot is using QNH).

On *Aerad* Charts for the the UK, where *QFE* is the altimeter setting most commonly used on final approach, the information is shown as OCH (in the box beside the field elevation, in the top LH corner of the chart).

On *Jeppesen* Charts, the minimum is shown as OCA(H). For example, on the Leeds Bradford ILS DME Rwy 32, the minimum is written as 832' (170') – the difference (662) equalling the runway threshold elevation. Different OCA(H)s are published for different categories of aeroplane, based on speed (and manoeuvrability) – most training planes are in Category A.

The pilot will take the greater of **OCA(H) plus required additions** and the **absolute minimum** to obtain his personal minimum for the approach. The absolute minima are:

- 500 ft *Decision Height* on QFE for a **precision approach,** such as an ILS; or
- 600 ft *Minimum Descent Height* on QFE for a **non-precision approach,** such as an NDB let-down or a VOR let-down.

Be very careful in calculating minima! This is covered in the next chapter.

5. **The Missed Approach Segment.** If the pilot has not become visual by a particular point or minimum height on final descent, then a Missed Approach must be made.

For a *Precision Approach,* such as the Instrument Landing System, the *Missed Approach Point (MAPt)* is defined by the intersection of the Glidepath with the pilot's Decision Height, and therefore is not shown on approach charts. Unless visual, the pilot should commence a Missed Approach **immediately** the DH is reached on an ILS.

Fig. 18-10. If not Visual, commence the Missed Approach on reaching the DA(H) on a Precision Approach.

For a *Non-Precision Approach,* the Missed Approach Point (MAPt) is defined by either a *fix, facility* or by *timing,* and is shown on both the plan and profile diagrams as a dotted line. It is also described in text. If a turn is specified in the Missed Approach procedure, then it should not be commenced until the aeroplane has passed the MAPt and is established in the climb.

Fig.18-11. Plan and Profile of the Blackpool NDB Rwy 10 Approach (Aerad).

The pilot may not descend below his calculated MDA(H) on a Non-Precision Approach unless he becomes visual, however (unlike on a Precision Approach), he may track in as far as the MAPt at or above this level in the hope of becoming visual, before having to commence a Missed Approach. It is possible that the aeroplane may become visual in a position from which it is not possible to complete a straight-in landing safely, in which case some manoeuvring to position the aeroplane will be necessary.

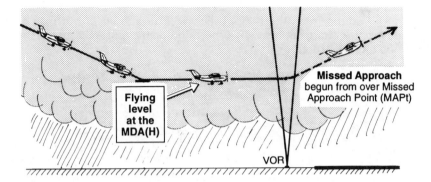

Fig. 18-12. If not Visual on a Non-Precision Approach, you may track in to the MAPt at the MDA(H) before executing a Missed Approach.

The Missed Approach Segment is considered to be completed at an altitude/height sufficent to allow either:
- initiation of another instrument approach;
- return to a designated holding pattern; or
- resumption of en route flight to a diversion aerodrome.

Instructions from ATC during the Missed Approach will be in terms of *altitude,* and so it may be necessary to alter the subscale setting from QFE to QNH once the Missed Approach is commenced (except at Military Aerodromes where a QFE Missed Approach procedure is used; see AIP RAC 4-3).

BECOMING VISUAL ON AN INSTRUMENT APPROACH

Of course, the aim of an Instrument Approach is to become visual and then to go ahead and make a safe landing. Some Instrument Approaches position you ideally for a straight-in landing, whereas others may put you in a position where some visual manoeuvring (circling) is necessary to position the aeroplane for a landing.

The subject of Visual Manoeuvring after an Instrument Approach is discussed in Chapter 20.

INSTRUMENT APPROACH CHARTS

Instrument Approach Charts provide a graphic presentation to the pilot of:
- Holding procedures (if required prior to commencing the instrument approach);
- the Instrument Approach procedure; and
- the Missed Approach procedure (in case the approach has to be discontinued at any time).

Instrument Approach Charts are designed to be readable in the cockpit, although some difficulty may be experienced in turbulence and/or poor light. The actual Instrument Approach will be shown in both plan and profile on the chart, along with other significant features such as aerodromes and obstructions.

Fig. 18-13. Excerpt from a (Jeppesen) Blackpool Chart, showing Warton Aerodrome and Obstructions.

Instrument Approach Charts are available for all aerodromes where instrument approach procedures have been established and approved by the CAA. The various types of chart in use that are acceptable to the UK CAA are those published by:

• British Airways/Aerad;

• Jeppesen; and

• the CAA itself.

Aerad and Jeppesen are the most commonly used charts in commercial operations. A chart list for CAA charts can be found in UK AIP MAP.

A pilot must study carefully the actual instrument approach charts that he will be using, since presentation of the same instrument approach by the different publishers is not identical. The symbols and abbreviations used will also differ. We have used a variety of charts in this manual to expose you to both publishers: *Aerad* and *Jeppesen.* A description of each approach is given in UK AIP RAC 4-2, and during your learning phase, it is worthwhile comparing this with the actual charts.

Use only current Instrument Approach Charts! They are regularly revised and amendments made available. Changes to the actual procedure, the appearance of significant new obstacles – such as buildings or masts in the Approach or Missed Approach areas – changes to radio frequencies, or the addition of new radio navigation facilities relevant to that approach, etc., will require issue of either a new chart or an amendment to the old chart.

Urgent amendments of a timely nature may be advised to pilots by NOTAM. Always check the date at the top of the chart, and check the NOTAMs for any amendments.

THE ELEMENTS OF AN INSTRUMENT APPROACH CHART

The information provided on an Instrument Approach Chart includes:
- identification of the particular approach;
- a plan view of the Approach and the Missed Approach;
- a profile view of the Approach and the Missed Approach;
- holding procedures associated with the Approach;
- full details of radio facilities associated with the Approach, Missed Approach and Holding;
- necessary aerodrome, topographical and cultural information (coastlines, significant lakes and rivers, relief, built-up areas, etc.) pertinent to the safe execution of the approach; and
- a *Landing Chart,* showing the runway layout.

IDENTIFICATION OF AN INSTRUMENT APPROACH CHART

An Instrument Approach Chart is normally identified in the top right hand side by:
- the name of the aerodrome;
- an abbreviation of the type of facility (further identified by the runway served in the case of a *Runway Approach* as against an *Aerodrome Approach);* and
- additional information to distinguish between separate charts for the same aerodrome.

There will be further information, such as the frequency of the radio navigation facility on which the approach is based, and its Morse Code identification signal. The Aerodrome Elevation (highest point on the landing area) is usually shown in this section of the chart. The **date** of the chart will also appear at the top.

RADIO COMMUNICATIONS FREQUENCIES

The relevant VHF communications frequencies, usually in the order in which a pilot will use them, are also listed near the top of the chart.

Fig. 18-14. The Top Section of the Chichester VOR Rwy 32 Aerad and Jeppesen Approach Charts, showing the Communications Boxes.

PLAN VIEW OF THE INSTRUMENT APPROACH

The plan view is a conformal projection that displays correct angular relationships. The scale is such that the Approach Charts are of a conveniently small size for use in the cockpit, yet large enough to show the Intermediate Approach area as well as the Final Approach and Missed Approach areas. A scale of 5 nm to the inch is typical. A graduated scale line will often be found down the left hand side of the plan view (remembering that 1 minute of latitude is 1 nm).

A reference circle of 5-nm radius or 10-nm radius is centred on the aerodrome to emphasise any obstructions or features close to the aerodrome. Horizontal distances along the approach are given in **nautical miles** to facilitate use of the DME (which reads in nm), however remember that Runway Distances and Runway Visual Range (RVR) are in **metres.**

The aerodrome is clearly shown on the plan view, including the runway pattern and any other distinctive patterns perhaps formed by taxiways or aprons. (Aerodrome Elevation is shown in the top LH box on *Aerad* charts, and in the top RH area of *Jeppesen* charts, immediately above the plan view.) Restricted and Danger Areas are shown, as are nearby aerodromes (to avoid mis-identification once visual). Even large aeroplanes have been landed at incorrect aerodromes, often in good weather when the Instrument-Rated Pilot has become visual well away from the destination aerodrome and not paid sufficient attention to tracking details to the aerodrome as shown on the Instrument Approach Chart. An aerodrome symbol on the chart will alert the pilot to this danger.

Even though Obstacle Clearance is provided for in the design of the Instrument Approach, significant topographical and other data, although not part of the actual Instrument Approach, may be shown on the chart to assist the pilot when and if he becomes visual. It is very handy, for instance, to know the runway layout and the position of any nearby obstacles to expect when and if becoming visual on Final Approach.

Information will appear regarding Minimum Sector Altitudes (MSA), or Sector Safe Altitudes (SSA), which are the lowest safe altitudes in the specified sectors within 25 nm of the homing facility.

The plan position of each of the radio aids required for the procedure is shown, with frequencies, *IDENT*, and defined tracks in **degrees Magnetic.**

The **main procedure track** is generally shown as a heavy, solid line with its magnetic direction and a directional arrow.

The **Missed Approach** is generally shown as a heavy, dashed line, with a directional arrow. The latest point at which to commence a Missed Approach according to the procedures is referred to as the Missed Approach Point (MAPt).

The **Holding Pattern** which, strictly speaking, is not part of most approaches, is generally shown as a light, solid or dotted line, with magnetic direction and a directional arrow. Some approaches, however, use the Racetrack Pattern as part of an alternative Intermediate Segment, replacing a Procedure Turn. The *Minimum Holding Altitude* may also be shown near the Holding Pattern, as may any special *distance* or *time* requirements.

PROFILE VIEW

The profile view of the Instrument Approach is published directly beneath the plan view. The aerodrome or a specific runway will be shown in the profile diagram, probably with its elevation stated nearby. Relevant radio facilities are also shown in profile.

The **main procedure track** is a solid line with a directional arrow and magnetic track. In the profile view, the angles shown are generally not to scale, but exaggerated for graphic effect. Approach slopes are really quite gentle (a typical ILS glideslope, for instance, is only 3° to the horizontal – a gradient of 1 in 20). The profile view of any reversal or procedure turn is shown as a horizontal line, which may have associated altitude, distance or time requirements stated nearby.

Vertical distances required along the instrument procedure are shown in **feet** on UK charts, both as *altitudes* (feet Above Mean Sea Level, AMSL) based on the QNH altimeter setting, and as *heights* Above Aerodrome Level (AAL) based on the QFE altimeter setting.

The heights of obstructions will be shown as feet AMSL. European charts may show vertical distances in *meters.*

The Missed Approach Procedure will generally be shown as a dotted line with a directional arrow, and with a written description nearby.

OBSTACLE CLEARANCE SECTION

Somewhere on the chart will be stated the Obstacle Clearance information for Final Approach, from which the pilot may commence calculating his Decision Altitude (Height) for a Precision Approach, or his Minimum Descent Altitude (Height) for a Non-Precision Approach.
- *Jeppesen* charts present the basic information as **OCA(H)**, the Obstacle Clearance Altitude (Height);
- *Aerad* charts specify the minimum as **OCH**, Obstacle Clearance Height (i.e. AAL, based on QFE). *(Aerad* also have a green page with Aerodrome Operating Minima at the front of each aerodrome group.)

GROUND SPEEDS versus RATES OF DESCENT ON FINAL, AND TIMING TO THE MAPt

Some charts have a table towards the bottom that provides guidance to the pilot regarding the *Rate of Descent* required at a particular *Ground Speed* to maintain the aeroplane on the published approach slope.

To maintain a given slope, the faster the aeroplane is moving over the ground, the greater its Rate of Descent must be. To use this table, the pilot needs to apply the wind component to his Airspeed to obtain Ground Speed, and then he can read off (or interpolate) the approximate Rate of Descent required to maintain the slope.

For a Non-Precision approach where the approach aid is well away from the aerodrome and acts as the Final Approach Fix (FAF), *Jeppesen* charts also show the **time** from the FAF to the MAPt. *Aerad* gives a time from the FAF to the Runway Threshold (see figure 18-15).

Gnd speed-Kts		70	90	100	120	140	160
Descent Grad. 6.0%		426	547	608	730	851	973
Lctr to MAP	4.3	3:41	2:52	2:35	2:09	1:51	1:37

Excerpted from *Glasgow NDB Rwy 05* Approach
Chart by permission of JEPPESEN & CO. GmbH

Fig.18-15. Ground Speed/Rate of Descent/Time tables: (above) Jeppesen Non-Precision Approach Chart; (right) Aerad Precision Approach Chart.

On ILS charts, the *GS/RoD/Time* information is useful in situations where the electronic glideslope is not available, and a Localizer Approach has to be made.

© BRITISH AIRWAYS AERAD

kt	fpm	FAF
200	1060	–
180	950	THR
160	850	2:15
140	740	2:34
120	640	3:00
100	530	3:36
80	430	4:30

Excerpted from *London/Stansted ILS/DME 23* Approach Chart by permission of BRITISH AIRWAYS AERAD

HOLDING PROCEDURES ASSOCIATED WITH THE APPROACH

Any Holding Patterns associated with the approach are shown on the plan diagram. Initially, they may appear to clutter the chart, but, with familiarity, it is easy to distinguish the various components. In some procedures the Holding Pattern may actually form part of the approach – a *reversal of the outbound track* using a Procedure Turn may sometimes be avoided by using a published alternative (and simpler) procedure of tracking outbound in the Holding Pattern and then turning inbound to intercept the Final Approach Track (FAT).

Fig.18-16. Alternative Reversal Procedure for the Birmingham Rwy 33 ILS/DME.

SOME TYPICAL INSTRUMENT APPROACH CHARTS

Examples of actual *Jeppesen* and *Aerad* Instrument Approach Charts for some UK approaches follow on the next pages, courtesy of these companies.

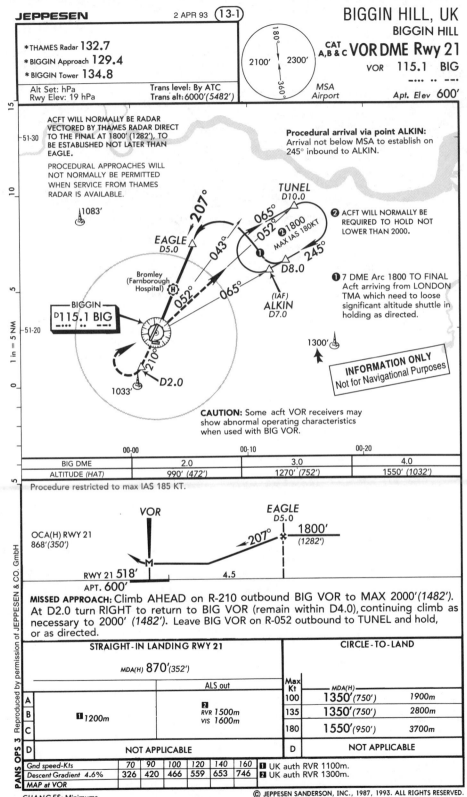

JEPPESEN   2 APR 93 (13-1)

BIGGIN HILL, UK
BIGGIN HILL

CAT A,B & C **VOR DME Rwy 21**

VOR **115.1 BIG**
---- .. ---

Apt. Elev **600'**

MSA Airport

2100' 2300'

* THAMES Radar **132.7**
* BIGGIN Approach **129.4**
* BIGGIN Tower **134.8**

| Alt Set: hPa | Trans level: By ATC |
| Rwy Elev: 19 hPa | Trans alt: 6000'(5482') |

ACFT WILL NORMALLY BE RADAR VECTORED BY THAMES RADAR DIRECT TO THE FINAL AT 1800' (1282'), TO BE ESTABLISHED NOT LATER THAN EAGLE.

PROCEDURAL APPROACHES WILL NOT NORMALLY BE PERMITTED WHEN SERVICE FROM THAMES RADAR IS AVAILABLE.

Procedural arrival via point ALKIN:
Arrival not below MSA to establish on 245° inbound to ALKIN.

1083'

TUNEL D10.0

207°   065°   052°   1800 MAX IAS 180KT

043°   052°

EAGLE D5.0

245°   D8.0

2 ACFT WILL NORMALLY BE REQUIRED TO HOLD NOT LOWER THAN 2000.

Bromley (Farnborough Hospital) (H)

052°   065°

1 7 DME Arc 1800 TO FINAL Acft arriving from LONDON TMA which need to loose significant altitude shuttle in holding as directed.

BIGGIN D 115.1 BIG
---- .. ---

(IAF) ALKIN D7.0

1300'

210°

D2.0

1033'

INFORMATION ONLY Not for Navigational Purposes

CAUTION: Some acft VOR receivers may show abnormal operating characteristics when used with BIG VOR.

	00-00	00-10	00-20
BIG DME	2.0	3.0	4.0
ALTITUDE (HAT)	990' (472')	1270' (752')	1550' (1032')

Procedure restricted to max IAS 185 KT.

VOR   EAGLE D5.0

OCA(H) RWY 21 868'(350')

207°   1800' (1282')

RWY 21 518'   M   4.5
APT. 600'

MISSED APPROACH: Climb AHEAD on R-210 outbound BIG VOR to MAX 2000'(1482'). At D2.0 turn RIGHT to return to BIG VOR (remain within D4.0), continuing climb as necessary to 2000' (1482'). Leave BIG VOR on R-052 outbound to TUNEL and hold, or as directed.

STRAIGHT-IN LANDING RWY 21				CIRCLE-TO-LAND		
MDA(H) **870'(352')**						
		ALS out	Max Kt	MDA(H)		
A	**1** 1200m	**2** RVR 1500m VIS 1600m	100	**1350'(750')**	1900m	
B			135	**1350'(750')**	2800m	
C			180	**1550'(950')**	3700m	
D	NOT APPLICABLE		D	NOT APPLICABLE		

Gnd speed-Kts	70	90	100	120	140	160
Descent Gradient 4.6%	326	420	466	559	653	746
MAP at VOR						

1 UK auth RVR 1100m.
2 UK auth RVR 1300m.

CHANGES: Minimums.

PANS OPS 3

CAMBRIDGE
L/DME or L 23

Elev 50	OCH L/DME A,B 350 C,D 380 L 540

CAMBRIDGE Approach 123·6	Tower 122·2	Radar 130·75	P2	Zd
			04 FEB 93	

Ahead to **2000** 1950 then left to CAM or as directed by ATC. Climb to **870** prior to level accel.

Var 4°W			T.Lev **ATC** T.Alt **3000**

L'CAM			T.Lev ATC T.Alt 3000
turn	kt	fpm	FAF
1:48	**200**	920	
2:00	**180**	830	THR
2:15	**160**	740	1:45
2:34	**140**	640	2:00
3:00	**120**	550	2:21
3:36	**100**	460	2:49
4:30	**80**	370	3:31

1. When approach is from NW: Pilots are advised to contact Wyton Approach.
2. *A/c normally required to hold min alt **3000** 2950.
3. Min alt to start procedure **2000** 1950 on ATC approval.
4. Cat A,B outbound leg Tr073M.
5. No DME: Cat A,B outbound leg for 2·5mins. Cat C,D outbound leg for 2mins. Max 185kt.
6. DME reads 0·3 at D.THR.
7. Figs in RH column compute at 2·6° angle of descent.

DME CAB		
5d	**1400**	1350
4d	**1140**	1090
3d	**860**	810
2d	**580**	530

Rev: Editorial

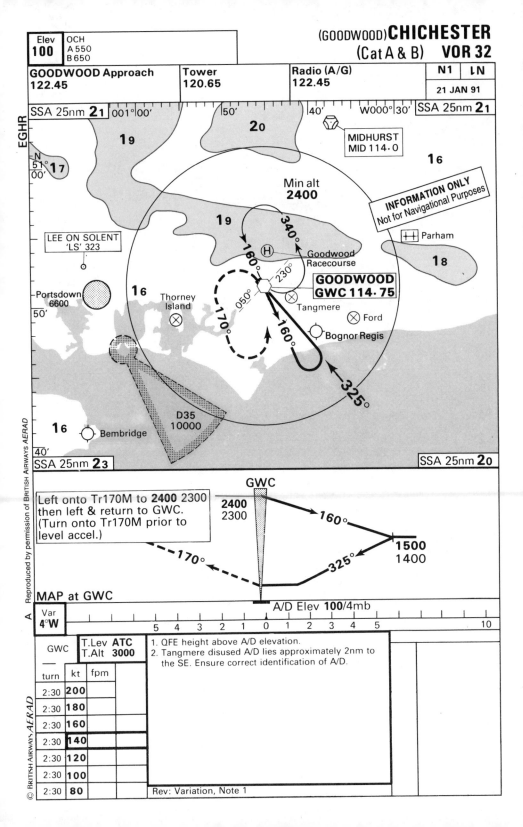

Elev	OCH
100	A 550
	B 650

		N1	LN
GOODWOOD Approach 122.45	**Tower** 120.65	**Radio (A/G)** 122.45	
		21 JAN 91	

EGHR

SSA 25nm **21** | 001°00' | 50' | 40' | W000°30' | SSA 25nm **21**

1 9

2 0

MIDHURST
MID 114·0

N 51° 00' **1 7**

1 6

Min alt **2400**

1 9

340°

160°

INFORMATION ONLY
Not for Navigational Purposes

LEE ON SOLENT
'LS' 323

H
Goodwood Racecourse

Parham

1 8

Portsdown
6600
50'

1 6

Thorney Island
⊗

230°

050°

**GOODWOOD
GWC 114·75**

⊗ Tangmere

⊗ Ford

170°

160°

Bognor Regis

325°

D35
10000

1 6 ○ Bembridge

40'

SSA 25nm **23**

SSA 25nm **20**

GWC

Left onto Tr170M to **2400** 2300 then left & return to GWC. (Turn onto Tr170M prior to level accel.)

2400
2300

160°

170°

1500
1400

325°

MAP at GWC

A/D Elev **100**/4mb

A | Var 4°W

5 4 3 2 1 0 1 2 3 4 5 10

GWC	T.Lev **ATC**		1. QFE height above A/D elevation.
—	T.Alt **3000**		2. Tangmere disused A/D lies approximately 2nm to
turn	kt	fpm	the SE. Ensure correct identification of A/D.
2:30	**200**		
2:30	**180**		
2:30	**160**		
2:30	**140**		
2:30	**120**		
2:30	**100**		
2:30	**80**		Rev: Variation, Note 1

DUNDEE
(Cat A,B) DDE 108.1 LLZ 10

| Elev 13 | OCH A,B 470 / No MKR A,B 600 |

DUNDEE Approach/Tower 122·9

M2 | ZW
09 NOV 92

EGPN

SSA 25nm **47** — SSA 25nm **45** — SSA 25nm **41** — SSA 25nm **25**

Leuchars/Perth Area of Intense Air Activity 4000 / 1000g

'DND' 394
MKR
Tealing
098° Perth
282°
LLZ
172° / 352° / 260°
Perth PTH 110·4
LUK 16d arc
Errol
102° Min alt 3000
Leuchars 'LU' 417
Leuchars
Leuchars LUK Ch 42 (110·5)
D604 1500 (9000 Notified)

INFORMATION ONLY Not for Navigational Purposes

'DND'

2500 / 2490
098°
1 min 260°
MKR
3000 / 2990
1670 / 1660
960 / 950
THR Elev 13/0 mb

To **2000** 1990 then left to 'DND' at **3000** 2990. (Acc. alt **1000**)
(If penetration of D604 unavoidable: After 2 min of missed approach, right to Tr130M & inform ATC. Await instructions to change to Leuchars (126.50), for radar assistance & return to 'DND' at **3000** 2990 clear of D604).

'DND' TO MAP(THR) 2·8nm

Var 7°W

5 4 3 2 1 0 1 2 3 4 5

'DND'	T.Lev **ATC** / T.Alt **3000**			
turn	kt	fpm	MKR	
2:00	200		—	
2:00	180		THR	
2:00	160		1:48	
2:00	140		2:03	
2:00	120		2:24	
2:00	100		2:52	
2:00	80		3:36	

1. Procedure not to be used when ATC unavailable.
2. When inbound to 'DND' within DDE 15d altitude may be reduced to **3000** 2990.
3. *Level segment of outbound leg 1 min 30 sec if less than 120kt.
4. Final turn clear of Perth ATZ (within LUK 16d).
5. Final app segment crosses high ground. **DO NOT** descend below proc min alts/hgts.
6. Min ROD: MKR to 'DND' 3.7°(384'/nm), 'DND' to TDZ 3.1°(324'/nm).
7. MKR fly through time may double when established on LLZ. MKR offset 0.27nm South of Centreline.
8. No MKR proc: Cross 'DND' at **1670** 1660.
9. At the extreme limit of the base turn OM indications may be received from Perth OM (dashes), these should not be confused with the Dundee Mkr (dots).

Rev: Text

Non Precision App

G/S 160 kt	
140	
120	
100	
80	

Reproduced by permission of BRITISH AIRWAYS AERAD

© BRITISH AIRWAYS AERAD

JEPPESEN   4 FEB 94   (11-2)   **EAST MIDLANDS, UK**
                                              EAST MIDLANDS
ATIS Arrival **128.22**   **ILS Rwy 09**
CASTLEDON Approach(R) **119.65**
CASTLEDON Tower **124.0**   LOC *109.9 IEMW
*Ground **121.9**   .. _ _ _ .__

| Alt Set: hPa | Trans level: By ATC |
| Rwy Elev: 11 hPa | Trans alt: 3000'(2695') |

2500'

MSA Airport

Apt. Elev **310'**

Λ804'

(IAF)
EAST MIDLANDS
393 EMW
_.. . _ _

Λ759'

ILS
093° *109.9 IEMW

Donington Park   MM

093°   273°   093°

048° 228°   3000
                  093°

Λ730'

INFORMATION ONLY
Not for Navigational Purposes

1027'
Λ

01-40   01-30   01-20   01-10

52-50
15 10 5 0 5
1 in=5 NM

Procedure restricted to max IAS 185 KT, except circling maneuver for CAT D.

Start turn at ½ Min
DESCENDING to **2000'**(1695')

273°   LOM
              _ _
              3000' (2695')

GS 1605'(1300')

LOC 1610'(1305')

093°

3.9   3.3

MM
_ _ _
GS 535'(230')

M

0.6   0   APT. **310'**

TCH 50'
RWY 09 **305'**

OCA(H) RWY 09
ILS AB: 485'(180')
CD: 505'(200')
GS out 655'(350')

MISSED APPROACH: Climb STRAIGHT AHEAD to 3000'(2695') then turn LEFT to Lctr maintaining 3000'(2695') or as directed.

STRAIGHT-IN LANDING RWY 09						CIRCLE-TO-LAND	
ILS DA(H) **505'**(200')		**LOC (GS out)** MDA(H) **660'**(355')					
	FULL	ALS out		MM out	ALS out	Max Kts	MDA(H)
A			900m			100	**860'**(550') / 1900m
B	RVR **1** 720m	**2** 1200m		NOT AUTH	**3** RVR 1500m VIS 1600m	135	**860'**(550') / 2800m
C	VIS 800m					180	**1160'**(850') / 3700m
D		**2** 1200m				205	**1160'**(850') / 4600m

Gnd speed-Kts	70	90	100	120	140	160
ILS GS 3.00° or LOC Descent Gradient 5.2%	377	485	539	647	755	862

1 UK auth RVR 600m. **2** UK auth RVR 900m.
3 UK auth RVR 1300m.
MAP at MM

PANS OPS 3   Reproduced by permission of JEPPESEN & CO. GmbH

CHANGES: ATIS established.

Elev **620**	OCH 570				
BRISTOL Approach 120·6		**Radar 124·35**		**Tower 133·85**	**Q 2**
					07 FEB 94

SSA 25nm **3o** | 00' | 50' | W002° 40' | 30' | SSA 25nm **22**

EGGD

2 2

N 51° 30'

'OF' 325
Filton

D 121 2000

BRISTOL HMR 120·6

←**269°**

111° *Cat C,D

INFORMATION ONLY Not for Navigational Purposes

20'

⊞ Weston

L 'BRI' 380

I-BTS Ch 38 (110·15)

3o

2 2

Yeovilton AIAA 5000 2000

D 119 5000

SSA 25nm **3o** | | | | SSA 25nm **3o**

VDF

3000 2400

Cat C,D **111°**

Ahead to **2500** 1900 then right to overhead VDF at **3000** 2400

1900 1300

269°

MAP at VDF

| Var 6°W | | 5 | 4 | 3 | 2 | 1 | 0 | 1 | 2 | 3 | 4 | 5 | | 10 |

D.THR Elev **601**/22mb

Reproduced by permission of BRITISH AIRWAYS *AERAD*

VDF —	T.Lev **ATC** T.Alt **3000**		1. Cat A,B outbound Tr 103M for 2 min 30 sec. 2. FAT off-set 3° right of runway centreline (272M)
turn	kt	fpm	
2:00	**200**		
2:00	**180**		
2:00	**160**		
2:00	**140**		
2:00	**120**		
2:00	**100**		
2:00	**80**		Rev:Approach/VDF freq.

© BRITISH AIRWAYS *AERAD*

SOME GENERAL COMMENTS ON MAKING INSTRUMENT APPROACHES

It is most important that the cockpit be **well organised** prior to commencing an Instrument Approach, since the workload during the approach will be high.

The **Instrument Approach procedures** to be used, including the Missed Approach, should be reviewed en route, preferably well before the aerodrome, and even prior to commencing descent from cruise level.

Given a choice of instrument approaches to an aerodrome or to a particular runway, a pilot will generally **opt for a Precision Approach,** such as an ILS, over a Non-Precision Approach. As well as making it easier to fly an accurate final descent, the glideslope guidance of a Precision Approach will permit a lower minimum height, possibly making the difference between becoming visual or having to make a Missed Approach.

The **charts** required should be arranged in order, calculations of minima completed, and determine the intended action in the case of a Missed Approach (e.g. diversion, return for second approach, etc.). *Fuel on Board* is an important consideration, especially if a diversion might be necessary.

The **Radio Navigation Aids** required for the approach should be set up as early as convenient, although there may be some delays necessary – for instance, if the VHF-NAV needs to remain selected to a VOR for en-route tracking prior to the commencement of an ILS approach. Make use of every available means of navigation to assist you in forming a picture of exactly where the aeroplane is. Do not leave the VHF-NAV, ADF or DME idle if they can be tuned to useful aids, even if those aids are not part of the published procedure.

Ensure that the **Altimeter** is set correctly for precise vertical navigation *(Aerodrome QNH* during the en-route descent and, normally in the UK, to *Aerodrome QFE* for an aerodrome approach, or to *Threshold QFE* for a runway approach – although some pilots may choose to use Aerodrome QNH).

If a **high speed** has been used on the cruise and descent, then it may be appropriate to slow the aeroplane down to a more suitable manoeuvring speed before reaching the Initial Approach Fix, and to complete any necessary cockpit checks at this time.

If the Instrument Approach uses the same facility for the Initial Approach Fix (IAF) and the Final Approach Fix (FAF), the pilot will track outbound from the IAF, reverse the track by making a **Procedure Turn** inbound, and then track to the Final Approach Fix.

Fig. 18-23. The Procedure Turn used to Reverse Direction.

Some Instrument Approaches are designed so that a Base Turn (rather than a Procedure Turn) is used to align the aeroplane on the Final Approach track.

Fig.18-24. The Base Turn as part of an Intermediate Segment.

Under Radar Control, however, a pilot may be radar vectored directly to the Final Approach track of any Instrument Approach, and cleared to descend to suitable altitudes by ATC, so that a smooth intercept of Final Approach May be made. If *Feeder Routes* are published for the particular approach, then the pilot will possibly be routed by ATC via one of these. Sometimes it is possible to track via a *DME Arc* from the en route track to intercept the Final Approach Track (FAT). In all of these cases, reversal turns may be avoided.

Fig.18-25. Different Methods used to avoid Reversal Turns.

The **minimum altitude (height)** at which the pilot may fly in any particular segment will be shown on the chart, although ATC may assign a higher level.

During the Intermediate Approach Segment, the aeroplane is being manoeuvred to be positioned on Final Approach at a suitable height and airspeed. The actual configuration of the aeroplane (i.e. the position of the flaps and undercarriage), and the speed at which it should be flown at various stages in the approach, will vary between aeroplane types, and clear instructions in this regard will be given by your Flying Instructor, and the Pilot's Operating Handbook.

During Final Approach, normal attitude-flying techniques should be used, with constant reference to the flight instruments, and regular reference to the navigation instruments. During an ILS, the glideslope should be maintained with small adjustments of pitch attitude on the Attitude Indicator using the elevator, and the airspeed should be maintained on the ASI with power adjustments made with the throttle. For a Non-Precision Approach, a suitable steady rate of descent should be set up, preferably that suggested on the Approach Chart for a particular *Ground Speed,* otherwise approximately 500 ft/min.

During Final Approach, the pilot should have clearly fixed in his mind his **minimum,** and the **Missed Approach procedure.** If not visual with the runway environment in sight at the calculated minimum height:

- for a *Precision Approach,* a Missed Approach should be commenced immediately at Decision Altitude (Height); and
- for a *Non-Precision Approach,* the aeroplane may continue tracking at the Minimum Descent Altitude (Height) to the Missed Approach Point (MAPt) if visual flight does not become possible.

What is 'VISUAL REFERENCE' at the DH or MDH?

Visual Reference is the **minimum visual reference** that the pilot should have in view before continuing the approach below the DH or MDH. The visual segment should contain sufficient physical features (approach lights, runway lights, runway markings, and features in the general runway environs) to ensure that the position of the aircraft relative to the desired flightpath can be positively ascertained. This then enables the pilot to make an informed judgement at DH/MDH, and thereafter maintain a stable descent path towards the runway.

Fig. 18-26. Visual or Not-Visual.

❏ Now complete **Exercises 18 – Instrument Approaches.**

19

INSTRUMENT MINIMA

CALCULATION OF MINIMA

A pilot is required to satisfy himself before take-off that a flight can be made safely. When poor weather exists, he must be certain (before taking off) that conditions at the destination or alternate aerodrome will allow a landing to be made. Take-off conditions at the departure aerodrome must also be suitable. Do not take off unless you are sure that you can land.

The UK Private Pilot must determine his own minima, based on the sound recommendations given in the UK AIP RAC 4-3. If the planned flight will be in instrument conditions, then the aeroplane must be properly equipped and the pilot property rated, with either an Instrument Rating or an IMC Rating. As well, the pilot needs to be in **current practice.**

Careful consideration should therefore be given to studying the available weather reports and forecasts, a detailed explanation of which can be found in the *Air Pilot's Manual, Volume 2.* **Bad weather** can be said to exist if conditions are:

- cloud ceiling worse than 1000 ft AAL;
- in-flight visibility worse than 1800 metres; and
- Runway Visual Range (RVR)/aerodrome visibility worse than 1500 metres.

Prior to operating, a pilot must consider:

- for **Take-Off** – the minimum visibility and cloud ceiling;
- for **Approach and Landing:**
  - the minimum height to which an approach on instruments should be continued for a straight-in landing (i.e. a Decision Height or a Minimum Descent Height) or a circling approach to land on another runway (i.e. Visual Manoeuvring Height); and
  - the minimum visibility and visual reference required to continue the approach to a safe landing.

The pilot must also consider:
- runway surface conditions (dry, wet, standing water, slush, ice);
- crosswind;
- aeroplane performance (take-off or landing distance required).

MINIMUM WEATHER CONDITIONS FOR TAKE-OFF

A prime consideration for take-off in a single-engined aeroplane is the ability for a safe forced landing to be made following engine failure. The UK AIP states that, for non-public transport flights, the minimum weather conditions for take-off should never be less than:
- **600 ft cloud ceiling (recommended);** and
- **1800 metres in-flight visibility (mandatory).**

Visibility is the distance at which prominent unlit objects by day, and a moderate intensity light by night, can be seen and identified.

Following an unexpected engine failure on take-off in these minimum conditions, an experienced and in-practice pilot of a relatively slow and manoeuvrable aeroplane will have a reasonable change of viewing a suitable forced landing area, and being able to avoid obstacles in attempting to reach it. Realistically, however, an IMC-Rated Pilot should be very wary about flying in conditions worse than 1500 ft cloud ceiling and 3 km visibility.

MINIMUM EN ROUTE WEATHER CONDITIONS

Following the take-off, the aeroplane should be climbed to a safe cruising level for the journey. Whilst the above minimum conditions might be suitable for take-off, they are **not suitable for a visual transit flight** cross-country or to another aerodrome. Flying visually cross-country under such poor conditions is generally not possible. **If a visual flight is to be undertaken, then the usual visual requirements** (shown below) **must be met.**

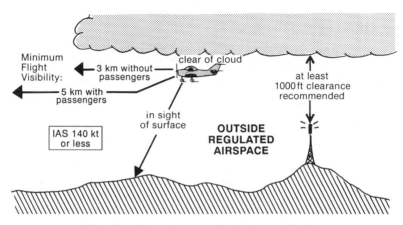

Fig. 19-1. Requirements for a Visual Flight.

If the flight is to proceed in **IMC Conditions,** however, then a suitable **Safety Altitude** must be used. It is suggested that you fly at least 1000 ft above the highest obstacle within 5 nm either side of track, or above the Maximum Elevation Figure (MEF) shown in latitude–longitude quadrangles on the $\frac{1}{2}$ million aeronautical chart series. The **Quadrantal Rule** should also be considered when selecting the cruise level. These aspects of 'Vertical Navigation' are fully covered in *Vol. 3 of the Air Pilot's Manual.*

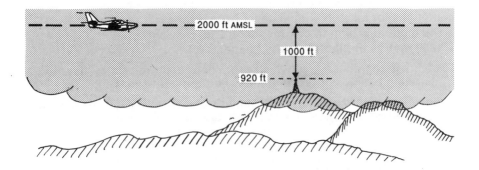

Fig. 19-2. In IMC, Maintain at least 1000 ft above any Obstacles within 5 nm.

MINIMUM CONDITIONS FOR LANDING

Determining the minimum conditions for landing is more complicated. The main considerations are as follows:

- Is there an *Instrument Approach Procedure* published for the destination?
- Is it a *Precision Approach* (ILS), or a *Non-Precision Approach* (NDB/VOR)?
- Is *Obstacle Clearance* a problem?
- What is the particular *System Minimum* (e.g. ILS 200 ft, NDB/VOR/VDF 300 ft, SRA 350 ft)?
- Is a correction for *Altimeter Position Error Correction* (PEC 50 ft) and *Aeroplane Error* (10 ft) required?
- What *Pilot qualification* do I hold – *IMC Rating* or *Instrument Rating?* (An IMC-Rated Pilot must add an extra 200 ft.)
- *Am I current,* i.e. with **recent experience?** (Either do not fly in instrument conditions if out of practice, or else add extra height to any Decision Height.)
- Is the *Visibility* at least 1800 metres (for IMC-Rated Pilots)?
- Is the *Runway* suitable (runway length, surface friction, crosswind component)?

An Instrument Approach consists of a **non-visual phase,** followed (hopefully) by a **visual phase** that will allow a safe touchdown and landing to be made. During the non-visual phase, the instruments will provide **tracking guidance,** and on some approaches, **slope guidance** is provided as well. This divides Instrument Approaches into two families.

A **Precision Approach** is one in which both **tracking** and **slope** guidance is given – the most common Precision Approach being the ILS. The minimum height calculated for a Precision Approach is known as a *Decision Height, DH* (based on QFE and height above the runway) or *Decision Altitude, DA* (based on QNH and height AMSL). The DA will be greater than the DH by the amount of the Runway Elevation.

Jeppesen charts show the two figures as, for example, DA(H) 227′ *(200′)*, with the Decision Altitude 227′ based on QNH coming first, followed by the Decision Height *200′* based on QFE in brackets and *italic* type. On *Aerad* charts, the two minima are shown one above the other, with the QNH figure at the top and in **bold** type.

The **visibility** required for an IMC-Rated Pilot to proceed below the DA(H) is 1800 metres. If satisfactory visual reference is not acquired at or before reaching the DA(H) on a Precision Approach, then a Missed Approach should be initiated **immediately.**

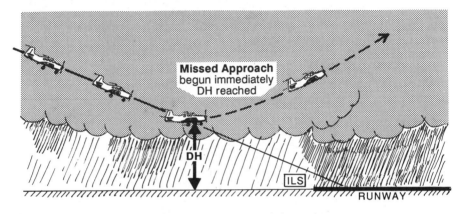

Fig. 19-3. The Precision Approach.

A **Non-Precision Approach** is one in which **tracking** guidance only is given, without accurate slope guidance. The NDB and VOR let-downs are Non-Precision Approaches, as is an ILS Approach without the Glideslope (known as a Localizer approach). The minimum height calculated for a Non-Precision Approach is known as a **Minimum Descent Height, MDH** (based on QFE) or **Minimum Descent Altitude, MDA** (based on QNH).

The aircraft should not be descended below the MDA(H) unless satisfactory visual reference is acquired. The **visibility** required for an IMC-Rated Pilot to proceed below the MDA(H) is 1800 metres.

If satisfactory visual reference is *not* acquired by the MDA(H), which may be reached some distance from the aerodrome, then the aircraft may be **flown level** at (but not below) this height until either adequate visual reference for landing is acquired or the Missed Approach Point (MAPt) reached and a Missed Approach begun.

This is different to the Precision Approach procedure where, if visual reference is not acquired on reaching the DA(H), the Missed Approach is begun immediately.

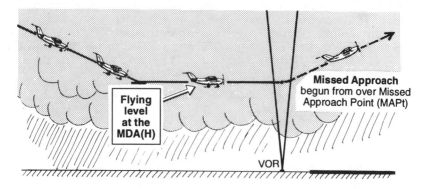

Fig. 19-4. Going Around from a Non-Precision Approach.

The minimum height to which it is safe to descend on instruments alone depends upon a number of items, the most important ones being:

• obstacles in the vicinity of the approach path (i.e. Obstacle Clearance Height, **OCH**);

• the minimum height to which a particular non-visual aid (e.g. ILS, VOR, NDB) may be flown (known as the **System Minimum**); and

• the qualifications and recent experience of the pilot.

Obstacle Clearance Height (OCH)

The designer of the approach calculates, according to strict criteria, a safe **Obstacle Clearance Height (OCH)**. The OCH at a particular aerodrome will be lower for the precision aids because of the smaller area in which obstacles need to be considered for a Precision Approach compared to a Non-Precision Approach. On a Precision Approach (e.g. an ILS Approach), the descent should be on slope, and the aeroplane should not arrive at the minimum height earlier than required.

For instance, the Blackpool Runway 28 ILS OCH for Category A aircraft is 135 ft, whilst the NDB OCH is 500 ft. The ILS provides excellent approach-slope guidance, whereas the NDB alone does not. If a Rwy 28 NDB/DME approach is carried out (i.e. with a DME to provide range, as well as the NDB to provide track guidance), more guidance on slope is given when compared to the NDB alone, the area to be considered for obstacles is less, and consequently the OCH has been lowered from 500 ft for the NDB alone to 450 ft AAL for the combined NDB/DME.

Another factor that can reduce OCH is **aeroplane speed.** A slower aero-plane is assumed to lose less height due to inertia when commencing a Missed Approach, whereas a faster aeroplane may lose more height during the transition from Final Descent to the Missed Approach climb-away.

As well as the lower Obstacle Clearance Height, there is a further advant-age for slower aircraft in the Visual Manoeuvring phase following the Instrument Approach and when circling to land on another runway. Because they are more manoeuvrable and have a smaller turning radius, slower aircraft such as Cessnas and Pipers can circle in a smaller area compared to Boeings and Airbuses, and therefore are likely to be exposed to fewer obstacles. Consequently (and logically), slower aeroplanes are permitted to operate at a Visual Manoeuvring Height (VMH) based on obstacles in a reduced circling area, which means their VMH may be lower than that for the faster aircraft.

The aeroplane categories are based on the **nominal threshold speed (V_{AT}),** which is *1.3 x Indicated Stalling Speed* in the approach configuration at the Maximum Landing Weight. V_{AT} is the speed at which you would normally plan to cross the threshold when at *Maximum Landing Weight,* so it is a fixed value at all times for the one aeroplane, which therefore is always in the one category. Most light aircraft fall into Category A or B. You should know the Category of your aeroplane. The Categories (which are listed in UK AIP RAC 4-2-2 & 4-3-4) are as follows:

Category **A** V_{AT} less than 91 kt.

Category **B** V_{AT} between 91–120 kt.

Category **C** V_{AT} between 121–140 kt.

Category **D** V_{AT} between 141–165 kt.

Category **E** V_{AT} between 166–210 kt.

A typical set of published OCHs for the different aeroplane categories is that for the Blackpool ILS/DME Rwy 28:

A 135, B 142, C 152, D 160.

If you are flying a Category A aeroplane (such as a typical training aeroplane), then OCH 135 is the figure you use when commencing to calculate your Decision Height.

NOTE: If you require visual manoeuvring to land (i.e. a circling manoeuvre) following the instrument approach, then the *Visual Manoeuvring OCH* should be substituted for the procedure OCH in determining your *Circle-to-Land MDH.*

System Minima (or Minimums)

A Precision Approach is capable of guiding a pilot to a lower height than a Non-Precision Approach. The minimum height to which a particular type of non-visual aid can be flown (i.e. the System Minimum as listed in UK AIP RAC 4-3) is considered to be as stated below. These are **not** the heights to which you should descend in Instrument Conditions – they (like OCH) are an early consideration to which additions must be made in the calculation of your **personal minimum height.**

Precision Approach System Minima

ILS . . . . 200 ft

Non-Precision Approaches System Minima

ILS (no glidepath) . . . . 250 ft

SRA (terminating at 1/2 nm) . . . . 250 ft

VOR, NDB, VDF (QDM or QGH) . . . . 300 ft

SRA (terminating at 2 nm) . . . . 350 ft

Calculation of DH for a Precision Approach, or MDH for a Non-Precision Approach

1. Take the higher value of OCH or System Minimum.

2. For a *Precision* Approach (ILS), **add 50 ft** Altimeter Position Error Correction (PEC) (50 ft is considered adequate for light aircraft). The correction has already been included for Non-Precision Approaches.

This, then, gives the DH/MDH for a pilot with an Instrument Rating (and is listed in UK AIP RAC 4-3-9 to -20).

3. An IMC-Rated Pilot must **add a further 200 ft** and then take the greater of this figure and the **absolute minima** of 500 ft for a Precision Approach and 600 ft for a Non-Precision Approach.

Example 1: Bristol Rwy 27 ILS/DME OCH for Category A is 176. What is the DH for an IMC-Rated Pilot?

1. Greater of OCH 176 and ILS System Minimum 200 ft is **200 ft** (i.e. the System Minimum is more limiting than any obstacles).

2. For ILS, add Altimeter PEC 50 ft to give **250 ft** (as in AIP RAC for an Instrument Rating).

3. For IMC Rating only, add 200 ft, to give 450 ft; compare with the IMC Rating absolute minimum for an ILS of 500 ft. The greater is **500 ft DH.**

It is suggested that a pilot who has not flown instrument approaches within the few previous weeks should deliberately avoid making an approach in bad weather. If, however, such an approach is unavoidable, then a further addition of at least 100 ft to the calculated DH is advisable.

Example 2: Blackpool NDB Rwy 10 OCH is 500 ft. What is the MDH for an IMC-Rated Pilot?

1. Greater of OCH 500 and NDB System Minimum 300 ft is **500 ft** (i.e. there *are* significant obstacles).

2. This is a Non-Precision Approach, so there is no requirement to add the Altimeter PEC. (The 500 ft calculated so far is listed in AIP RAC for a pilot with an Instrument Rating.)

3. For an IMC Rating only, add 200 ft, to give 700 ft: compare with the IMC absolute minimum for a Non-Precision Approach of 600 ft. The greater is **700 ft MDH.**

It is perhaps easier to calculate DH or MDH using a Table, such as the one illustrated in the next figure, since there is quite a bit to remember.

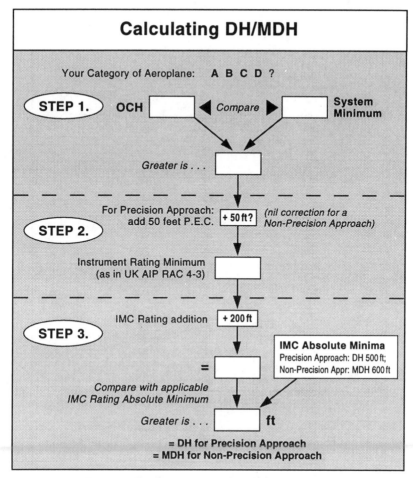

Fig.19-5. Tabular Form of calculating DH/MDH.

SOME NOTES ON MINIMA IN PUBLICATIONS

The **Obstacle Clearance Heights (OCH)** can be found:
- on *Jeppesen* and *Aerad* approach plates;
- UK AIP RAC 4-3-9 to -20 for Category A aeroplanes, and in RAC 4-2 for all categories;
- on CAA Instrument Approach Charts; and
- in Pooley's Flight Guide for Category A aeroplanes only.

Missed Approach Points are shown on the approach charts.

Jeppesen, Pooley's Flight Guide and AIP RAC 4-3-9/-20 also give DH/MDH and the required RVR/visibility for each procedure. Aerad and RAC 4-3 minima are calculated in the manner described above, except that *Aerad* does not include the Altimeter correction in the DH. The *Jeppesen* method for calculating minima is acceptable if the Altimeter correction to the DH is added. *Pooley's Flight Guide* minima are for IMC-Rated Pilots.

Fig.19-6. A typical Approach Plate (Jeppesen excerpt, East Midlands Rwy 09 ILS).

The pilot planning to use this procedure for a *straight-in* landing may descend to his calculated Decision Height, which is the latest point at which he must become visual for the approach to be continued. The pilot planning to use this procedure for a *circle-to-land* approach onto Runway 27 must not descend in instrument conditions below his calculated circle-to-land minimum.

Air Traffic Services may advise Instrument Rating Minima

In conditions where the visibility is 1500 metres or less, or the cloud ceiling at or below the Visual Manoeuvring Height, the Aerodrome Traffic services in the UK will advise the Pilots of non-public transport flights of the recommended minima for approach and landing. These minima apply only to Pilots with Instrument Ratings flying in Category A aeroplanes. Pilots with an **IMC Rating** must make further additions to the advised height, as previously discussed. This is an **advisory** service only by ATS, and does not absolve the Pilot from determining his own minima, but merely serves as a reminder.

AERODROMES WITHOUT INSTRUMENT APPROACH PROCEDURES

Instrument approaches are to be made only using published Instrument Approach Procedures. If desiring to land at an aerodrome for which there is no *published* IAP, then two possibilities are:

- Descend en route to the Minimum Safe Altitude (allowing 1000 ft clearance above the highest obstacle within 5 nm of track) and not contravening any Low Flying Rules. If the aeroplane encounters visual conditions, then the flight can proceed visually to the destination aerodrome; or

- use a published Instrument Approach Procedure at a nearby aerodrome to become visual, and then proceed visually to the destination aerodrome.

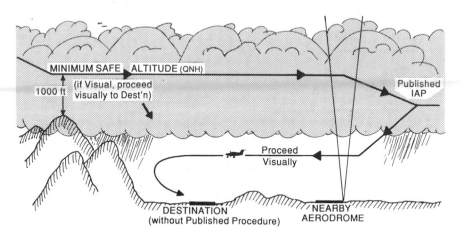

Fig.19-7. Approaching an Aerodrome without a Published Instrument Approach Procedure.

☐ Now complete **Exercises 19 – Instrument Minima**.

20

VISUAL MANOEUVRING

If the final approach direction of an Instrument Procedure does **not** align the aeroplane within +/−30° of the landing runway, or position it suitably so that a reasonable flight path to the touchdown point can be achieved comfortably, then it is technically no longer a *straight-in* procedure, and significant **visual manoeuvring** (probably involving at least a partial circuit) will be required to align the aeroplane with the landing runway.

Visual manoeuvring is also known as *circling*, or as a *circle-to-land* manoeuvre, and these terms are used to describe the **visual** phase of flight after completing an Instrument Approach, with the aim of manoeuvring an aircraft into position for a landing on a runway which is not suitably located for a straight-in approach.

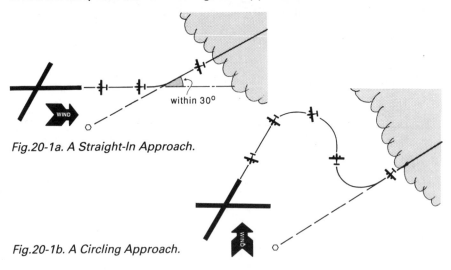

Fig.20-1a. A Straight-In Approach.

Fig.20-1b. A Circling Approach.

The most common use of Visual Manoeuvring in the UK is after becoming visual at or above the *circle-to-land* minimum following an instrument approach based on an out-of-wind runway, and then manoeuvring visually for a landing on the into-wind runway, e.g. using a Runway 27 ILS to become visual, followed by a circling approach and landing on Runway 09.

The flight path that the Pilot chooses to fly will vary depending upon the situation — for instance, he might choose to circle in a direction that avoids high terrain, low cloud, a heavy shower, etc.

A circling approach is a more difficult manoeuvre than a straight-in approach, because it often involves close-in manoeuvring under a low cloud base and in rain or poor visibility. It will require **precise attitude flying** by the Pilot, with close attention paid to maintaining height, whilst flying a suitable flight path to position the aeroplane for a landing and **keeping a very good lookout**.

VISUAL
At or Above
Minimum

Fig.20-2. Typical Manoeuvring (Circling) after becoming Visual following an Instrument Approach.

The **circle-to-land MDH** for a particular approach procedure that is aligned with a runway will generally be higher than the **straight-in DH**.

THE VISUAL CIRCLING MANOEUVRE

If the Pilot becomes visual at or above the Minimum Descent Height for the Instrument Approach, then he should maintain this height until within the Circling Area. When within the Circling Area, and remaining visual, the Pilot may fly at the **Visual Manoeuvring Obstacle Clearance Height** (which at some aerodromes is lower than the MDH for the Instrument Approach). The Visual Manoeuvring Obstacle Clearance Height may be referred to as the Visual Manoeuvring OCH, the Circling Height, or the Visual Manoeuvring Height **VMH**.

A circling approach is a **visual** flight manoeuvre, and the Pilot **must** remain visual throughout, otherwise a Missed Approach is to be carried out.

Each circling situation is different because of variables such as:
• the final approach direction of the Instrument Approach;
• the runway layout;
• **wind direction and speed**, and the selected runway for landing;
• local terrain;
• meteorological conditions (especially **cloud base** and **visibility**).

For instance, wind direction and strength usually determine which runway should be used for landing. Cloud base usually determines what circuit height (at or above Visual Manoeuvring OCH) is flown. If there is a fog bank on one side of the aerodrome, then a circling approach on the other side of the aerodrome in good visibility is preferable, irrespective of whether a left or right circuit is involved.

All things being equal, however, it is advisable to follow the normal circuit pattern, which at most aerodromes is left-handed to provide the Captain in the left seat with a good view of the runway, and at the usual 1000 ft AAL. If the cloud is lower, however, then a circling approach is legal at heights down to the Visual Manoeuvring OCH.

The term *circling* does **not** imply that the visual manoeuvring should follow a circular pattern, but rather that the circuit pattern should be adjusted to suit the conditions. As a general rule, however, **Circling should be as close to a normal circuit as conditions allow**. This helps other traffic in the circuit, as well as ATC, and keeps things as standard as possible for the Pilot.

If, for instance, the Pilot becomes visual at 2000 ft AAL on the Instrument Approach, well above the permitted minimum, then he should continue descent to normal circuit height and fly a normal circuit, rather than descend to the Visual Manoeuvring Obstacle Clearance Height which may be as low as 400 ft AAL. Whilst training, however, your Instructor may ask you to fly a circuit assuming a particular cloud base even though *actual* conditions do not require it.

Good attitude control is essential in the circling manoeuvre, with **bank angle** limited to 20° or Rate 1 (maximum 30°), **altitude maintained** at or above Visual Manoeuvring Obstacle Clearance Height, and **airspeed** as desired. The aeroplane must also be configured for landing (with the landing gear and flaps extended as required), and all checks completed, before the landing is made.

A well-flown circling approach is the sign of a competent Pilot.

Descent Below the Visual Manoeuvring Height

Descent below the Visual Manoeuvring Obstacle Clearance Height should not be made until:

- visual reference with the aerodrome environment is established and maintained;
- the landing threshold is in sight; and
- the required obstacle clearance can be maintained on approach and the aeroplane is in a position to carry out a landing.

The most appropriate time to commence the descent from the Visual Manoeuvring OCH for a landing is when the normal landing descent profile is intercepted. The lower the Circling Height, the closer this will be to the aerodrome. If, for instance, the aeroplane is circling at the lowest permissible Visual Manoeuvring OCH at an aerodrome with no obstacles (which is 400 ft AAL), the landing descent would not be commenced until on final. For higher Visual Manoeuvring OCHs, the descent for a landing may be commenced earlier to avoid unnecessarily high descent rates on final.

Fig.20-3. Achieve a Normal Landing Profile.

Pilot Initiative and Judgement is Required

It is impossible to design a single procedure that will cater for all situations – this is an area for **Pilot judgement and decision**. Because the circling manoeuvre may have to be carried out in poor conditions, the Pilot must be able to **make firm decisions fairly quickly**. This ability will come with experience and with good planning. The basic assumption in circling approaches is that, after initial visual contact, the **runway environment** (i.e. the runway, the runway threshold or approach lighting aids, or other markings identifiable with the runway) should be kept in sight whilst manoeuvring in the circuit at or above the Visual Manoeuvring Height.

The **actual height** to be flown whilst manoeuvring in the Circling Area will be governed by the **Visual Manoeuvring Obstacle Clearance Height** and the **cloud ceiling**. It is unusual for a cloud base to be dead flat; normally it is rather *furry* or *lumpy,* and fluctuates in height. For this reason, it is recommended that a gap of at least 200 ft exist between the aeroplane (flying at Visual Manoeuvring Height or higher) and the estimated cloud base. This gap is impossible to measure accurately of course, so it requires **realistic estimation by the Pilot** who must:

• remain visual; and

• not descend below the Visual Manoeuvring Obstacle Clearance Height until in a position for a safe descent for landing.

If, for example, the Visual Manoeuvring OCH published for a particular aerodrome is 550 ft AAL, then the Pilot, seeing a forecast cloud base of 800 ft AAL, knows that he will probably be operating in marginal conditions where 200 ft above the Circling OCH may or may not exist. He **must not** circle at a lower height than the Visual Manoeuvring OCH, no matter what the cloud does. His way out, of course, is a Missed Approach.

Another consideration (besides cloud base) is **visibility** and, whilst not laid down in the AIP, it is recommended that **to continue a circling approach there should be a visibility of at least 2000 metres,** assuming a circuit speed of 100 kt or less. (Faster aeroplanes with a greater turning radius and requiring more manoeuvring area may need greater visibility – about 200 metres for each additional 10 kt).

The precise visibility is impossible for the Pilot to measure in flight, but he can estimate it, and he must feel confident and comfortable that sufficient visibility exists for safe visual manoeuvring. Ideally, he will keep the runway in sight at all times.

If at any time during the visual manoeuvring for a circling approach the Pilot feels uncomfortable for any reason (such as a lowering cloud base, decreasing visibility, heavy rain or hail, turbulence, windshear, or if he loses visual contact, etc.), then he should execute a Missed Approach.

THE VISUAL MANOEUVRING (CIRCLING) AREA

The Visual Manoeuvring Area (or Circling Area) is the area around an aerodrome in which **Obstacle Clearance** has been considered by the *State Authority* (which in the UK is the CAA) for aircraft having to manoeuvre visually before landing. To avoid penalising slower and more manoeuvrable aircraft (which require less manoeuvring area than faster aeroplanes), different aircraft categories based on Maximum Speed for Circling have been devised.

Most training aeroplanes have a Maximum Speed for Circling of less than 100 kt (known as Category A for Visual Manoeuvring purposes), and the Circling Area considered for Obstacle Clearance under the current *ICAO PANS-OPS* requirements for such aeroplanes is 1.68 nm radii from the runway thresholds.

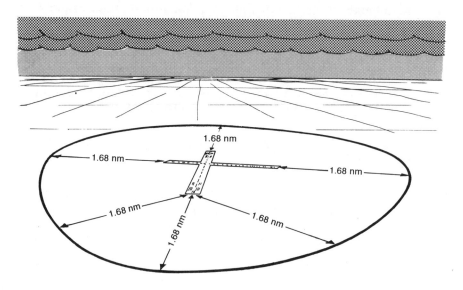

Fig.20-4. The Visual Manoeuvring Area for Category A Aeroplanes (less than 100 kt).

NOTE: For aeroplanes with a Maximum Speed for Circling between 100–135 kt, the radii are increased to 2.66 nm.

Obstacle Clearance in the Visual Manoeuvring (Circling) Area

Once the *State Authority* has established its Circling Area, obstacles within this area are surveyed and a **safety margin** added to ensure clearance from these obstacles. A Visual Manoeuvring (Circling) Obstacle Clearance Height, VM(C) OCH, is then determined for each category of aircraft.

For Category A aeroplanes, the circling area is radius 1.68 nm and maximum circling speed 100 kt – AIP RAC 4-1-5. The safety margin for visual manoeuvring in the Circling Area is a minimum of 300 ft above obstacles.

- If, for instance, the highest obstacle in the circling area is a tower 290 ft AAL, then the Visual Manoeuvring Obstacle Clearance Height, VM(C) OCH, is (290 + 300 =) 590 ft AAL.
- If there are **no specific obstacles,** then 100 feet is allowed for the growth of trees, etc., and the 300-ft safety margin added to this to give a **lowest permissible VM(C) OCH** at any aerodrome of (100 + 300 =) **400 ft AAL.**

Fig.20.5. Calculation by the State Authority of Visual Manoeuvring OCH.

Where to Find the Visual Manoeuvring Obstacle Clearance Height

The Visual Manoeuvring OCH (or Circling OCH) for each aerodrome is published in AIP RAC 4-2.

	CAMBRIDGE - General		
1	**Minimum Sector Altitudes** (ft):	Northeast: **1800**	Southeast: **1800**
2	Visual Manoeuvring (Circling) **OCH** by Aircraft Category (ft aal):	A/B: 600	

Fig.20-6. The Visual Manoeuvring OCH for Circling at Cambridge.

Cambridge obviously has a significant obstacle in its circling area raising its Circling OCH to 600 ft AAL for Category A aircraft, whereas Alderney (below) does not, since its Circling Height is the lowest permitted, i.e. 400 ft AAL.

	ALDERNEY - General		
1	**Minimum Sector Altitudes** (ft):	Northeast: **2000**	Southeast: **2000**
2	Visual Manoeuvring (Circling) **OCH** by Aircraft Category (ft aal):	A: 400	

Fig.20-7. The Visual Manoeuvring OCH for Circling at Alderney.

The 'Visual Manoeuvring OCH' may be lower than the circling 'Minimum Descent Height' for the Instrument Approach Procedure.

The Visual Manoeuvring OCH (the lowest height permitted for manoeuvring in the Circling Area to achieve adequate obstacle clearance) should not be confused with the Minimum Descent Height MDH for the Instrument Approach itself when used prior to a *circle-to-land* manoeuvre. The two are arrived at using different criteria:

1. The **Instrument Approach MDH** provides safe obstacle clearance along the Instrument Approach path and also throughout the Missed Approach;

2. The **Visual Manoeuvring OCH** provides safe obstacle clearance in the Circling Area around the aerodrome.

It is possible that the Visual Manoeuvring Obstacle Clearance Height is less than the appropriate *circle-to-land* Minimum Descent Height for the Instrument Approach procedure. In such cases, once the Pilot is indeed visual and within the Circling Area around the aerodrome, it is permissible to descend to the Visual Manoeuvring Obstacle Clearance Height if necessary. This situation could arise if there is a significant obstacle beneath the Instrument Approach Obstacle Clearance Plane, but lying outside the Visual Manoeuvring (Circling) Area.

Fig.20-8. Visual Manoeuvring OCH at Some Aerodromes is less than MDH for the Instrument Approach.

NOTE: It is also possible that Visual Manoeuvring OCH is the same as the *circling* MDH, but it will **never** be greater, since this would lead to the illogical procedure of becoming visual on the Instrument Approach, and then having to climb to a greater Circling Height.

Since Visual Manoeuvring Obstacle Clearance Height and the Instrument Approach *circling* MDH may differ, the Pilot, therefore, must be very clear in his mind (even before commencing the Instrument Approach) which minimum height applies to which phase of the approach:

- Minimum Descent Height (MDH) applies to the Instrument Approach; and

- Visual Manoeuvring OCH applies once within the Circling Area.

SECTORISED VISUAL MANOEUVRING (CIRCLING) AREAS

The lower the Visual Manoeuvring Obstacle Clearance Height, the more accessible the aerodrome is in poor weather, since it will allow a pilot to operate beneath a lower cloud base. In an attempt to achieve lower Circling Heights, the State Authority can exclude from the Circling Area a sector that contains a particularly high and restrictive obstacle, provided that it lies outside the Final Approach and Missed Approach areas.

If the State Authority does exercise this option, and thereby lowers the Visual Manoeuvring OCH, then the pilot is **prohibited** from circling at this lowered height within the excluded sector that contains the obstacle(s).

For instance, an obstacle 800 ft AAL in the normal Circling Area requires a Visual Manoeuvring Height of (800 + 300 =) 1100 ft AAL, which operationally is very restrictive. By removing a sector that contains this obstacle from the permissible circling area, the State Authority may lower the Visual Manoeuvring Obstacle Clearance Height appropriately, in the case illustrated below to (150 + 300 =) 450 ft AAL.

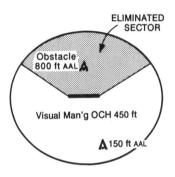

Fig.20-9. A Sectorised Circling Area.

A typical example of the advantages to be obtained using a sectorised Circling Area is Blackpool.

BLACKPOOL - General
1   **Minimum Sector Altitudes** (ft):   Northeast: **2900**   Southeast: **3500**
Note: Subject to ATC approval, aircraft may descend to not below **2000** ft after passing 15 DME
2   **Visual Manoeuvring (Circling) OCH** by Aircraft Category (ft aal):   A: 550
Sectorized VM(C) OCH for aircraft south of Runway 10/28 :   A: 400
3   **Holding Procedure:**
1-minute race-track pattern approaching NDB(L) BPL on track 098° MAG turning right at the facil
4   **Notes:**
4.1   Reversal Procedures to Runway 28: During reversal procedures to Runway 28 using DME aircra
4.2   Lowest altitude to start procedure **2000** ft after holding or missed approach.

Fig.20-10. Extract for Blackpool in AIP RAC 4-2.

Obviously, if the cloud base at Blackpool is as low as 600 ft, a Pilot is better off confining his manoeuvring to that part of the Circling Area south of Runway 10/28, where the Visual Manoeuvring Obstacle Clearance Height is only 400 ft AAL. If he operates in the area to the north of this runway, the Visual Manoeuvring OCH becomes 550 ft AAL.

Fig.20-11. Sectorised Circling Area at Blackpool.

THE MISSED APPROACH PROCEDURE WHEN CIRCLING

If the Pilot loses visual reference when circling to land after an Instrument Approach, then the Missed Approach procedure for that particular Instrument Approach should be followed.

The aeroplane may be in a slightly awkward position for a Missed Approach depending upon its position in the circuit, however it is expected that the Pilot will make an initial climbing turn towards the landing runway and overhead the aerodrome where he will continue climbing on the published Missed Approach track to the required altitude. This should keep the aeroplane clear of obstacles, first of all in the Circling Area, and then in the Missed Approach area.

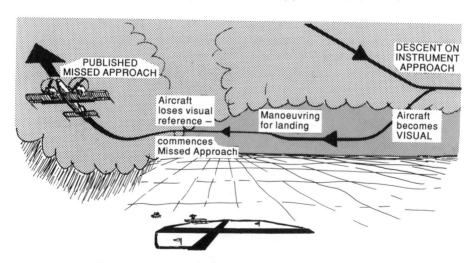

Fig.20-12. Making a Missed Approach When Circling.

Since the Circling Manoeuvre may be accomplished in more than one direction, and since the aeroplane could be anywhere in the circuit when visual reference is lost, the Pilot will have to devise and follow a suitable flight path to establish the aeroplane on the prescribed Missed Approach track. This would depend upon the aeroplane's position in the Circling Manoeuvre at the time visual reference is lost and the climb-away commenced, and also on the nature of the Missed Approach track.

When the Pilot decides to execute a Missed Approach, he must fly the aeroplane according to the procedure laid down in the aeroplane's Flight Manual – transitioning smoothly to a climb-away in a positive manner with prompt and precise attitude and power changes. A typical Missed Approach procedure may be:

- adopt the Missed Approach **attitude** and simultaneously apply go-around **power**;
- assume the Missed Approach **configuration** (gear up when a positive climb is achieved, flaps as required).

As soon as comfortably established in the climb (there need be no rush!), the Pilot should turn towards the runway and the Missed Approach track. **Attitude Flying** will require most of the Pilot's attention, so at least from the time he commences the Circling Manoeuvre he should have in mind:

- an Initial Heading to turn onto if he loses visual contact;
- the Missed Approach Track; and
- the Missed Approach Altitude.

When convenient, and once comfortably established in the climb-away, the Pilot should advise ATC that he has commenced a Missed Approach. Remember that any **altitude** given by ATC at this time (e.g. *'climb to three thousand'*) will be based on QNH (height AMSL). If QFE has been set in the altimeter subscale, it should be reset to QNH.

Remember the order of importance:

- aviate (fly the aeroplane!);
- navigate (head it towards where you have to go); and, finally,
- communicate (advise ATC).

CIRCLING AT AN AERODROME WHICH HAS NO APPROACH

If arriving at an aerodrome which does not have a published Instrument Approach Procedure, the pilot should, where possible, become visual well away from the aerodrome to allow time for orientation and planning the visual circuit. The options available to achieve this are:

1a. Descend in Visual Meteorological Conditions (VMC) and with visual contact with the ground, and then fly to the destination in compliance with the Visual Flight Rules and the Minimum Height Rule; *or*

1b. Descend through cloud using a published Instrument Approach Procedure at a nearby aerodrome, and transit visually to the destination aerodrome (in accordance with the Visual Flight Rules and the Minimum Height Rule). *If either of these options is not available:*

2. Obtain an accurate en route fix and descend to not lower than 1000 ft above the highest obstacle within 5 nm of the aircraft and, once visual, proceed visually to the destination aerodrome (in accordance with the Visual Flight Rules and the Minimum Height Rule).

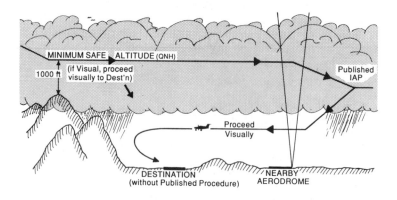

Fig.20-13. Arriving at a Destination Aerodrome which does NOT have a Published Instrument Approach.

Having become visual, the pilot needs to remain visual for the transit to the destination aerodrome, and for the circuit and landing.

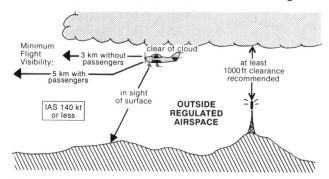

Fig.20-14. Requirements for a typical Visual Private Flight.

In the **Circling Area** around an aerodrome, the minimum cloud ceiling recommended is the higher of:
- 600 ft above the highest obstacle within 4 nm of the aerodrome; or
- 800 ft Above Aerodrome Level (AAL).

Fig.20-15. *Visual Criteria in the Circuit of an Aerodrome.*

NOTE: Information on obstacles within 4 nm of an aerodrome may be found in UK AIP AGA 2 and 3-4.

For **more experienced pilots** (for example those with at least 100 hours as pilot-in-command) flying circuits at aerodromes with which they are familiar, the minimum cloud ceiling may be reduced to allow only 400 ft above the highest obstacle within a 4-nm radius of the aerodrome. Flying a circuit at a low level requires a lot of concentration and makes it more difficult for a pilot to cope with problems such as an unexpected forced landing, or a circuit and landing with one or more engines inoperative.

READ THE UK AERONAUTICAL INFORMATION PUBLICATION.

It is recommended that you now read those sections of AIP RAC 4-1 & 4-2 related to Visual Manoeuvring (Circling).

A Warning Contained in the AIP:

Pilots should never commence or continue an Instrument Approach when:
- **cloud ceiling** is reported to be at or below their calculated DH; or the
- reported **RVR/Visibility** is below minimum required (1800 m, IMC-Rating).

Therefore a flight should not be planned to terminate in conditions below the relevant minima. Should the destination weather deteriorate below minima after departure, a diversion to a suitable planned Alternate should be made forthwith (AIP RAC 3-1 and 4-3).

SPECIAL VFR

The IMC Rating (Aeroplanes) entitles holders to be Pilot-In-Command of an aeroplane, provided:
(i) they do not fly on a Special VFR (SVFR) flight in a Control Zone in a flight visibility less than 3 km; and
(ii) they do not act as such when the aeroplane is taking off or landing at any place if the flight visibility below cloud is less than 1800 m.

☐ Now complete **Exercises 20 – Visual Manoeuvring.**

Intentionally Blank

4

NIGHT FLYING

21

AERODROME LIGHTING

The main aeronautical lighting provided at an aerodrome to assist a Pilot to manoeuvre his aeroplane at night consists of:
- taxiway lighting;
- runway lighting;
- approach lighting; and
- Visual Approach Slope Indicators (VASI).

Particulars of aerodrome lighting are shown in the Aeronautical Information Publication UK AIP AGA 2, and on Landing and Approach charts.

TAXIWAY LIGHTS

Taxiways are lit in one of two ways for the guidance of Pilots with either:
- one line of **centreline green** taxiway lights; or
- two lines of taxiway **blue edge** lights.

At some aerodromes, there is a mixture on the two types, centreline green on some taxiways, and blue edge on others.

At certain points on the taxiway, there may be taxiway **red stop bars**, to indicate the position where an aeroplane should hold — for instance, before entering an active runway.

Fig.21-1. Taxiway Lighting.

RUNWAY LIGHTS

Runway edge lighting is **white**. The runway edge lights may be directional (i.e. visible only to aeroplanes aligned with the runway), or they may be visible equally in all directions. Some runway lights are flush with the surface, and others are elevated (indicated in AIP AGA by the word *elev*). If *paraffin flares* only are available (rather than electrical lighting), this will be indicated in AGA by the word *goosenecks.*

The approach threshold of the runway will have **green threshold lights** across its width if the lights are of the flush type – if they are of the elevated type, the central area of the approach threshold may be left clear. Sometimes there are wingbars outboard of the runway edge lights for use in poor visibility or to mark a displaced threshold.

At the far end of the runway there will be **red runway end lighting**

Fig.21-2. Basic Runway Lighting at Night.

On certain **instrument runways** (i.e. runways for which there is a published instrument approach), the colour of the runway edge lighting over the *caution zone,* which is the last 600 metres, may be yellow. This is an indication to a Pilot landing in very poor visibility conditions (far less than that allowed for an IMC-Rated Pilot), that the aeroplane on its landing run is approaching the stopping end of the runway.

Precision Approach runways at major aerodromes may have flush **runway centreline lights** that are white, but becoming red at the stopping end of the runway. There may also be **touchdown zone lighting**, which consists of rows of white lights on either side of the runway during its first 900 metres.

APPROACH LIGHTING

At many major aerodromes, Approach Lighting extends out from the approach end of the runway, to well beyond the physical boundaries of the runway. It consists of extended centreline lighting, with up to three crossbars sited at 300 metre intervals back along the approach path from the threshold. If more crossbars are used, they may be sited at 150 metre instead of 300 metre intervals.

The Approach Lighting, because of its extent, may have components outside the boundaries of the aerodrome, possibly in forested or even built-up areas. Approach Lights do **not** mark the boundaries of a suitable landing area – they simply act as a lead-in to a runway.

To a Pilot making an approach, the Approach Lighting provides a visual indication of how well the aeroplane is aligned with the extended runway centreline, as well as helping in estimating the distance the aeroplane has to fly to touchdown. They are very useful to a Pilot who has become *visual* during the latter stages of an instrument approach, especially in conditions of low visibility. In situations where no visible horizon exists, they can assist the Pilot to judge bank angle visually.

Advanced Precision Approach runways may have additional red approach lights, but these need not concern an IMC-Rated Pilot.

Fig.21-3. Approaching an Instrument Runway.

VISUAL APPROACH SLOPE INDICATORS (VASI or VASIS)

In conditions of poor visibility and at night, when the runway environment and the natural horizon may not be clearly visible, it is often difficult for a Pilot to judge the correct approach path of the aeroplane towards the touchdown zone of the runway. A number of very effective devices have been invented to assist a Pilot in this situation.

The Typical Two Bar VASI has two pairs of wingbars extending outboard of the runway, usually at 150 metres and 300 metres from the approach threshold. It is sometimes known as the *red/white* system, since the colours seen by the Pilot tell him if he is right on slope, or too high or too low. He will see:

• all bars white if high on approach;

• the near bars white and the far bars red if right on slope; and

• all bars red if low on slope.

LEGEND ▨ Red Bar Light ☐ White Bar Light

Fig.21-4. Perspectives on Approach using a Two Bar VASI.

During the approach, the aeroplane should be maintained on a slope within the white sector of the near bars and the red sector of the far bars. If the aeroplane flies above or below the correct slope, the lights will change colour, there being a pink transition stage between red and white.

The plane of the VASI approach slope provides obstacle clearance in an arc 10° left or right of the extended centreline out to a distance of 4 nm from the runway threshold. Before using VASI information, therefore, the aeroplane should be within this arc, and preferably aligned with the extended runway centreline.

Fig.21-5. The Extent of Useful VASI Information.

In general, therefore, an approach descent using VASI should not be initiated until the aeroplane is visually aligned with the extended runway centreline. On instrument approaches, once the VASI comes into view the Pilot may use it to adjust his approach path.

There are some other operational considerations to be borne in mind when using the red/white VASI. At maximum range, the white bars may become visible before the red bars, because of the nature of red and white light. In haze or smog, or in certain other conditions, the white lights may have a yellowish tinge about them. When extremely low on slope, the two wingbars (all lights red) may appear to merge into one red bar – at close range to the threshold this would indicate a critical situation with respect to obstacle clearance, and the Pilot should take urgent action.

Some VASI systems use a reduced number of lights, in which case they may be known as an *Abbreviated* VASI or *AVASI.*

At some aerodromes there is a Low Intensity Two Colour Approach Slope System (*LITAS*), which is similar to the VASI, but is composed of lower intensity indicators installed **singly** in the upwind and down wind VASI wingbar positions, usually on the left hand side of the runway only. It is interpreted in the same way as the Two Bar VASI.

The Three Bar VASI has an extra far wingbar added to assist the Pilots of long-bodied aeroplanes such as the Boeing 747 or the Airbus A300. The approach slope guidance given by any VASI depends on the position of the Pilot's eyes. Since the wheels of a long-bodied aeroplane will be much further below the Pilot's eyes, it is essential that his eyes follow a parallel but higher slope to ensure adequate clearance over the runway threshold. An additional wingbar further into the runway makes this possible.

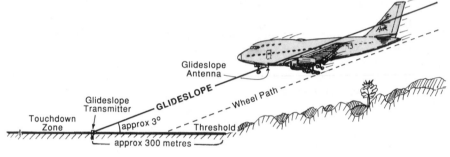

Fig.21-6. Wheel Clearance over the Threshold.

Pilots of such aeroplanes should use the second and third wingbars, and ignore the first. When the Pilot's eyes are positioned on the correct slope for a long-bodied aeroplane, he will see the top bar red, the middle bar white (and ignore the lower bar which is also white).

Fig.21-7. The Pilot of Long-Bodied Aeroplane using the Three Bar VASI.

Pilots of smaller aeroplanes should refer to only the two nearer wingbars, and ignore the further 'long-bodied' wingbar. On slope, the indications should be (top bar red and ignored), middle bar red and lower bar white.

Fig.21-8. The Pilot of a Smaller Aeroplane using the Three Bar VASI.

The Precision Approach Path Indicator (PAPI) is a development of the VASI, and also uses *red/white* signals for guidance in maintaining the correct approach angle, but the lights are arranged differently and their indications must be interpreted differently. PAPI has a single wingbar, which will consist of four light units on one or both sides of the runway adjacent to the touchdown point. There is no pink transition stage as the lights change from red to white.

If the aeroplane is on slope, the two outer lights of each unit are white and the two inner lights are red. Above slope, the number of white lights increase, and below slope the number of red lights increase.

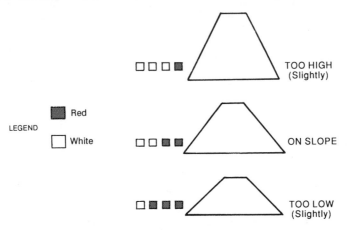

Fig.21-9. Slope Guidance using PAPI.

22

NIGHT FLYING AT AN AERODROME

Night Flying involves a mixture of visual and instrument flying skills. The take-off run at night, for instance, is made with *visual reference* to the runway. Shortly after take-off, however, there may be no visible features at all to be seen, and transferring your attention from outside the cockpit to *the instruments* in the cockpit at or before that time is essential, whereas by day and in good weather conditions your attention can remain outside the cockpit.

ADAPTATION OF THE EYES TO DARKNESS

Your eyes are very important when flying, and they should always be looked after. However, at night there are some special considerations regarding your vision. Since your attention during Night Flying will be both inside and outside the cockpit, care should be taken to ensure that eyes can function at near maximum efficiency. **It takes the eyes some minutes to adapt to a dark environment**, as most of us have experienced when walking into a darkened cinema (late!), and stumbling across other patrons in an attempt to find an empty seat.

The rate at which **Dark Adaptation** of the eyes occurs depends to a large extent upon the contrast between the brightness of light previously experienced, and the degree of darkness of the new environment.

Whilst bright lighting within the previous few minutes has the strongest effect, that experienced for some period within the previous few hours will also have an effect. Bright lighting, therefore, is best avoided prior to Night Flying. Generally, this is difficult to achieve, since flight planning in a well-lit room and pre-flight inspections with a strong torch or on a well-lit tarmac will almost always be necessary. The best that can be achieved in many cases is to dim the cockpit lighting prior to taxying, and to avoid looking at bright lights during those few minutes prior to take-off.

Night Vision can also be affected by the **lack of oxygen**, so ensure that you use oxygen when flying above 10 000 ft AMSL. On a more mundane level, **avoid cigarette smoke in the cockpit at night**, since it will displace oxygen in your blood to some extent, and consequently reduce your Night Vision by an amount comparable to an extra 5000 ft in altitude. In the long term, **a good diet** containing foods with Vitamins A and C can improve your Night Vision.

Since **bright lights will impair your outside vision at night**, it is good airmanship to keep the cockpit lighting at a reasonably low level, but not so low that you cannot see your charts, or find the Fuel Selector.

There are some occasions, however, when bright cockpit lighting can help preserve your vision. This can occur on an instrument flight, for instance, if flying in the vicinity of electrical storms. Nearby lightning flashes can temporarily degrade your dark adaptation and your vision, particularly if it is in contrast to a dim cockpit. Bright lighting in the cockpit can minimise this effect and, although your external vision will not be as good as with dim cockpit lighting, you will avoid being temporarily blinded by the lightning flashes.

Note that **flying near electrical storms is not recommended**. They should be avoided by at least 10 miles and, if you are not an instrument-rated Pilot in a suitably-equipped aeroplane, then possibly you should stay on the ground at night if there are storms around.

PREPARATION FOR NIGHT FLIGHT

Night flying requires careful attention to **pre-flight preparation and planning**. Unlike daylight hours, when weather conditions in the vicinity of the aerodrome are visible, at night the situation is different. Whilst stars might be clearly visible overhead one minute, the next they may be covered unexpectedly by low cloud, which could have a significant effect on flight in the area.

Study the available **weather reports and forecasts**, paying special attention to any item that could affect visibility and your ability to fly at a safe operating height. Some of the main items to consider are:

• cloud base and amount;

• weather – such as rain, snow, fog, mist, etc.;

• temperature/dewpoint relationship – the closer they are, the more likely fog is to form as temperature drops further;

• wind direction and strength – from the point of view of runway choice, the possibility of fog being blown in, and the likelihood of windshear due to the diurnal effect (a light surface wind with a strong wind at height as a result of less vertical mixing).

Check any **special procedures** for night flying at that aerodrome and in the vicinity.

For a cross-country flight, carry the appropriate **aeronautical charts**, and have them prepared for quick use in the cockpit. The greater the pre-flight preparation of the charts, then the lower the in-flight workload.

Note that, if red light is to be used in the cockpit, then red print on the chart will not be easily seen. All lines drawn on the chart should preferably be in heavy black, since even white light in the cockpit will probably be dimmed to ensure that good external night vision is retained. If you are instrument-qualified, carry the Instrument Approach Charts for the expected aerodromes of operation, as well as for any other suitable aerodromes nearby just in case unexpected cloud rolls in.

Note on the chart any **well-lit landmarks** that may be useful, including rotating aerodrome beacons, towns, major roads, railway yards, etc., as well as any **radio navigation aids** available for use. Be especially aware of significant lit or unlit obstructions.

Check personal equipment, including the normal daylight items such as a Navigation Computer, a Plotter (or a Protractor and Scale Rule) and pencils. A definite requirement for night flying is a good **Torch** – essential for your external pre-flight checks, and very useful in the cockpit in case of electrical failure.

EXTERNAL PRE-FLIGHT CHECK

A strong **Torch** is essential for the external pre-flight check to be carried out successfully at night. Not only must the aeroplane be checked, but also the surrounding area should be scanned for obstructions, rough ground and other aircraft. Tie-down ropes and wheel chocks are also more difficult to see (and remove) at night.

Whilst the normal external checks will be made, some additional *night* items must also be included. These should be incorporated into the check if any night flying at all is to occur, even though the take-off might be made in daylight.

A check of the aircraft lights is important. A typical technique during the Pre-Flight Check is to position yourself near (or in) the cockpit and:

- place the **Master Switch** *ON;*
- check the instrument lighting and dimmers (if fitted);
- check the cabin lighting;
- check the Taxi Light, Landing Lights and Anti-Collision Beacon by switching them *ON,* and then *OFF* again so that they do not drain the Battery unnecessarily;
- switch the Navigation Lights *ON,* and leave them *ON* for the walk-around, since it may be impossible to check them from the cockpit.

During the **walk-around**:

- all of the lights and their covers should be checked for cleanliness and serviceability;
- the Navigation Lights should be carefully checked (red-left, green-right, white-tail), as **Navigation Lights are essential for night flight**. **The Taxi Light is essential** for safe taxying, but the Landing Lights, whilst useful, are not essential for flight – good take-offs and landings can be made without them; and

- for a neat external check, a test of any electrical Stall Warning device can be made at this time, before returning to the cockpit and placing the Master Switch back to *OFF* to minimise electrical load on the Battery.

Take great care in the night pre-flight check, focussing the torch on each specific item as it is checked, and also running its beam over the aeroplane as a whole. Ensure that the windscreen is clean and free of dust, dew, frost or ice. If ice or frost is present, check the upper leading edge of the wing (the main lift-producing part of the aeroplane) to ensure that it is also clean. Any ice, frost or other accretion should be removed from the aeroplane (especially from the lift-producing surfaces such as wings and tailplane) prior to flight. Do not forget to remove the Pitot Cover, otherwise there will be no airspeed reading on the ASI.

INTERNAL PRE-FLIGHT CHECK

Carry out the internal pre-flight check. Ensure that spare fuses, if required, are available. Place all items that might be required in flight in a handy position, especially the torch, which should be placed where you can lay your hands on it in complete darkness. Whilst handy, it should still be secure, otherwise it could become a dangerous *missile* in the cockpit during turbulence.

Cabin lighting should be set at a suitable level. Dim the cabin lights so that external vision is satisfactory, and reflection from the canopy minimised, but do not have them so dim that you cannot see the controls or fuel selector. It is unwise to commence night flying immediately after being in a brightly lit environment. Allow your eyes time to adjust to natural night light.

START-UP AT NIGHT

Make sure that you have the **Park Brakes ON** before starting the engine, especially since any movement of the aeroplane will be more difficult to detect than during daylight hours. To avoid draining the Battery, any unnecessary electrical services should be *OFF* until after start-up. Ideally, the Anti-Collision Beacon should be turned *ON* just prior to engine start, to warn any person nearby that the aeroplane is *active.*

Keep an extremely good **Look Out** before starting the engine – a spinning propeller is deadly, and may be difficult to see at night. With dim cabin lights, an open window and a loud warning that you are about to start the engine – **'CLEAR PROPELLER'** – and the flashing of the Taxi Lights or Landings Lights several times, the risk will be minimised.

Once the engine is running, check outside to make sure that the aeroplane is not moving. The **Alternator**/Generator should be checked to ensure that it is functioning correctly, with the Ammeter showing a positive reading after the start-up. Adjust the engine rpm if necessary to achieve a suitable charging rate. If the Anti-Collision Beacon was *OFF* for the start-up, it should now be turned on for added safety. **Adjust the cockpit lighting** to assist your eyes adapt to the darkness outside.

TAXYING AT NIGHT

The responsibility for all movement of the aeroplane, on the ground and in the air, lies with the Pilot. Take advantage of any assistance provided by a **Marshaller**, but remember that **you carry the final responsibility**. Use the Taxi Light, but *avoid blinding* the Marshaller or Pilots in other aeroplanes, if possible. The Taxi Light not only assists you to see obstructions and avoid them, it also makes it more obvious to other people that the aircraft is moving, or about to.

Taxi slowly and carefully. Taxying at night requires additional attention because:

- Distance at night is very deceptive – stationary lights may appear to be closer than what they really are.

- Speed at night is very deceptive, and there is almost always a tendency to taxi too fast. Consciously check taxi speed by looking at the wingtip area where reflected light off surface objects will help you to judge speed, and slow down if necessary.

- Other aircraft and any obstacles will be less visible at night. An aeroplane ahead on the taxiway may be showing just a single white tail-light that can be easily lost in the multitude of other lights. So, **keep a good Look Out**.

Follow taxi guide lines or lights. Taxiway lighting will be either two lines of *Sideline Blue* along the taxiway edges, or one line of *Centreline Green*. White taxi guide lines may be marked on hard surfaces, and will be visible in the Taxi Light. Stay in the centre of the taxiway to preserve wingtip clearance from obstacles. The ground reflection of the wingtip navigation lights, especially on a high-wing aeroplane, are useful in judging the clearance between the wingtips and any obstacles at the side of the taxiway.

If there is any doubt about your taxi path, slow down or stop. If you stop, set the Park Brakes *ON*. In an extreme situation, say on a flooded or very rough taxiway, it may be advisable to even stop the engine, seek assistance, or check the path ahead on foot. The Landing Lights may be used to provide a better view ahead, but they will draw more power, and (depending upon the aeroplane) their continuous use on the ground may not be advisable.

Pay attention to the welfare of other Pilots. Some taxiways run parallel to the runway, so avoid shining your bright lights into the eyes of a Pilot taking-off or landing, or taxying, either by switching them off, or positioning the aeroplane conveniently. Avoid looking into the Landing Lights of other aircraft yourself, since this could seriously degrade your Night Vision.

Following start-up and prior to take-off, all of the vital radio-navigation equipment should be checked for correct functioning. This includes VHF-COM, VHF-NAV, DME, ADF/RMI, Marker Lights and Transponder. The Altimeter should be checked for the correct subscale setting — check QFE and QNH give a sensible value of airfield elevation between both readings.

During the taxying run, the instruments should be checked.

Turning left:
- DI/RMI/Compass decreasing;
- ADF/RMI tracking;
- Turn Coordinator shows left turn;
- Balance Ball shows skidding right;
- AI steady.

Turning right:
- DI/RMI/Compass increasing;
- ADF/RMI tracking;
- Turn Coordinator shows right turn;
- Balance Ball shows skidding left;
- AI steady.

At the Holding Point

The holding point or holding bay may have special lights or markings. **Do not intrude upon the runway** until you are **ready**, you have a **clearance** (if appropriate), and the runway and its approaches are **clear of other possibly conflicting aircraft**.

Whilst completing the pre-take-off checks at the holding position, ensure that your Taxi and/or Landing Lights do not blind other Pilots. Ensure that the **Park Brakes** are *ON* – an aeroplane can easily move during the power check, and at night there are few visual cues to alert the Pilot. During the pre-take-off checks, do not have the cabin lighting so bright that it impairs your night vision. If bright cabin lighting is not desired, then the torch can be used.

Pay special attention to the **fuel selection**, since the Fuel Selector may be in a poorly lit area. Ensure that any item required in flight is in a handy position.

Although probably included in the normal daylight Pre-Take-Off Check, checking the **Direction Indicator** for alignment with the Magnetic Compass whilst the aeroplane is stationary is especially important at night, since it will be used for heading guidance, both in the circuit area and on cross-country flights.

A final check of cabin lighting should be made. Ensure that it is adjusted to a suitable minimum, bright enough to see the major items and instruments in the cockpit, but not so bright as to seriously affect your outside vision.

THE NIGHT TAKE-OFF

When ready to line up for take-off, make any necessary **radio call**, and look carefully for other traffic on the ground and in the air. Clear the approach path to the runway, checking both left and right – '**Clear left, clear right**'. Conditions are often calm at night, making either direction on the runway suitable for operations – so ensure that the approach areas at **both** ends of the runway are clear. The landing lights of an approaching aeroplane are generally quite visible, but often a Pilot will choose to practise a night landing without using them, in which case the aeroplane will be more difficult to see – unless of course it has strobe lights.

Do not waste runway length when lining-up for take-off, especially on a short runway. Line up in the centre of the runway, check that the DI agrees with the runway direction and, with the **Brakes *OFF*** and the feet well away from the brakes and on the rudder pedals, **smoothly apply maximum power**.

Directional control during a night take-off is best achieved with reference to the Runway Edge Lighting, using your peripheral vision, since your eyes should be focussed well ahead of the aeroplane towards the far end of the runway. Runway Centreline Markings may also assist. Avoid overcontrolling during the ground run – keeping straight with rudder, and wings level with ailerons.

The take-off is the same by night as it is by day. Fly the aeroplane away from the ground at the normal lift-off speed, and adopt the normal climb-out attitude. The big difference is that, at night, **visual reference to the ground is quickly lost after lift-off**, and any tendency to settle back onto the ground will not be as easily noticed. As soon as the aeroplane is airborne, therefore, **transfer your attention to the Flight Instruments**.

Try to be on instruments *before* losing the last visual references, which typically will be the last set of Runway Lights, since the first 300-400 ft of the climb-out will probably have to be totally on instruments until you are high enough to regain usable visual references.

Fig.22-1. Transfer to Instruments after Lift-Off, and maintain a Positive Climb.

Maintain the normal take-off Pitch Attitude and the wings level on the Attitude Indicator. Climb power and climb attitude should result in a **positive climb away from the ground**, reflected in a climb rate on the VSI and a gradually increasing Altimeter reading.

The ASI should be checked to ensure that a suitable **airspeed** is being maintained on the climb-out, with minor adjustments being made on the Attitude Indicator as necessary and, once well away from the ground and comfortable in the climb-out, the Direction Indicator can be checked for heading.

In a retractable-undercarriage aeroplane, the gear should not be raised until a positive climb is indicated on both the Altimeter and the VSI. Flaps should not normally be raised until at least 200 ft AAL, and no turns should be made until a safe height is reached. Normally, a steady straight climb is maintained until 500 ft AAL before turning onto the crosswind leg.

With little or no natural external horizon visible, the instruments become very important. If glare from the landing lights is distracting in the cockpit, turn them off when established in the climb. Mist, haze, smoke or cloud will reflect a lot of light.

If an **engine failure** occurs during the climb-out, follow the normal daylight procedures. Lower the nose to the gliding attitude to ensure that a stall does not occur, and use the landing lights to assist in ground recognition. Maintain control of the aeroplane. Ideally, if sufficient height is available, re-start the engine and climb away. Fuel selection may have been the cause (a very serious error to make!).

If a problem occurs during the take-off ground run prior to lift-off, close the throttle and apply the brakes as necessary, keeping straight with rudder.

THE NIGHT CIRCUIT

The circuit pattern at night is usually the same as that by day, except that it is flown mainly by instruments, with reference to the aerodrome lighting to assist in positioning the aeroplane suitably. The normal techniques of **attitude flying** apply. There is often a tendency to overbank at night, so special attention should be paid to bank angle.

Once the aeroplane makes the first turn, the **Runway and Aerodrome Lights** will be easily seen and should be referred to frequently. **Well-lit landmarks** may also be useful for positioning in the circuit.

Allow for drift on the crosswind leg, and level off using normal instrument procedures. Maintain height accurately, and carefully scan outside before making any turn. A good **look out** for other aircraft must be maintained at all times, and the usual radio procedures followed. Recognising the navigation lights of other aeroplanes, and responding with an appropriate heading change, will avoid collisions. This is well-covered in *The Air Pilot's Manual*, Volume 2, Chapter 1.

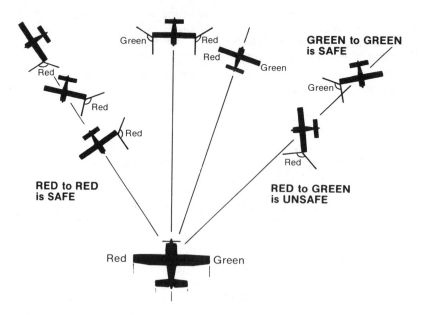

Fig.22-2. Using Navigation Lights to avoid Collision.

Whilst *green to red* is not safe, this will be the situation with two aeroplanes flying parallel on downwind. An especially careful look out will need to be maintained.

Listening to radio transmissions will help you maintain a picture of what else is happening in the circuit.

The **turn from downwind onto base leg** should be made at the normal position, with reference to the Runway Lights and any Approach Lighting. The descent on base leg should be planned so that the **turn onto final** commences at about 600-700 ft AAL, ideally with a 20° bank angle, and certainly no more than 30°.

THE NIGHT APPROACH

A powered approach is preferable at night, rather than a glide approach. In modern training aircraft, the powered approach is generally used by day also. Power gives the Pilot **more control**, a lower Rate of Descent and, therefore, a less steep slope. The approach to the aiming point should be stable, using any available aids, such as the **Runway Lighting** and a **VASIS** (Visual Approach Slope Indicator System) if available.

Using the **Runway Edge Lighting** only, correct tracking and slope is achieved when the **runway perspective** is the same as in daylight. For **correct tracking,** the runway should appear symmetrical in the wind-screen. Guidance on achieving the **correct approach slope** is obtained from the *apparent* spacing between the Runway Edge Lights. If the aeroplane is getting low on slope, the Runway Lights will appear to be closer together. If the aeroplane is flying above slope, then the Runway Lights will appear to be further apart. Attention should also be paid to the ASI throughout the approach, to ensure that the correct **airspeed** is being maintained.

Fig.22-3. Perspectives on Approach using Runway Edge Lighting.

If no VASIS is available, then the **aiming point** during the approach should be a point selected somewhere between two to four Runway Edge Lights along the runway from the approach threshold.

If there is a VASI available, however, the **aiming point** during the approach should be the VASIS. Because it is an approach aid and not a landing aid, the VASIS should be disregarded once below about 200 ft Above Aerodrome Level, and attention placed on the perspective of the Runway Edge Lighting in anticipation of the flare. Following the landing flare and hold-off, the aeroplane will of course touch down some distance beyond the aiming point used during the approach.

Fig.22-4. Perspectives on Approach using a VASIS.

Stay on centreline during the approach. Any tendency to drift off the extended centreline can be counteracted with coordinated turns, and drift can be laid-off if a crosswind exists. Be prepared for wind changes as the descent progresses – the difference between the wind at 1000 ft AAL and at ground level is likely to be more pronounced at night than by day. It is common for the wind speed to decrease and the wind direction to back as the aeroplane descends.

Stay on slope during the approach. Any variations in slope should be corrected with coordinated use of power and attitude. The aiming point should stay, on average, in the same position in the windscreen. **Stay on airspeed during the approach.** Check airspeed on the ASI, and do not be afraid to use power. Occasionally check the altitude.

Once approaching the threshold, the Runway Lights near the threshold should start moving down the windscreen, and certain runway features may become visible in the landing lights. The VASIS guidance will become less valuable below about 200 ft and should not be used in the latter stages of the approach, and certainly not in the flare and landing. The VASI is an approach guide only. It is Pilot judgement that counts in the landing.

THE FLARE, HOLD-OFF AND LANDING AT NIGHT

The aeroplane should be flown on slope towards the aiming point, where the landing flare will occur. The best guide to **flare height and round-out** is the runway perspective given by the Runway Edge Lighting. As the aeroplane descends towards the runway, the Runway Edge Lighting that the Pilot sees in his peripheral vision will appear to rise. The appearance of the ground can sometimes be deceptive at night so, even when using landing lights, **use the Runway Lighting as your main guide in the flare and hold-off**, both for depth perception as well as tracking guidance. For this reason, your introductory landings may be made *without* the use of Landing Lights. When using Landing Lights, however, do not stare straight down the beam, but to one side.

There is a common tendency to flare and hold-off a little too high in the first few landings at night, but this tendency can soon be modified with a little practice. The runway perspective on touchdown should resemble that on lift-off, and an appreciation of this is best achieved by looking well ahead towards the far end of the runway. Avoid trying to see the runway under the nose of the aeroplane. This will almost certainly induce a tendency to fly into the ground before rounding-out.

As the aeroplane is flared for landing, the **power should be gradually reduced as the aeroplane enters the hold-off phase**, and the **throttle fully closed** as the aeroplane settles onto the ground during touchdown. **Keep straight** during the landing ground run with rudder and, in any crosswind, keep the wings level with aileron.

Keep on the centreline until the aeroplane has slowed to taxying speed, using brake if necessary. Taxi clear of the runway, stop the aeroplane, set the brakes to *PARK,* and complete the after landing checks.

THE GO-AROUND AT NIGHT

The flying technique for a go-around at night is the same as by day, except that it is done primarily by reference to instruments.

Whereas the eyes may be concentrated on the Runway Lighting during the latter stages of the approach, these lights are no longer necessary when full power is applied and the Pitch Attitude raised. There will be strong pitch and yaw tendencies due to the power increase that must be controlled with reference to the Flight Instruments. **Hold the desired attitude on the AI**, monitor vertical performance on the Altimeter, monitor airspeed on the ASI, and hold direction on the DI.

Fig.22-5. The Go-Around at Night.

Do not change configuration (flaps/gear) until established in the go-around, with a positive Rate of Climb indicated on both the Altimeter and the VSI.

WIND VARIATIONS WITH HEIGHT

The Surface Wind at Night may differ significantly from the Wind at Height. The term **Surface Wind** refers to the wind measured 10 metres (30 feet) above open and level ground, i.e. where *windsocks* and other wind indicators are generally placed. **The Surface Wind is generally weaker than the wind at height** because of the friction forces existing between the lower layers of the airflow and the Earth's surface, which slow it down. The rougher the surface, the greater the slowing-down effect. The Wind well away from the influence of the surface, typically some thousands of feet above it by day and possibly only 500 ft above it by night, is known as the **Gradient Wind**.

There will be some vertical mixing in the air mass near the Earth's surface, depending upon a number of things, including **heating**, which will cause thermal eddies in the lower layers. During a typical day, the Earth's surface is heated by the Sun. The Earth's surface, in turn, heats the air near it, causing the air to rise in turbulent eddies and mix with the upper air. This vertical mixing in the lower levels of the atmosphere brings the effect of the Gradient Wind closer to the Earth's surface.

With vigorous heating (such as over land on a sunny day), the friction layer is deep, and so the stronger upper winds are brought down to lower levels; if the thermal eddying is weak (such as by night or over a cool sea), then the vertical mixing is less, and the friction layer shallower.

At night, therefore, with less heating and less mixing, the effect of a strong Gradient Wind will **not** be brought as close to the Earth's surface, resulting in a Surface Wind that is lighter at night than by day. A light wind of 10 kt by day may fall to become practically calm by night, even though the upper winds have not changed.

A consequence of a reduced wind speed is a reduced *Coriolis Effect* (as explained in the Chapter on *WIND* in *The Air Pilot's Manual* Volume 2), hence **the Surface Wind will *back* compared to the wind at height**, i.e. the wind direction will move anticlockwise as the aeroplane descends. (The effect is opposite in the Southern Hemisphere.)

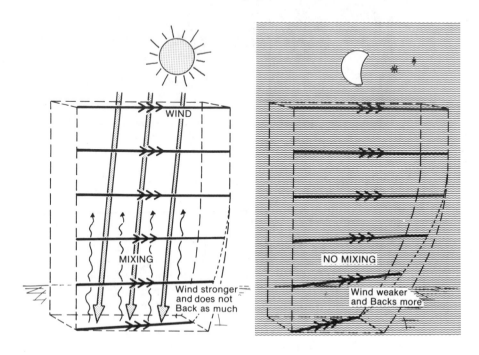

Fig.22-6. The Diurnal (Daily) Variation of Wind.

Expect stronger and sharper wind changes as you climb out by night. The difference in wind strength between the surface and at height will generally be more marked at night and, if there is a **sudden** transition from the lower winds in the shallow friction layer to the undisturbed upper winds at a particular height, say at about 500 ft, then **windshear** could be experienced as the aeroplane passes through this level.

A Surface Wind of 5 kt at take-off may suddenly become 20 kt at some low level on a clear night (possibly with a significant change in direction as well), yet only 10 kt at 1000 ft on a clear and sunny day.

EMERGENCIES AT NIGHT

ENGINE FAILURE

A Forced Landing at night away from an aerodrome is obviously a more dangerous event than by day, when better vision will allow the easier selection of a suitable field. Moonlight may help at night, but do not count on it! Normal daylight procedures should be followed if the engine fails at night, with the emphasis on **keeping the aeroplane at flying speed** and **restarting the engine.**

Flying the aeroplane at a low forward airspeed consistent with retaining full control will help achieve a lower Rate of Descent, and allow more time for remedial action and for carrying out a Forced Landing if necessary. A **MAYDAY** call should be made fairly promptly to alert the rescue services.

Time available for action will depend upon height above the ground, so reference to the Altimeter is important. With QNH set, it will read altitude AMSL. With QFE set, it will read height above the aerodrome, which may be at a different level to surrounding terrain. **Make a commonsense judgement of your height above the ground**, and keep a good look out. If sufficient height and time is available, the aeroplane should be glided (at a safe speed) back towards the aerodrome, whilst trouble-shooting the problem continues.

The full procedures for rectifying the problem and restarting the engine should be carried out if time permits. Fuel selection is a major item to consider. If, however, a landing has to be made, then consideration should be given to landing into-wind, using only a partial flap setting (rather than full flap) to avoid a steep nose-down gliding attitude with a high descent rate, and to minimise the flare required prior to touch-down. It is preferable to touch down in a fairly flat attitude. Landing lights may be useful during the last few hundred feet, especially in making visual contact with the ground.

ELECTRICAL FAILURE

Electrical failure may cause the loss of instrument lighting , which can be easily compensated for by using the **torch** (kept in a handy position and with good batteries). A sudden failure of lighting should only deprive you of the instruments for a few seconds but, in this time, make use of visual clues such as the natural horizon.

The natural horizon will generally be of more value when the aeroplane is well above the ground. Close to the ground, shortly after take-off for instance, there may be insufficient ground lighting to provide a horizon and, in any case, the lights could possibly be on a hillside giving a *false* horizon, or there could be so few that the aeroplane will quickly fly over them anyway. Scan the Flight Instruments!

If the electrical failure is only partial, then alternative lighting may be available in the cockpit from another light source or, perhaps, by interchanging bulbs. Panic action is **not** required – calm and careful consideration is. Do not be distracted from controlling the attitude of the aeroplane!

The Attitude Indicator, if it is electrical, will gradually run down if its electrical power is removed, but it could remain useful for a brief period. Attention should be paid to the **Air Speed Indicator**, however, to ensure that flying speed is maintained. The first step following a failure of any kind is – **fly the aeroplane!**

Once flying the aeroplane is under control following engine failure, with a suitable gliding attitude and airspeed achieved, try to **rectify the problem**, and follow the appropriate Emergency Procedures or Check Lists. For an electrical failure, check the switching, monitor the alternator/generator or battery discharge rate, and check circuit breakers and fuses (if convenient) without disturbing your control of the aeroplane. If the electrical failure is only partial, but with a high discharge rate, then off-load the alternator or battery by switching off non-essential services, such as some radios, the Landing Lights, etc. A landing as soon as reasonably possible should be considered.

A return to the airfield should be planned, making a radio call if possible, and certainly keeping a good **look out** for other aircraft. If it is only a **radio failure**, then ATC can perhaps be alerted by flying a circuit, descending, and then flying above the landing runway, flashing the Landing Lights and/or Navigation Lights. Without radio, light signals from the ATS personnel on the ground may be used – the main ones being:

- *continuous RED* – give way to other aircraft and continue circling;
- *RED flashes* – do not land; aerodrome not available for landing;
- *GREEN flashes* – return to the aerodrome; wait for permission to land;
- *continuous GREEN* – you may land.

If the **Navigation Lights** have failed, then the aeroplane should be landed normally as soon as it is safe to do so, unless ATC authorises the continuation of the flight. ATC should be informed of the lack of Navigation Lights as soon as possible, so that other aircraft can be warned. Loss of the Navigation Lights will not affect control of the aeroplane in any way – in fact, the Pilot generally cannot even see these lights, however it will affect the ability of other aeroplanes to see you and remain clear. A normal circuit and landing should be made.

If the **Landing Lights** have failed, then this is of little importance. They are not required for a Pilot to make a normal, safe landing.

FAILURE OF AERODROME LIGHTING

Most aerodromes have a standby power supply that will come into play within seconds of an aerodrome power failure, however there is a possibility (fairly remote) that a complete power failure could occur. Aeroplanes in the vicinity of an aerodrome without any Runway Lighting at night should hold at a safe height, and maintain a very good look out. Radio contact should also be maintained, preferably with ATC on the ground, but if that is not possible, with other aircraft in the circuit or with ATC on an alternative frequency.

If the lighting is not returned to service, then consideration should be given to **diverting** (at a safe height) to a nearby aerodrome where Runway Lighting is available. A Radar Service may be available to assist in tracking. **A Minimum Safe Altitude of 1000 ft above the highest obstacle within 5 nm either side** of the diversion track should be allowed for, possibly higher if conditions permit.

LOST

If you become temporarily uncertain of your position, follow the same procedures as you would during daylight hours. Radio Navigation Aids, if available in the vicinity, should always be taken advantage of – if you know how to use them. If you are really lost, then navigational assistance may be available from ATC, either by Radar or with VHF Direction Finding using the VHF-COM radio. The choice of alternative aerodromes will be more limited at night, of course, since Runway Lighting will be required.

It is always advisable to carry sufficient fuel at night for an unexpected journey to an alternative field.

23

NIGHT NAVIGATION

Navigating at night follows the same basic principles as navigating by day, except that ground features are more difficult to see, distances are more difficult to estimate, and the likelihood of encountering unexpected cloud or areas of restricted visibility is greater.

The best ground features to use at night are usually the **light patterns of towns**, and the **beacons** of any nearby aerodromes. Cities like London and Manchester are generally too large for distinctive light patterns to be meaningful to a novice Night Flyer, but small towns, especially if they have areas of darkness around them, are generally good. Busy **Motorways** delineated by a stream of car headlights may also be useful.

On moonlit nights, reflections off the surface of lakes and other large bodies of water may make them very visible (especially when viewed against the moon), although this should not be relied upon for navigation purposes just in case clouds cover the sky unexpectedly.

Aeronautical Light Beacons, which are installed at various civil and military aerodromes in the UK, are good landmarks. Provided it is during the aerodrome's hours of operation, they can be expected to be on at night and by day in bad visibility. The different types include:

- **Identification Beacons**, which flash a two-letter morse code group every 12 seconds (*green* at civil aerodromes and *red* at military aerodromes; and

- **Aerodrome Beacons** give an alternating-colour flash signal instead (usually *white/white* or less commonly *white/green*). They are not normally provided in addition to an identification beacon.

Sometimes, **Marine Beacons** and **Lightships** may be useful if you are navigating near the sea by night. They appear on some aeronautical charts with a description of their lighting characteristics.

Fig.23-1. Marine Beacons on an Aeronautical Chart.

Radio Navigation Aids are very useful at night — if you know how to use them correctly. Some aids experience errors at night, e.g. NDB *Night Effect* which may be greatest during the periods around dawn and dusk. The hours of service should be checked in the AIP to ensure that the aids will indeed be available at the time of your flight. In general, you can expect major en route VORs and NDBs to be operating H24 (i.e. all hours), but some aids tied to a particular aerodrome may not be available outside its hours of operation. This could apply to a Radar Service, a VDF Service, an ILS, Locator, etc. Better to check first, and be sure.

THE AVAILABILITY OF AERODROMES

Many aerodromes close down at night, both civil aerodromes and MATZs. It is always advisable to check in the AIP and NOTAMs which aerodromes are available at night and which are not. Call a Briefing Office if you are unsure. Check not only your planned departure and destination aerodromes, but also those aerodromes which might be useful as Alternates in case of a diversion. You must be certain that **runway lighting** will be available for your landing. As well as some aerodromes closing down, there are some Danger Areas that are not active at night.

FLIGHT PLANNING

Good flight planning is especially important at night, since there will be fewer ground features to assist in determining navigation errors, as well as less assistance available from ATSUs in the form of Communications, Radar or VDF bearings.

The **Weather** takes on special importance at night. All relevant information should be studied carefully, especially the Aerodrome Forecasts for your destination, as well as those for a number of Alternates and your aerodrome of departure. Remember that the closeness of the *temperature/dewpoint* figures provides some clue as to the possibility of mist or fog forming as the temperature falls even further during the night. Fewer Observers on duty at night will mean fewer updates of *actual* weather. Attention should be paid to the possibility of low cloud, mist or fog, and also to the wind strength and direction, at altitude as well as at the surface.

A **suitable route** should be chosen that utilises the best features available at night (the lights of small towns, Aerodrome Light Beacons, operating Radio Navigation Aids, Marine Beacons, Motorways, etc.), even if this route is slightly longer than the direct route. Rugged and/or high terrain is best avoided, and a **Safety Altitude** to ensure adequate terrain clearance should be calculated. A vertical clearance of 1000 ft above the highest obstacle within 5 nm of track is required.

Tracks should be marked on the chart with dark lines, to ensure that they will be clearly seen in a dimly-lit cockpit. The **Flight Log** should also be filled in with a dark pencil or pen, so that it is easily read in dim lighting. Red lines will not be visible in red lighting, and certain colours on the map may not be as distinguishable by night as by day, which may lead to some difficulties.

Care should be taken in measuring Tracks and Distances, and then in calculating Headings and Ground Speeds. Always re-check! Dead-Reckoning is very important at night, and a correct Flight Log is a much better starting point than an incorrect one.

Night Flights must operate according to the Instrument Flight Rules (IFR), and so Quadrantal Levels will apply above 3000 ft AMSL. A Safety Altitude providing at least 1000 ft vertical clearance above obstacles within 5 nm of track must be used for all cruising levels, both above and below 3000 ft AMSL.

Calculate an accurate **Fuel Log**, ensuring that there is sufficient fuel available for a successful diversion and landing, with adequate reserves remaining.

It is *recommended* that a **Flight Plan** be submitted for a night cross-country flight, since this increases the protective Search and Rescue cover.

FLY ACCURATE HEADINGS AND AIRSPEED

Distance at night can be deceptive, since there will be fewer ground objects visible and available for comparison in terms of size and location. The usual tendency at night is to underestimate distance. Height and speed may also be difficult to estimate, so careful attention should be paid to the Altimeter and to the Air Speed Indicator.

The aeroplane should be navigated, according to a predetermined Flight Log, by flying planned Heading and True Air Speed. From time to time occasional track corrections and revised ETAs may be required, using reliable pinpoints and Radio Navigation Aids. **Accurate heading and time-keeping is essential**, and changes should only be made when absolutely certain that a change is required.

If you become **lost** on a night cross-country flight, follow the normal daylight procedures. Use available pinpoints and Radio Navigation Aids to fix your position, or request assistance from an ATSU which may be able to provide a radar fix or a VDF bearing. However, with good flight planning and accurate flying in terms of airspeed and heading, you will always know where you are, even at night.

APPENDIX 1

The IMC Rating

The following two-page excerpt from CAA Publication **CAP 53** (The Private Pilot's Licence and Associated Ratings) covers the main details of the UK IMC Rating. Further reading in CAP 53 is recommended for such things as *Exemptions,* and Appendices G & H – *The Ground and Flight Training Syllabuses,* and *Flight Test Requirements for the IMC Rating.*

The Instrument Meteorological Conditions Rating

1   RATING PRIVILEGES

1.1   An Instrument Meteorological Conditions (IMC) Rating extends the privileges of a PPL(A) holder to allow flight as PIC:

(a)· out of sight of the surface;

(b) in a control zone on a special VFR clearance with flight visibility less than 10 km but not less than 3 km;

(c) when in IMC outside controlled airspace notified for the purposes of Schedule 8 to the ANO;

(d) carrying passengers above 3000 ft amsl in IMC or in a flight visibility less than 5 km at or below that height, when outside controlled airspace notified for the purposes of Schedule 8 to the ANO;

(e) during take-off or landing with a flight visibility below cloud of not less than 1800 m.

1.2   The rating confers no privileges for flight in controlled airspace under circumstances requiring compliance with Instrument Flight Rules (IFR). It is not recognised in other States, and is only of use in UK territorial airspace, and in Channel Islands and Isle of Man airspace.

2   EXPERIENCE AND TRAINING REQUIREMENTS

2.1   An applicant for the grant of an IMC rating must have 25 hours experience as an aeroplane pilot since the date of application for his PPL(A). The 25 hours must include 10 hours as pilot-in-command (PIC), of which at least 5 hours must be on cross-country flights, and may include the 15 hours dual instrument instruction specified in paragraph 2.2.

2.2   An applicant must also hold an FRTO licence and, unless exempted under paragraph 6, complete a recognised course of training for the rating before taking the Ground Examination and Flight Test. The course must include 15 hours training in instrument flying in a suitably equipped dual control aeroplane, except for up to 2 hours which may be in a simulator recognised by the Authority as being suitable for the training. Not less than 10 of the 15 hours must be flown by sole reference to instruments. These minimum course requirements assume that the applicant has completed the 4 hours of dual instruction in instrument flying specified in the PPL requirements. An applicant, who has not had these 4 hours training, must satisfy the FTO that he has reached an equivalent standard of ability before starting the course.

2.3   Where an applicant wishes to be tested for the IMC Rating on a multi-engine aeroplane the flying training must ensure that in simulated instrument flight conditions the pilot can maintain stable flight after an engine failure at climb power, then climb at the recommended speed and execute the normal range of flight manoeuvres under asymmetric power.

2.4   A student's ability and experience may be taken into account in deciding how much time should be allotted to each of the following items but the course must cover all of them:

2.4.1 *Basic Stage*

    (a)   Instrument attitude flight.

    (b)   Basic flight manoeuvres.

    (c)   Intermediate flight manoeuvres.

    (d)   Simulated loss of gyroscopic instruments.

    (e)   Simulated loss of pitot/static pressure.

2.4.2 *Applied Stage*

    (a)   Flight planning.

    (b)   Departure and en-route techniques.

    (c)   Approach and let-down procedures.

    (d)   Bad weather circuits and landing (a simulator must not be used for this item).

2.6   Ability and experience may be taken into account when deciding on the amount of ground instruction needed by an individual. Normally, however, the course should provide for a minimum of 20 hours covering:

    (a)   Physiological factors.

    (b)   Flight instruments.

    (c)   Aeronautical Information Service.

    (d)   Flight planning.

    (e)   Privileges of the IMC rating.

3   GROUND EXAMINATIONS

Unless exempted under paragraph 6, an applicant must pass, in the 12 months before the date of application for the rating, a written examination covering subjects drawn from the IMC Rating course syllabus and the PPL(A) syllabus including questions on the planning and execution of a typical flight under IFR outside controlled airspace.

5   VALIDITY OF IMC RATING

5.1   The IMC Rating C of T is valid for a period of 25 months from the date of the successful flight test.

APPENDIX 2

The Night Rating

The following information on the UK Night Rating is also extracted from CAP 53.

The Night Rating (Aeroplanes)

1 INTRODUCTION

1.1 The experience requirements and the flying training syllabus for the PPL(A) do not call for any night flying training. However, in order to fly as PIC at night, with or without passengers, the holder of a PPL(A) must have a Night Rating. For this purpose, 'night' means the time between half-an-hour after sunset and half-an-hour before sunrise, sunset and sunrise being determined at surface level.

1.2 The privileges of the Night Rating are set out in Schedule 8 of the Air Navigation Order 1989.

1.3 A PPL(A) which includes a Night Rating and a valid IR(A) allows the holder to carry passengers at night, without meeting the night currency requirement (see paragraph 3).

2 EXPERIENCE REQUIREMENTS

2.1 An applicant for a night rating must produce evidence of having completed satisfactorily a total of 50 hours as pilot of aeroplanes. Before starting a recognised course of night flying an applicant must have at least 20 hours as pilot-in-command of which 10 hours must have been gained since making application for a PPL(A).

2.2 The training requirements are:

(a) dual instruction in instrument flying of which not less than 5 hours must be flown by sole reference to instruments; up to 3 hours of the 5 hours may have been achieved during PPL(A) training. Not more than 2.5 hours may be tuition in instrument flying in a simulator recognised by the Authority as being suitable for training;

(b) satisfactory completion of a course of at least 5 hours night flying conducted by a flying instructor to a syllabus recognised by the Authority. This shall consist of:

    (1) at least 3 hours dual instruction including at least one hour night navigation;

    (2) 5 take-offs and 5 landings as PIC, when the depression of the centre of the sun is not less than 12 degrees below the horizon (ie. the end of evening or beginning of morning civil twilight). In at least one instance take-off and landing should be separated by a complete departure from, and rejoining of, the aerodrome traffic pattern.

2.3   The flights as PIC must have been obtained within the 6 months immediately preceding the date of qualifying for the rating. The holder of a Flying Instructor's Rating must certify, on the application form, that this requirement has been fulfilled. 'Touch and Go' take-offs and landings are not acceptable, each flight must terminate in a full stop landing.

3   VALIDITY

3.1   The holder of a Night Rating, or a Licence including the privileges of a Night Rating, may not fly as PIC at night unless he either holds a valid Instrument Rating or has within the immediately preceding 13 months carried out, as PIC, not less than 5 take-offs and 5 landings at a time when the depression of the centre of the sun was not less than 12 degrees below the horizon.

3.2   A pilot who has qualified to fly as PIC at night but is unable to meet the recency requirements must undertake dual refresher training in night flying with a qualified flying instructor. The pilot must satisfy the PIC recency requirements detailed in paragraph 3.1 by flying solo, with the authority and under the supervision of a flying instructor, who is present during the take-off and landing at the aerodrome from which the instruction is to begin and end, before acting as a PIC at night.

NOTE: Where PIC is stipulated this does not include PIC U/S or P/UT.

4   APPLICATIONS

An application for inclusion of a Night Rating in a PPL(A) must include:

(a)   Personal Flying Log Book;

(b)   Existing Licence;

(c)   Form FCL 111;

(d)   Prescribed Charge.

APPENDIX 3

Radio Failure Procedures

The following information on Radio Failure procedures is extracted from UK AIP RAC 6.

3   Radio Failure Procedures For Pilots

3.2   Failure of Radio Navigation Equipment

3.2.1   If part of an aircrafts radio navigation equipment fails but two-way communication can still be maintained with ATC, the pilot must inform ATC of the failure and report his altitude and approximate position. ATC may, at its discretion, authorize the pilot to continue his flight in or into Controlled Airspace. When radar is available it may, subject to workload, be used to provide navigational assistance to the pilot.

3.2.2   If no authorization to proceed is given by ATC, the pilot should leave, or avoid Controlled Airspace and areas of dense traffic, and either:

    (a) Go to an area in which he can continue his flight in VMC or (if this is not possible);

    (b) select a suitable area in which to descend through cloud, fly visually to a suitable aerodrome and land as soon as practicable.

But before doing so, however, he should consult ATC who may be able to give him instructions or advice. He should also take into consideration the latest meteorological information and terrain clearance and should make full use of ground VHF D/F stations. He must at all times keep ATC informed of his intentions.

3.3   Failure of two-way radio Communications Equipment

3.3.1   The basic procedure to be adopted by pilots experiencing two-way radio communications failure is given in paragraph 3.3.2. Other procedures which may be required in certain circumstances because of weather conditions, the last ATC instruction received, etc, are tabulated in paragraph 3.3.3. Similarly, additional procedures are described in paragraph 3.3.4 for departing aircraft flying in Controlled Airspace on certain ATC clearances but which have not reached cruising level.

3.3.2   The basic procedure is:

    (a) Continue the flight in accordance with the current flight plan to the holding point at the aerodrome of first intended landing. Maintain the last acknowledged cruising levels for the portion of the route for which levels have been assigned and thereafter maintain the cruising levels shown in the flight plan. Operate secondary radar transponder on Mode A, Code 7600, with Mode C;

    (b) if the aircraft's transmitter is thought to be still functioning, transmit position reports on the appropriate frequency when over the routine reporting points;

    (c) arrange the flight to arrive over the holding point as closely as possible to the ETA last acknowledged by the appropriate ATC Unit. If no such ETA has been acknowledged, the pilot should use an ETA computed from the last acknowledged position report and flight plan times for the subsequent sections of the flight. Pilots must follow the appropriate inbound route for the Control Zone or Control Area concerned (see RAC 3);

    (d) begin to descend over the holding point at the last acknowledged EAT. If no EAT has been acknowledged the descent should be started at the ETA calculated in (c) above. The rate of descent to the lowest level of the holding stack must be not less than 500 ft a minute. It is essential that aircraft should maintain a strict timing; a descent may only be started within the ten minutes immediately following the time that it ought to have begun. If 'Delay not determined' has been given, and no subsequent EAT, do not attempt to land at the destination aerodrome but fly to another aerodrome following the procedure outlined in (e) below;

(e) land within 30 minutes of the time descent should have been started (ie the EAT or ETA referred to in (d) above). If unable to land within this time, but able to complete an approach and landing visually, do so. If not able to land within the specified time, nor to approach and land visually, leave the vicinity of the aerodrome and any associated Controlled Airspace at the specified altitude and on the specified route (see RAC 3). If no altitude or route is specified, fly at the last assigned altitude or Minimum Sector Altitude (MSA), whichever is the higher and avoid areas of dense traffic. Then, either:

(i) fly to an area in which flight may be continued in VMC and land at a suitable aerodrome there, or (if this is not possible);

(ii) select a suitable area in which to descend through cloud, fly visually to a suitable aerodrome and land as soon as practicable.

In either case, inform ATC as soon as possible after landing.

(f) In the event of a missed approach:

(i) land at the aerodrome of destination if this can be achieved within 30 minutes of the time descent from the holding point should have started, or (if this is not possible);

(ii) fly to another aerodrome following the procedure outlined in (e) above.

3.3.3   The procedures to be adopted in certain circumstances are tabulated below.

Table II

Paragraph	Flight Conditions	Details of Circumstances	Procedure to be Adopted
3.3.3.1	VMC	(a) Flight in VMC can be maintained.	Continue flight in VMC, land at the nearest suitable aerodrome and report arrival by the most expeditious means to the appropriate ATC Unit.
		(b) Flight in VMC cannot be maintained.	Adopt the IMC procedure appropriate to the circumstances.

EXERCISES

PREPARATION FOR THESE EXERCISES

The aim of the *Air Pilot's Manual* has been, where possible, to treat each topic once, but thoroughly – so, as a Private Pilot, you should already have a very sound knowledge of much of what is required for an IMC Rating. It is recommended, however, that you review the following Chapters of the *Air Pilot's Manual* (especially if you have any difficulty with the following Exercises):

- Volume 2, Chapters L1, L2, L3, L4, M9 & M11;
- Volume 3, Chapters 2, 3, 4, 5 & 6;
- Volume 4, Chapters 25, 26 & 27; and
- Volume 6, Chapters 2 & 3.

NOTE: The questions in these Exercises are organised in different ways:
- *Optional answers* within questions are bracketted, and divided by an oblique stroke (/).
- Options in multi-choice questions are preceded by (a), (b), (c), etc.
- Where questions are divided into *Parts*, these are shown as (i), (ii), (iii), etc.

REFERENCES

In developing expertise as an IMC-Rated Pilot it is important to refer to appropriate chapters of the *Air Pilot's Manual* and also the *UK Aeronautical Information Publication (AIP)*. This vital operational document, published by the CAA, is kept up-to-date using the CAA's AIP Amendment Service.

In many cases, you may have to search through the AIP for the required information, but this in itself is a worthwhile exercise since you must become familiar with the document. Make use of its Indexes, especially that at the end of the RAC section. You should also study the *Instrument Charts* that you decide to use, in particular those published by the *British Airways/Aerad* or *Jeppesen* chart companies.

The answers to a few of our questions have to be obtained from the UK AIP and will require amending from time to time, since the AIP is amended regularly. Use your common sense in such cases. Also, please feel free to advise us in writing of any significant changes that you notice – this will assist us in ensuring that the changes are included in our next printing.

SECTION 1

EXERCISES – ATTITUDE FLYING (covering entire Section 1)

1. During manoeuvres, to determine the attitude of the aircraft, the pilot should use (the flight instruments and what his eyes tell him/his bodily feel and what his balance mechanism tells him).

2. Having settled into a steady banked turn, the balance mechanism will send a message of (level/banked) flight. You should use your .... to verify the true situation.

3. Immediately after rolling level out of a lengthy, banked turn to the left, the balance mechanism will send a message of (level/right-banked/left-banked) flight. This is known as the .... You should ... ...

4. To minimise balance illusions in instrument flight, you (should/need not) hold your head upright relative to your body, and use your .... .

5. A strong forward acceleration can cause an illusion of pitching nose (up/down) and tumbling (forwards/backwards). You should ... .

6. A strong deceleration can cause an illusion of pitching nose (up/down) and tumbling (forwards/backwards). You should ... .

7. An illusion of rotation when no rotation is occurring, or vice versa, is known as ....

8. Vertigo (can/cannot) be caused by accelerations, strong nose-blowing, and sneezing.

9. What pressures are fed to the ASI?

10. What pressures are fed to the VSI and Altimeter?

11. What Altimeter subscale setting is used when cruising below the Transition Altitude (usually 3000 ft AMSL in the UK)?

12. What Altimeter subscale setting is used when cruising at a Flight Level above the Transition Level?

13. What Altimeter subscale setting is used when descending from a Flight Level and approaching an aerodrome at which you plan to land?

14. What Altimeter subscale setting is normally used in the UK when on final approach to land?

15. If a Missed Approach is made following an Instrument Approach in which the pilot did not become visual, climb instructions may be passed by ATC in the form of an Altitude. What Altimeter subscale setting would be the most suitable following the commencement of the Missed Approach?

16. Some Attitude Indicators are operated electrically, others are operated by .... ?

17. Some Direction Indicators, or Heading Indicators, are operated electrically, others are operated by .... ?

18. If the Static Vent ices over during descent, the Altimeter will:
    (a) continue to read correctly.
    (b) show a constant indication.
    (c) indicate an altitude lower than what it really is.

19. If the Static Vent ices over on the climb, the Altimeter will:
    (a) continue to read correctly.
    (b) show a constant indication.
    (c) indicate an altitude higher than what it really is.

20. If the Static Vent ices over on the cruise, the ASI will:
    (a) show a constant indication, even if the airspeed changes.
    (b) read too high if the aeroplane climbs, and too low if it descends.
    (c) read too low if the aeroplane climbs, and too high if it descends.
    (d) continue to read correctly if the aeroplane climbs or descends.

21. If the Static Vent ices over on the climb, the VSI will:
    (a) continue to read correctly.
    (b) show a constant positive indication.
    (c) indicate zero.

22. If the Static Vent ices over at any time, a suction-driven Attitude Indicator will ....

23. Which flight instruments will be affected by a blocked pitot tube?

24. Pitot pressure equals .... pressure plus static pressure. The Air Speed Indicator measures the difference between .... pressure and ...... pressure and converts this to an indicated airspeed.

25. A blocked pitot tube will mean that the measured (pitot/static) pressure will be incorrect.

26. If a pitot tube is blocked, then during the take-off run the pitot tube will not measure the increase in (dynamic/static) pressure, and so the ASI will read (too high/too low/zero).

27. A pitot tube becomes blocked on the cruise, with its measured total pressure remaining constant, then during descent, as the actual static pressure (increases/decreases), the ASI will read (too high/too low/correctly/zero).

28. Whilst cruising at 5000 ft AMSL under ISA conditions, the Air Speed Indicator shows 100 kt. The True Air Speed is approximately:
    (a) 100 kt.   (b) 102 kt.   (c) 108 kt.   (d) 120 kt.

29. What is the True Air Speed cruising at FL 70, OAT –5°C, and IAS 105 kt?

30. Whilst parked at a level aerodrome, Elevation 810 ft, the Altimeter reads 900 ft, 90 ft too high, with 1015 mb set. What is the Aerodrome QNH and QFE?

31. You are cruising at FL40 in cloud. Regional QNH is 980 mb. What is your vertical distance AMSL? Does this provide adequate clearance above an obstacle within 5 nm of track that is 2560 ft AMSL.

32. When turning through North in the Northern Hemisphere, the Magnetic Compass will be (sluggish/lively) and will (lag behind/overshoot).

33. Turning Errors of the Magnetic Compass are greatest when turning through .... ?

34. In the Northern Hemisphere, you should (overshoot/undershoot) the desired Magnetic Heading when turning through North.

35. In the Northern Hemisphere, you should (overshoot/undershoot) the desired Magnetic Heading when turning through South.

36. Turning Errors of the Magnetic Compass are (the same/reversed) in the Southern Hemisphere.

37. Turning Errors of the Magnetic Compass are (greater/smaller/the same) near the Equator, compared to when the aircraft is at high latitudes.

38. Acceleration Errors of the Magnetic Compass are greatest on headings of .... ?

39. Name three gyroscopic instruments found in most aircraft.

40. What effect would a low suction pressure have on a vacuum-driven AI?

SECTION 2

EXERCISES 9 – RADAR

1. The process of separating aircraft and positioning them by an ATC Radar Controller passing headings-to-steer is known as Radar V........ .
2. If a Radar Service is not available, then ATC will separate aircraft using procedures based on their estimated positions and known altitudes. This is known as:
   (a) Non-Radar Separation.
   (b) Procedural Separation.
   (c) Standby Separation.
3. Primary Surveillance Radar can detect signals from aircraft, even if they carry no airborne equipment. Secondary Surveillance Radar, SSR, on the ground detects strong responding signals transmitted from aircraft equipped with a T......... .
4. An approach to a runway under the guidance of a Radar Controller who passes tracking and descent advice is known as a S...... R........ A......... .
5. What approximate RoD in ft/min is required to achieve a 3° glideslope, which is 300 ft per nm, if the Ground Speed of the aeroplane is 60 kt?
6. What approximately RoD in ft/min is required to achieve a 3° glideslope, which is 300 ft per nm, if the Ground Speed of the aeroplane is 90 kt?
7. The minimum visibility required for an SRA by an IMC-Rated Pilot is ....
8. The Decision Height for an SRA carried out by an IMC-Rated Pilot will depend upon the Obstacle Clearance Height (plus additions), but in no case may be less than an Absolute SRA Minimum of ...... ft AAL.
9. The approximate range of any VHF signals for an aeroplane at 6000 ft above the level of a ground station is ..... nm.
10. The approximate range of any VHF signals for an aeroplane at 2000 ft above the level of a ground station is ..... nm.
11. The approximate range of any VHF signals for an aeroplane at 2500 ft above the level of a ground station is .... nm.
12. Where in the UK AIP can you find the *Special Purposes* Codes used for Secondary Surveillance Radar?

EXERCISES 10 – DME

1. The letters DME are an abbreviation for D......... M......... E....... .
2. DME measures:
   (a) horizontal distance.
   (b) vertical distance.
   (c) slant distance.
3. The DME is selected on the ...... radio, usually along with a co-located VOR.
4. If an aircraft tracking directly towards a DME ground station is at 37 DME at time 0115, and at 27 DME at time 0120, what is its Ground Speed?
5. If an aircraft tracking directly away from a DME ground station is at 22 DME at time 1223, and at 32 DME at time 1230, what is its Ground Speed?
6. Tracking abeam a DME ground station, the DME readings change in the following manner as time passes: 25, 21, 17, 15, 14, 15, 17, 21. What was your abeam distance from the DME ground station?

7. A DME can provide a:
   (a) circular position line.
   (b) straight position line.

EXERCISES 11a – NDB/ADF

1. The letters NDB are an abbreviation for N....... D....... B......... .
2. The NDB is (a ground-based transmitter/an airborne receiver).
3. NDBs transmit in either the .... or ...... frequency bands.
4. The letters ADF are an abbreviation for A...... D........ F......... .
5. The ADF is (a ground-based transmitter/an airborne receiver).
6. A particular NDB may be identified by ....
7. The Morse Code is shown on many aeronautical charts. What is the Morse-code *IDENT* of the Blackpool NDB, 'BPL'?
8. The three basic steps that a pilot should follow before using a particular NDB or Locator beacon are ....
9. QDM is the (Magnetic/True) bearing (from/to) the ground station.
10. QDR is the (Magnetic/True) bearing (from/to) the ground station.
11. The term RBI is an abbreviation for R..... B....... I......... .
12. If an aircraft on Heading 250°M has a reading of 030 on its Relative Bearing Indicator, what is:
    (i) the magnetic bearing of the NDB from the aircraft?
    (ii) the magnetic bearing of the aircraft from the NDB?
13. If an aircraft on Heading 250°M has a reading of 350 on its Relative Bearing Indicator, calculate:
    (i) the magnetic bearing of the NDB from the aircraft.
    (ii) the magnetic bearing of the aircraft from the NDB.
14. Determine the range of the Chiltern NDB from UK AIP COM 2.
15. An NDB used to locate the aircraft on an Instrument Approach is called a ....
16. An NDB positioned so that it provides a fix for an aircraft during an Instrument Approach, and co-located with the Outer Marker for the Approach, may be designated on the Instrument Approach Chart with the letters .... .
17. Atmospheric conditions, such as electrical storms or the periods of sunrise and sunset, (may/will not) distort NDB signals, making ADF indications less reliable.
18. Mountains (may/will not) reflect and distort NDB signals, making ADF indications less reliable.
19. The range promulgated in the UK AIP for NDBs is based on a daytime protection ratio between wanted and unwanted signals that limits bearing errors to +/– ...° or less.
20. Write down the Morse Code in dots (·) and dashes (–) for all the letters of the alphabet.

EXERCISES

EXERCISES 11b – RBI

1. An aircraft has a Heading of 035°M. Its RBI indicates 040. The Magnetic Variation in the area is 4°W. Calculate:
   (i) QDM; (ii) QDR; (iii) QTE.

2. An aircraft has a heading of 335°M. Its RBI indicates 355. The Magnetic Variation in the area is 4°W. Calculate:
   (i) QDM; (ii) QDR; (iii) QTE.

3. MH 080; RBI 000. Onto what heading should you turn to make a 90° intercept of a track of 040°M to the NDB? What will the RBI indicate at the point of intercept?

4. MH 080; RBI 000. Onto what heading should you turn to make a 60° intercept of a track of 040°M to the NDB? What will the RBI indicate at the point of intercept?

5. MH 070, RBI 010. Which way should you turn to intercept 075°M to the NDB?

6. MH 155, RBI 180. Which way should you turn to intercept a track of 140°M away from the NDB?

7. MH 155, RBI 180. Which way should you turn to intercept a track of 180°M away from the NDB?

8. When tracking towards an NDB, the ADF readings are:
   Time 1: MH 055, RBI 005; *Time 2:* MH 055, RBI 005.
   What track is the aircraft maintaining to the NDB?

9. When tracking towards an NDB, the ADF readings are:
   Time1: MH 055, RBI 005 and on track; *Time 2:* MH 055, RBI 002.
   Is the aircraft off track to the left or right?

10. To track towards an NDB on a track of 340°M, with an expected crosswind from the right causing 5° of drift, what Magnetic Heading should you steer, and what do you expect the RBI to indicate?

11. To track away from an NDB on a track of 120°M, with an expected crosswind from the right causing 8° of drift, what Magnetic Heading should you steer, and what do you expect the RBI to indicate?

12. You wish to track 360°M in nil-wind conditions. What Magnetic Heading should you steer? What will the RBI indicate as you pass abeam an NDB which is 10 nm to the right of track, i.e. when the NDB is on a bearing of 90° to the track?

13. You wish to track 360°M and you expect 10° of drift caused by a wind from the East. What Magnetic Heading should you steer? What will the RBI indicate as you pass abeam an NDB which is 10 nm to the right of track?

14. You wish to track 030°M in nil-wind conditions. What Magnetic Heading should you steer? What will the RBI indicate as you pass abeam an NDB which is 10 nm to the right of track?

15. You are heading 030°M in nil-wind conditions. What is your track? What will the RBI indicate as you pass abeam an NDB which is 10 nm to the left of track?

16. You wish to track 030°M and expect 7° left drift. What Magnetic Heading should you steer? What will the RBI indicate as you pass abeam an NDB which is 10 nm to the left of track?

17. You are tracking 278°M with 6° of port drift. You can determine your position abeam an NDB which is to the right of track by waiting until the RBI indicates ....

18. You are tracking 278°M with 6° of port drift. You can determine your position abeam an NDB which is to the left of track by waiting until the RBI indicates ..... .

19. You are tracking 278°M with 5° of starboard drift. You can determine your position abeam an NDB which is to the left of track by waiting until the RBI indicates ....

EXERCISES 11c – RMI

1. An aircraft has a Heading of 035°M. Its RMI indicates 075. The Magnetic Variation in the area is 4°W. Calculate:
   (i) QDM;   (ii) QDR;   (iii) QTE.

2. An aircraft has a Heading of 335°M. Its RMI indicates 330. The Magnetic Variation in the area is 4°W. Calculate:
   (i) QDM;   (ii) QDR;   (iii) QTE.

3. MH 080; RMI 080. Onto what heading should you turn to make a 90° intercept of a track of 040°M to the NDB? What will the RMI indicate at the point of intercept?

4. MH 080; RMI 080. Onto what heading should you turn to make a 60° intercept of a track of 040°M to the NDB? What will the RMI indicate at the point of intercept?

5. MH 070, RMI 080. Which way should you turn to intercept 075°M to the NDB? What will the RMI indicate at the point of intercept?

6. MH 155, RMI 330. Which way should you turn to intercept a track of 140°M away from the NDB? What will the RMI indicate at the point of intercept? What will the tail of the RMI pointer indicate?

7. MH 155, RMI 130. Which way should you turn to intercept a track of 090°M away from the NDB? What will the RMI indicate at the point of intercept? What will the RMI tail indicate?

8. When tracking towards an NDB, the ADF readings are:
   Time 1: MH 055, RMI 060;   *Time 2:* MH 055, RMI 060.
   What track is the aircraft maintaining to the NDB?

9. When tracking towards an NDB, the ADF readings are:
   Time 1: MH 055, RMI 060 and on track;   *Time 2:* MH 055, RMI 057.
   Is the aircraft off track to the left or right?

10. To track towards an NDB on a track of 340°M, with an expected crosswind from the right causing 5° of drift, what Magnetic Heading should you steer, and what will you expect the RMI to indicate?

11. To track away from an NDB on a track of 120°M, with an expected crosswind from the right causing 8° of drift, what Magnetic Heading should you steer, and what do you expect the RMI to indicate?

12. You wish to track 360°M in nil-wind conditions. What Magnetic Heading should you steer? What will the RMI indicate as you pass abeam an NDB which is 10 nm to the right of track?

13. You wish to track 360°M and expect 10° of drift caused by a wind from the East. What Magnetic Heading should you steer? What will the RMI indicate as you pass abeam an NDB which is 10 nm to the right of track?

14. You wish to track 030°M in nil-wind conditions. What Magnetic Heading should you steer? What will the RMI indicate as you pass abeam an NDB which is 10 nm to the right of track?

15. You are heading 030°M in nil-wind conditions. What is your track? What will the RMI indicate as you pass abeam an NDB which is 10 nm to the left of track?

16. You wish to track 030°M and expect 7° left drift. What Magnetic Heading should you steer? What will the RMI indicate as you pass abeam an NDB which is 10 nm to the left of track?

17. You are flying on a Magnetic Track of 239° with 7° of port drift. At a position directly abeam an NDB which is to the left of track, the RMI will read ..... ?

EXERCISES 12 – VOR

1. The VOR is a (VHF/LF/MF) Radio Navigation Aid.

2. Many VORs in the UK are coupled with an (ILS/DME/NDB/VDF).

3. An aeroplane at 3000 ft AMSL should be able to receive a VOR situated at sea level out to a range of approximately .... nm.

4. A 'Radial' is the (Magnetic/True) Bearing (to/away from) a VOR ground station.

5. *Radial* is expressed in the 'Q-Code' as ....

6. You are instructed to track outbound on the 070 radial from a VOR. The more suitable heading is (070/250).

7. You are instructed to track inbound on the 050 radial. The more suitable heading is (050/230).

8. A particular VOR may be identified by its ....

9. A VOR ground station should transmit to an accuracy of at least +/– ...°.

10. 'VOR' stands for ... .

11. The radio set in the cockpit used to select a VOR is the (VHF-COM/VHF-NAV/ADF).

12. The needle in the VOR Cockpit Display is known as the CDI, i.e. the C.... D...... I...... .

13. Any one of 360 tracks may be selected in the VOR Cockpit Display using the OBS, i.e. the O... B...... S...... , with the selected track displayed on the O..... B..... I......... .

14. A 1-dot deviation of the CDI on the VOR Cockpit Display indicates a displacement of ...° from the selected track.

15. A 2-dot deviation of the CDI on the VOR Cockpit Display indicates a displacement of ...° from the selected track.

16. A 3-dot deviation of the CDI on the VOR Cockpit Display indicates a displacement of ...° from the selected track.

A 4-dot deviation of the CDI on the VOR Cockpit Display indicates a displacement of ...° from the selected track.

18. A 5-dot deviation of the CDI on the VOR Cockpit Display indicates a displacement of ...° from the selected track.

19. If the CDI is centred with 090 selected on the OBI, and the *FROM* flag showing, what radial is the aircraft on?

20. If the CDI is centred with 090 selected, and the *TO* flag showing, what radial is the aircraft on?

21. If the CDI is 2 dots right with 090 selected, and the *TO* flag showing, what radial is the aircraft on?

22. If the CDI is 1 dot left with 090 selected on the OBI, and the *FROM* flag showing, what radial is the aircraft on?

23. Check an Aeronautical Chart and determine the frequency of the Cranfield VOR (some 40 nm NW of London) and its Morse-code *IDENT*.

24. What radial from the Cranfield VOR would keep you just to the North of D206?

25. Check an Aeronautical Chart and determine the frequency of the Newcastle VOR and its Morse-code *IDENT*.

26. What *NEW* radial would you track on to the Dean Cross VOR (DCS)?

27. What *DCS* radial would you be tracking in on from NEW?

28. On the reciprocal track, from DCS to NEW, you would track on the ...... DCS radial and the ...... NEW radial.

29. Specify three means of fixing your position in IMC conditions somewhere along the DCS to NEW track.

30. You depart over DCS at 1427 UTC and pass abeam 'CL' NDB at 1438 UTC. At what time do you estimate NEW?

31. What is the specified Designated Operational Coverage, DOC, of the Dean Cross VOR?

32. You are flying MH 080, with the OBI selected to 080, CDI needle showing 2 dots right, and the *FROM* flag showing. Your desired track is the 080 radial outbound. Is this track out to your left or your right?

33. You are flying MH 300, with the OBI selected to 300, the CDI needle showing 3 dots left, and the *TO* flag showing. Your desired track is 300°M to the VOR. Is this track out to your left or right?

34. You are flying MH 300, with the OBI selected to 300, the CDI needle showing 3 dots left, and the *TO* flag showing. If the aircraft is now turned onto the reciprocal heading of MH 120, would the indications in the VOR Cockpit Display change in any way, assuming the OBI is left unaltered?

35. Specify which of the aircraft illustrated below could have the VOR indications depicted in Instruments (i), (ii) and (iii).

Fig. 1.

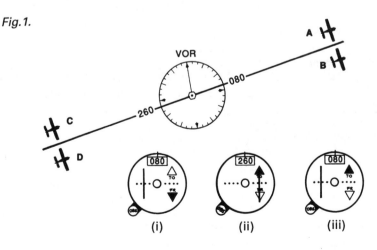

(i)   (ii)   (iii)

EXERCISES

EXERCISES 13 – ILS

1. The letters *ILS* represent I..... L..... S...... . The ILS is a (Precision/ Non-Precision) Approach.

2. Name three components of a typical ILS.

3. The ILS is normally selected in the cockpit using the (VHF-COM/VHF-NAV/ADF) radio.

4. In an aircraft fitted with only one VHF-NAV, is it possible to have an ILS and a VOR selected simultaneously?

5. In an aircraft fitted with two VHF-NAVs, is it possible to have an ILS and a VOR selected simultaneously?

6. With the Localizer selected, a full-scale deflection of the CDI indicates that the aircraft is ...° or more off the centreline.

7. The Localizer track from full-scale deflection left to full-scale deflection right covers an arc of ...°.

8. A 1-dot deflection of the CDI with the Localizer selected represents ...°, which makes the instrument ..... times as sensitive compared to when it is tuned to a VOR.

9. Localizer coverage is ... nm within +/–10° of the front-course line, and ... nm within 10°–35° of the front-course line.

10. The Glideslope is automatically selected when the Localizer frequency is selected on the VHF-NAV. (True/False)?

11. A 3° Glideslope, which is typical for an ILS, represents a loss of height of approximately .... ft per nautical mile.

12. At 5 nm from the runway threshold, an aircraft that is *on glideslope* will be at approximately ...... ft AAL.

13. At 2 nm from the runway threshold, an aircraft *on glideslope* will be at approximately ...... ft AAL.

14. To maintain the Glideslope at a Ground Speed of 60 kt requires a RoD of .... ft/min.

15. To maintain the Glideslope at a Ground Speed of 120 kt requires a RoD of .... ft/min.

16. To maintain the Glideslope at a Ground Speed of 100 kt requires a RoD of ..... ft/min.

17. There may be false Glideslopes:
    (a) only above the correct Glideslope.
    (b) only below the correct Glideslope.
    (c) both above and below the correct Glideslope.

18. The Glideslope should always be intercepted from (above/below).

19. As an aeroplane flies in at 1500 ft AAL and intercepts the Glideslope from below, the Glideslope needle should:
    (a) descend from the top of the Cockpit Indicator.
    (b) rise from the bottom of the Cockpit Indicator.

20. Descent on the Glideslope:
    (a) should not be commenced unless on track, within half-scale of the Localizer.
    (b) may be commnced upon intercept of the Glideslope, even if off track.

21. If the Glideslope fails, is it permissible to use the Localizer?

22. If the Localizer fails, is it permissible to use the Glideslope?

23. Can Marker Beacons be used for homing to a station?

24. Passage over an Outer Marker is indicated in the cockpit by ....

25. The Localizer usable coverage sector specified in UK AIP COM is +/– ...° either side of the nominal course line.

26. The Glidepath coverage is out to ... nm unless otherwise specified in UK AIP COM, and is accurate if the aircraft is within +/– ...° left or right of the Localizer centreline.

27. The Glideslope is nominally ....° to the horizontal. It (may/will never) differ from this.

28. The Glideslope, which is nominally 3° to the horizontal, is protected so that it will not give false signals if the aircraft is in the range of ....° to ....° to the horizontal.

EXERCISES 14 – VDF

1. The letters *VDF* stand for V..... D....... F....... .

2. Another abbreviation for VDF is ..... .

3. The airborne radio used for VDF is the (ADF/VHF-NAV/VHF-COM).

4. QDM is defined as ....

5. QDR is defined as ....

6. A Class-B VDF bearing is accurate to +/– ...°.

7. When tracking towards a ground station using the QDMs passed by ATC, the pilot (should/should not) allow a Wind Correction Angle to counter any crosswind effect.

8. When tracking towards a ground station, the QDMs gradually increase: QDMs 340, 342, 345. The aircraft is moving to the (left/right) of track and should turn (left/right).

9. When tracking towards a ground station, the QDMs gradually decrease: QDMs 340, 336, 330. The aircraft is moving to the (left/right) of track and should turn (left/right).

10. When tracking away from a ground station, the QDMs gradually increase: QDMs 360, 006, 010. The aircraft is moving to the (left/right) of track and should turn (left/right).

11. When tracking away from a ground station, the QDMs gradually decrease: QDMs 360, 355, 350. The aircraft is moving to the (left/right) of track and should turn (left/right).

12. The difference between a VDF Approach, in which a pilot requests QDMs from an ATSU, and a QGH Approach is ....

SECTION 3

EXERCISES 15 – PREPARATION FOR FLIGHT

This topic will be thoroughly tested in the IMC-Rating Ground Examination. Almost all of it is knowledge that you will have gained from your study of *Navigation* and *Flight Planning* in the *Air Pilot's Manual, Volume 3* (especially Chapter 13 – *Compiling a Flight Log*), and Volume 2 – *Meteorology* section. The Exercises that follow serve merely to test this knowledge. Reference to the UK AIP will also be required – use its Indexes to assist you.

Meteorology

1. An Aviation Routine Weather Report is known as a (METAR/TAF); whereas an Aerodrome Forecast is known as a (METAR/TAF).

2. Sketch the symbol found on a Meteorological Chart to indicate the following:
    (i) a cold front at the surface.
    (ii) snow.
    (iii) widespread fog.
    (iv) moderate turbulence.
    (v) hail.
    (vi) freezing precipitation.
    (vii) severe line squall.
    (viii) thunderstorm.
    (ix) rain.
    (x) drizzle.
    (xi) showers.
    (xii) severe aircraft icing.

3. Temporary variations lasting less than one hour may have this indicated in a Forecast by the use of the word ....

4. The system of providing Meteorological Information via the Public Telephone Network as well as by AFTN, Telex and facsimile equipment is known as ....

5. The *AIRMET* service consists of (1/2/3/4) routine Area Forecasts in (plain/coded) language, issued (1/2/3/4) times daily, covering the (UK only/UK and near Continent) with vertical coverage from the surface to (5000/10,000/15,000/18,000) ft AMSL, with Winds and Temperatures to (5000/10,000/15,000/18,000) ft AMSL.

6. When are METARs usually issued at those aerodromes providing the service?

7. What is the validity period of a Trend or Landing Forecast?

8. The Forecasts that are available continuously via the Public Telephone Network are issued ...... times daily.

9. When the term *NOSIG* is used in a Trend or Landing Forecast, it means ..... during the ..... hours after the observation time.

10. If you require a special forecast to cover a flight of less than 500 nm, you should give at least ..... hours notice.

11. If you require a special forecast to cover a flight of more than 500 nm, you should give at least ..... hours notice.

12. Decode the following Meteorological Information for Dundee (EGPN):
TAF EGPN 1322 18015KT 3000 OVC030 BECMG 1518 1000
Can you operate on an IMC Rating throughout the period of the TAF? Explain.

13. Decode the following Meteorological Information for Lydd (EGMD):
TAF EGMD 1018 28020KT 6000 SCT014 BECMG 1215 1200
Can you operate on an IMC Rating throughout the TAF period? Explain.

14. Decode the following Meteorological Information for Oxford (EGTK):
TAF EGTK 1220 35015G25KT 1500 OVC010 BECMG 1518 28015KT 2500 BKN015
Can you operate on an IMC Rating throughout the TAF period? Explain.

15. Decode:
TAF EGBN 0814 12015KT 1800 OVC008 BECMG 1012 BKN012
Can you operate on an IMC Rating throughout the TAF period? Explain.

16. Decode:
SAUK 0820 EGNT 12005KT 8000 HZ SCT014 06/05 Q1018

17. Does the following Forecast attached to the METAR for Halfpenny Green indicate that the aerodrome is suitable for an IMC-Rated Pilot to operate? Explain.
METAR EGBO 0940 23015G25KT 6000 BKN035 12/09 Q1003 NOSIG

18. Does the following Forecast for Aberdeen indicate that the aerodrome is suitable for an IMC-Rated Pilot to operate throughout the period? Explain.
TAF EGPD 0716 28016KT 8000 HZ BKN010 BKN035 BKN100 TEMPO 1214 28025G35KT 1000 RA+ OVC008

19. If you were unable to obtain a forecast for Inverness/Dalcross, which Forecast Office would you contact, and on what telephone number?

Safety Altitudes

20. For an IMC flight, a vertical clearance of .... ft is required above the highest obstacle within ... nm of track.

21. High obstacles close to your planned track are:
   (i) 1237 ft AMSL 3 nm left of track;
   (ii) 2598 ft AMSL 7 nm right of track; and
   (iii) 1610 ft AMSL 4 nm right of track.
   What is the lowest required Safety Altitude?

22. What is the altitude of an aircraft that is cruising at FL55 if the Regional QNH is 1023 mb?

23. What is the altitude of an aircraft that is cruising at FL55 if the Regional QNH is 1003 mb?

24. What is the altitude of an aircraft that is cruising at FL55 if the Regional QNH is 963 mb?

25. Which of the following are suitable Quadrantal Levels for an aircraft cruising on a Track of 137°M? (FL50/FL55/FL60/FL65/FL70/FL75/FL80).

26. The highest obstacle within 5 nm of track is 1950 ft. The Regional QNH is 973 mb. Planned Track is 085°M. What is the lowest suitable Flight Level according to the Quadrantal Rule?

27. The highest obstacle within 5 nm of track is 2350 ft. The Regional QNH is 953 mb. Planned Track is 045°M. What is the lowest suitable Flight Level according to the Quadrantal Rule?

Computer Calculations

28. RAS (CAS) is 95 kt. Calculate TAS at FL50, OAT +5°C.

29. RAS (CAS) is 95 kt. Calculate TAS at FL50, OAT −10°C.

30. RAS (CAS) is 95 kt. Calculate TAS at FL80, OAT +5°C.

31. IAS 95 kt, FL50, OAT −8°C, W/V 300/20, Track 010. Calculate Heading and Ground Speed.

32. What time interval is required to cover a distance of 127 nm to the destination at an average Ground Speed of 87 kt? If you depart at 0117 UTC, what is your ETA at the destination?

Charts

For these Exercises, refer to your CAA 1:500,000 ICAO Aeronautical Chart for Southern England (Sheet 2171CD). Consider the area between the aerodromes at Bristol (N51 22.9, W002 42.8) and Bournemouth (N50 46.6, W001 50.3).

33. What is the elevation of Bristol aerodrome?

34. What is the frequency of the Bristol NDB, and what is its Morse identifier?

35. What is the elevation of Bournemouth aerodrome?

36. What is the bearing and distance from Bristol aerodrome to the Bournemouth Locator, BIA, which is on the aerodrome? What is a reasonable Safety Altitude for this leg, and what approximate time interval could you expect for the flight if your expected average Ground Speed is 120 knots?

37. There is an NDB at Compton Abbas which you plan to use en route. What is its frequency and Morse-code identifier?

38. What aerial activity occurs in the vicinity of Compton Abbas?

39. What Altimeter Setting Regions will you be passing through when flying from Bristol to Bournemouth?

40. Is a full Position Report required as you cross from one ASR to the next?

41. Are you required to give a full Position Report as you pass from one FIR (Flight Information Region) to another – say on a flight North, passing from the London FIR into the Scottish FIR?

42. What is the Transition Altitude at Bristol?

43. What is the FIS frequency that you would use on the flight from Bristol to Bournemouth?

44. What is the large area surrounded by a thick purple-shaded border which is marked on the chart about 10 nm South of Bristol?

45. What is the nature of the airspace around Yeovilton aerodrome?

46. On what frequency would you request a Lower Airspace Radar Service, LARS, in the vicinity of Yeovilton?

47. Within what distance of a participating ATSU is LARS normally available?

48. How could you identify the Yeovilton Aerodrome Identification Beacon, if it is in operation?

49. If, while en route, you decided to penetrate a MATZ, where could you find the appropriate procedures to use, and what would be your initial radio call?

50. What are the radio frequencies for Bristol Tower and Bristol Approach?

51. Who operates Bristol Aerodrome?

52. What is the length of the longest runway at Bristol?

53. Where in the UK AIP would you look to determine the Air Traffic Control rules specific to the Bristol Class D controlled airspace?

54. What is the radio navigation facility situated approximately 22 nm Northeast of Bournemouth, and what is its frequency and IDENT?

55. What is the nature of the airspace surrounding Bournemouth aerodrome?

56. On what VHF-COM frequency would you request permission to enter the Southampton Class D Control Area, if you need to do so?

57. What details would you specify in your radio call?

58. Where are the Loss of Communications procedures specified for an aircraft being radar vectored at Bournemouth?

59. About 17 nm SW of Bournemouth is an area labelled P047. What is its significance?

60. About 26 nm SW of Bournemouth is an area labelled D020. What is its significance, and who can assist with crossing information?

61. On what frequency would you listen to a VOLMET covering Bournemouth?

62. A locator beacon, IDENT *BIA,* is situated at Bournemouth. What is the range of the locator, and where is it in relation to the aerodrome?

Fuel Calculations

63. You need to uplift 15 US gallons of AVGAS. How many litres would you order from the fuel agent?

64. Fuel required at start-up is 43 US gallons. The fuel remaining in your tanks is 13 US gallons. How many litres will you order?

65. Calculate the fuel required for a flight of 100 minutes duration at an average consumption rate of 9.5 USG per hr, allowing 60 mins reserve. What is the margin (in US gallons and in minutes) if there is 48 USG on board?

66. Flight time is 73 minutes. Fuel consumption on the cruise is 7.0 USG/hr, with an additional allowance of 2.5 USG for start-up, take-off and climb to cruise level. Descent and landing may be calculated at cruise rate. What is the minimum required fuel on board (FOB) at start-up, allowing 45 minutes reserve at cruise rate? Give the answer in US Gallons and Litres. If the Specific Gravity is 0.72, what is the weight of the FOB in kg and lb?

67. What total fuel is required at take-off for a flight of 63 minutes to a destination for which an alternate aerodrome is required because of poor weather conditions forecast for the time of arrival.
    - Flight time to the alternate is 17 minutes.
    - Cruise consumption rate is 8 USG/hr.
    - Allow 2 USG for climb to cruise altitude.
    - Descent and landing may be calculated at cruise rate, although 2 USG should be allowed for an NDB Approach at the destination.
    - Allow 10.0 USG Reserve Fuel.

    If the Fuel on Board at take-off is 30.0 USG, how much of this is available for contingencies, calculated at cruise rate?

68. Calculate the fuel required in US gallons for the following flight:
    Start-up, taxi, take-off .... 3 USG
    Flight fuel to destination (1 hr 30 mins at 12 USG per hr)
    Approach and missed approach .... 3 USG
    Alternate fuel .... (20 mins at 12 USG per hr)
    Holding .... (45 mins at 12 USG per hr)
    Approach and landing .... 3 USG
    Reserve fuel .... (30 mins at 12 USG per hr)

Weight-and-Balance

69. An aeroplane (may/must not) be flown overloaded.

70. Compared with a correctly loaded aeroplane, an overloaded aeroplane will have (a higher/a lower/the same) stalling speed, (a higher/a lower/the same) acceleration during the take-off run, requiring (a longer/a shorter/the same) take-off distance, (a poorer/a better/the same) rate of climb, (a higher/a lower/the same) maximum operating altitude, (a longer/a shorter/the same) landing distance.

71. An aeroplane that is loaded incorrectly, with the Centre of Gravity outside limits, (may/will not) be difficult, or even impossible, to control.

72. 1 US gallon of AVGAS weighs .... lb.

73. What payload can be carried if the following conditions apply?
    Maximum take-off weight authorised .... 2200 lb
    Pilot weight .... 180 lb
    Aircraft empty weight (including oil and unusable fuel) ..... 1450 lb
    Fuel at take-off .... 25 USG (SG = 0.72)

74. What payload can be carried if the following conditions apply?
    Maximum take-off weight authorised .... 2550 lb
    Pilot weight .... 180 lb
    Aircraft empty weight (including oil and unusable fuel) ..... 1730 lb
    Fuel at take-off .... 39 USG (SG = 0.72)

IFR

75. Which of the following Instrument Flight Rules apply to a flight by an IMC-Rated Pilot operating completely Outside Controlled Airspace?
    (a) Rule 29: the Minimum Height Rule.
    (b) Rule 30: the Quadrantal Rule.
    (c) Rule 31: Flight Plan and ATC Clearance
    (d) Rule 32: Position Reports

76. May a Flight Plan be submitted for any flight?

77. Must a Flight Plan be submitted for a flight of 130 nm outside regulated airspace by an IMC-Rated Pilot in an aeroplane whose Maximum Total Authorised Weight is less than 5700 kg, or is it optional?

78. Must a Flight Plan be submitted for a flight of 130 nm outside regulated airspace by an IMC-Rated Pilot in an aeroplane whose Maximum Total Authorised Weight exceeds 5700 kg, or is it optional?

En Route Calculations

79. If 25 nm is covered in 12 minutes, what is the Ground Speed? How long will it take to cover a further 15 nm?

80. If the aeroplane is 3 nm left of track after 30 nm, what heading change is required to regain track:
    (i) in another 30 nm?
    (ii) in 15 nm?

EXERCISES

Flight Procedures

81. To within what distance of an Approach Control unit is a Radar Advisory Service normally limited?

82. Specify the components of a standard Position Report.

83. Any Emergency Message or Urgency Message should be passed on the frequency in use or on the Emergency VHF frequency of .... MHz, and be prefixed by the words ..... or ..... .

84. Flight over a congested area should be at an altitude of at least ..... ft above the highest fixed object within ..... ft of the aircraft or at a height at which it can ...... clear in the event of engine failure, whichever is (higher/lower). These low flying regulations are specified in Rule (5/17/21).

85. You are given the following departure clearance, *"Turn right on track, not above 2500 ft QNH until East of the city."* You should fly (at/at or below/at or above) 2500 ft until East of the city, and not lower than ....

86. You are given the following departure clearance, *"Turn left on track, not above 2000 ft QNH until North of the city."* The highest obstacle within 2000 ft of the aircraft is 350 ft AMSL, and the estimated height needed to glide clear of the small town in case of engine failure is 1500 ft AMSL. You should cross the city at or between the altitudes of ....

87. When a pilot is using the Radar Information Service, RIS, or the Radar Advisory Service, RAS, the responsibility for maintaining adequate terrain clearance rests with the (pilot/radar service controller).

88. RIS controllers will give (traffic information only/traffic information plus advice on collision avoidance action).

89. RAS controllers will give (traffic information only/traffic information plus advice on collision avoidance action).

90. Whilst en route, you call the nominated Air Traffic Service Unit to establish if a particular Danger Area is active. You do not get a response. You should assume that the Danger Area is (active/inactive).

91. To cross a Control Zone in Class D airspace around a busy controlled airport, you (should/need not) file a flight plan on the ground or in the air, and then obtain an .... before entering the airspace. Two-way radio communications with ATC (are/are not) required.

92. If you experience radio failure before entering controlled airspace, you should (continue and land at the controlled aerodrome/remain clear of the controlled airspace and land as soon as possible at a suitable aerodrome).

Visual Illusions

93. Sloping cloud banks by day or town lights on a hillside at night (can/will not) cause visual illusions of a false horizon.

94. The normal approach path to an upwards-sloping runway will appear to be too (steep/shallow), causing a tendency to fly too (high/low) on slope.

95. During a night approach, the apparent gap between the runway edge lights is reducing. The aeroplane is flying to an aiming point (before/at/beyond) the normal aiming point.

96. Making a 'black-hole approach' at night in clear conditions, with no approach-slope guidance, the runway may appear to be (closer/further away) than what it really is, causing a tendency for the pilot to (undershoot/overshoot) the approach.

425

EXERCISES 16 – INSTRUMENT DEPARTURES

1. The minimum recommended conditions for take-off by an IMC-Rated Pilot in a single-engined aeroplane are:
   (i) a cloud ceiling of .... ft AAL; and
   (ii) a visibility of ..... metres.

2. SID charts are produced for some busy aerodromes. The term 'SID' is an abbreviation for S....... I........ D........ .

3. When climbing to cruise at 3000 ft AMSL, the Altimeter subscale setting should be on ..... mb(hPa).

4. When climbing to cruise above the Transition Level, the Altimeter subscale setting should be changed to ....

5. Shortly after departure, you will be passing near a MATZ with a stub. Sketch a typical MATZ and stub with its vertical and horizontal dimensions.

EXERCISES 17 – HOLDING AND MANOEUVRING

1. The shape of a typical Holding Pattern is a:
   (a) circle.　　　　(b) racetrack.
   (c) rectangle.　　 (d) ellipse.

2. A complete one-minute Holding Pattern will take .... minutes if flown perfectly.

3. In strong head/tailwind conditions, on the outbound leg of a Holding Pattern the timing should be adjusted by .... second(s) per knot of the estimated head/tailwind component.

4. With an estimated 15-knot tailwind component on the outbound leg of a Holding Pattern, it is reasonable to adjust the timing by ..... .

5. Whilst tracking guidance is usually available to you on the inbound leg to the Holding Fix, on the outbound leg there is generally none. In strong crosswind conditions, it is suggested that a drift correction of .... be applied on the outbound leg.

6. If a WCA of 5° to the left is required to track correctly on the inbound leg of a Holding Pattern, then a suitable correction on the outbound leg is .... .

7. Sketch three diagrams of a Holding Pattern, showing the three Sector Entries.

8. A Sector-1 Entry is also known as a .... Entry.

9. A Sector-2 Entry is also known as a .... Entry.

10. A Sector-3 Entry is also known as a .... Entry.

11. Sketch the pattern of a 45°/180° Procedure Turn used to reverse direction.

EXERCISES 18 – INSTRUMENT APPROACHES

1. The Altimeter Setting given to arriving aircraft will initially be:
   (a) Standard Pressure 1013.2 mb.
   (b) Aerodrome QNH.
   (c) Aerodrome QFE.
   (d) Threshold QFE.

2. The MSA, an abbreviation for M..... S....... A....., published on *Jeppesen* Instrument Approach Charts will provide at least ..... metres, ... ft, vertical clearance within ..... nm of the Homing Facility. *Aerad* Approach Charts show a similar minimum altitude as S..... S.... A....... .

3. The tracks shown on Instrument Approach Charts are in (°Magnetic/°True).

4. On Final Approach of an instrument let-down that is closely aligned with the landing runway, it is usual in the UK to have ...... set in the Altimeter subscale, so that the Altimeter indicates ....

5. When circling to land on a runway with which the Final Segment of the Instrument Approach is not aligned, it is usual in the UK to have ...... set in the Altimeter subscale so that the Altimeter indicates ....

6. Name the five possible segments of an Instrument Approach.

7. A *Feeder Route* or *Terminal Route* is an .... Segment.

8. *Crossing Heights* and *Step-Down Fixes* shown on an Instrument Approach Chart (are/are not) limiting heights, and (should/need not) be crossed at or above their minimum crossing heights.

9. Descent on the Final Approach Segment of an ILS should not be commenced until the aircraft is within ..... scale deflection of the Localizer.

10. Descent on the Final Approach Segment of an NDB or VOR let-down should not be commenced until the aircraft is within .... of the Final Approach Track.

11. An Instrument Approach in which both tracking guidance and electronic glideslope guidance is provided is a (Precision/Non-Precision) Approach.

12. The term *Decision Height* applies to a (Precision/Non-Precision) Approach.

13. The term *Minimum Descent Height* applies to a (Precision/Non-Precision) Approach.

14. The appropriate Decision Height for an ILS:
    (a) will be given to the pilot by ATC.
    (b) must be calculated by the pilot.

15. If a pilot does not become visual during a Precision Approach, then he:
    (a) should commence a Missed Approach at or above his calculated Decision Height.
    (b) should commence a Missed Approach at or above his calculated Minimum Descent Height.
    (c) may track in at his calculated MDH or DH to the aid, from where he should commence a Missed Approach.
    (d) should descend lower in IMC conditions in an attempt to become visual.

16. If a pilot does not become visual during a Non-Precision Approach, then he:
    (a) should commence a Missed Approach at or above his calculated Descision Height.
    (b) should commence a Missed Approach at or above his calculated Minimum Descent Height.
    (c) may track in at his calculated MDH to the MAPt, from where he should commence a Missed Approach.
    (d) may track in at his DH to the MAPt, from where he should commence a Missed Approach.
    (e) should descend lower in IMC conditions in an attempt to become visual.

As an Exercise, compare *Aerad* or *Jeppesen* Instrument Approach Charts for the following let-downs with the descriptions and information given in UK AIP RAC 4 and AGA, and consider the following quesions (to which we will not give answers, since the let-downs will change from time to time). Terms used include: IAF – Initial Approach Fix; IF – Intermediate Fix; FAF – Final Approach Fix; FAT – Final Approach Track; MAPt – Missed Approach Point.

East Midlands NDB Rwy 09

- What is the date of the chart?
- What radio communications frequencies should be used?
- What is the MSA for an aircraft arriving from the North?
- What is the Transition Altitude over East Midlands?
- What is the NDB frequency?
- Which radio set is used to select this frequency?
- How would you identify the NDB?
- What is the Aerodrome Elevation?
- What is the Runway 09 Threshold Elevation?
- What is your calculated MDH for this approach?
- Why is it MDH, and not DH?
- What visibility do you require to continue the approach to a landing?
- What runway length is available for landing?
- What is your calculated Visual Manoeuvring OCH if you were to use this approach to become visual for a circling approach onto Rwy 27?
- At or above what height should you be when commencing the outbound leg from the LOM?
- What is the outbound track, and is it stated as °M or °T?
- At or above what minimum height should you be during the procedure turn?
- What is the inbound track?
- What angular deviation from track is considered to be sufficiently on track when inbound before commencing further descent (+/–5° or +/–10°)?
- At or above what height should you remain prior to the Locator?
- If not visual at your calculated MDH, may you track in to the aerodrome at this height, or must you immediately commence a Missed Approach?
- What is the Missed Approach Point for the approach?
- Describe the Missed Approach.
- What two radio navigation aids can be used for tracking guidance during the Missed Approach?
- Any climbing instructions passed to you by ATC during the Missed Approach will be in terms of (Altitude/Height AAL).

Scilly Isles NDB Rwy 28

- What is the date of the chart?
- What is the MSA for an aircraft approaching the Scilly Isles NDB from the Northeast?
- For what Aeroplane Categories is the chart valid?
- What is the frequency of Scillies Approach/Tower?
- What is the Transition Altitude over the Scilly Isles?
- What is the frequency of the NDB?
- How would you identify it?
- Describe the Direct Arrival procedure whereby the Final Approach Track is intercepted off the direct track from the VOR LND 242 radial.
- What radio set is tuned to the LND VOR to enable this intercept?

- What radio set is tuned to the STM NDB to enable this intercept?
- At what DME distance from LND should the FAT be intercepted?
- How is the DME selected in the aircraft?
- What is the nominal distance from this point to the Runway Threshold?
- Is there a DME available at Scilly Isles to assist you?
- Describe the Holding Pattern.
- What is the inbound track of the Racetrack Procedure?
- What is the minimum height at which the procedure may be commenced?
- How close to the inbound track should the ADF indications be before you commence further descent?
- What is your calculated MDH for this approach? *(see our Chapter 19 and UK AIP RAC 4-2 and 4-3)*
- What is your calculated Visual Manoeuvring OCH for circling, if necessary? *(see UK AIP RAC 4-2)*
- What is the Elevation of the aerodrome?
- What runway length is available for landing?
- At what RoD in ft/min should you descend to achieve a 3° descent gradient if your Ground Speed is 90 kt?
- What is the Missed Approach Point (MAPt)?
- Describe the Missed Approach Procedure.
- Are you permitted to use the procedure if your aircraft is not fitted with VOR/DME?

Kirkwall VOR/DME Rwy 27

- What is the date of the chart?
- What radio communications frequencies should be used?
- What is the MSA for an aircraft arriving from the Southeast?
- What is the Transition Altitude over Kirkwall?
- On which navigation facilities is the approach based?
- What is the VOR frequency and which radio set is used to select it?
- Can you make the approach if your DME is unable to receive the KWL DME?
- What is the Aerodrome Elevation?
- What is the Runway 27 Threshold Elevation?
- What runway length is available for landing?
- What is your calculated MDH for this approach?
- Why is it an MDH rather than a DH?
- What visibility do you require to continue the approach to a landing?
- What is your calculated Visual Manoeuvring OCH if you were to use this approach to become visual for a circling approach onto Rwy 33?
- What is the Track for the outbound leg?
- What angular deviation from track is indicated by a two-dot deviation on the CDI? (VHF-NAV tuned to the VOR)
- At what DME distance do you commence the base turn right?
- At or above what minimum height should you be during the base turn?
- What is the Final Approach Track?
- What is the Final Approach Fix?
- How do determine the IAF when making a Direct Arrival from the South?
- How do you join the FAT if making a Direct Arrival from the South?
- What is the minimum height on the DME arc?
- If making the approach without DME, how do you determine the position at which to commence the reversal procedure?

- What percentage is the Final Approach Gradient?
- On this gradient, at what height should you be passing 3 DME on Final Approach?
- If not visual at your calculated MDH, are you permitted to track in to the aerodrome at this height, or must you immediately commence a Missed Approach?
- What is the MAPt for the approach?
- Describe the Missed Approach.
- Any climbing instructions passed to you by ATC during the Missed Approach will be in terms of (altitude AMSL/height AAL).

East Midlands ILS Rwy 09

- What is the date of the chart?
- What radio communications frequencies should be used?
- What is the MSA for an aircraft arriving from the South?
- What is the transition altitude over East Midlands?
- What is the Localizer frequency?
- Which radio set is used to select this frequency?
- Does the ILS Glideslope have to be selected separately, or is it automatically selected with the Localizer?
- What is the Aerodrome Elevation?
- What is the Runway 09 Threshold Elevation?
- What runway length is available for landing?
- What is your calculated DH for this approach?
- Why is it DH and not MDH?
- What visibility do you require to continue the approach to a landing?
- What is your calculated Visual Manoeuvring OCH if you were to use this approach to become visual for a circling approach onto Rwy 27?
- What does 'LOM' mean?
- How do you recognise passage of the LOM?
- At or above what height should you be when commencing the outbound leg from the LOM?
- At or above what minimum height should you be during the procedure turn?
- Should the Localizer have been intercepted before descent is commenced using the glideslope?
- Before descent on the Glideslope can be commenced, what Localizer CDI deviation is considered to be sufficiently on track: (full-scale/half-scale/precisely on track)?
- What height at the LOM verifies the accuracy of the Glideslope? Is this height AMSL (QNH) or AAL (QFE)?
- If not visual at your calculated DH, are you permitted to track in to the aerodrome at this height, or must you immediately commence a Missed Approach?
- What is the MAPt for the approach?
- Describe the Missed Approach.
- Any climbing instructions passed to you by ATC during the Missed Approach will be in terms of (altitude AMSL/height AAL).

Bristol VDF 27
- What is the date of the chart?
- What is the VHF-COM frequency to be used during the approach?
- What is the MSA if the aircraft is approaching Bristol from the Northeast?
- What is the Transition Altitude over Bristol?
- What is the Airport Elevation?
- What is the commencement height of the VDF/DF procedure?
- What is the track outbound, and what QDM would indicate that you are on track? What QDR would indicate that you are on track?
- If the QDMs gradually increase on the outbound leg, would you turn left or right to regain track?
- To what height may you descend on the outbound leg?
- What QDM would indicate that you are on track when proceeding inbound?
- If the QDMs gradually increase on the inbound leg, would you turn left or right to regain track?
- What is your calculated MDH?
- What is your minimum required visibility to make a landing?
- What runway length is available for landing?
- What is the MAPt for the approach?
- Describe the Missed Approach Procedure.

Edinburgh SRA Rwy 07
- What is the date of the Approach Chart?
- What is the MSA for an aircraft arriving from the Southeast?
- What is the Rwy 07 ILS frequency, to assist with your final approach?
- How would you identify it?
- What is the Radar Termination Range (RTR) for the SRA procedure?
- What is the FAF and what is the minimum height prior to passing it?
- At what distance and minimum height is the Step Down Fix?
- What Locator beacons would you tune to assist in orientation as ATC vectors you towards Runway 07?
- How would you identify them?
- What is the MAPt?
- Descibe the Missed Approach Procedure.
- You break clear of cloud in the final approach area, but suddenly lose radio contact. What flight path would you follow until contact is re-established?
- State the SSR Transponder code to squawk if radio contact is not regained?

EXERCISES 19 – INSTRUMENT MINIMA

Take-Off and Landing
1. When planning a take-off in minimum conditions of visibility, a prime consideration, if flying a single-engined aircraft, is to be able to make a safe .... in the event of engine failure.
2. The UK AIP states that the minimum conditions for take-off should never be less than .... ft cloud ceiling or ..... metres visibility.
3. The minimum visibility required for landing for an IMC-Rated Pilot is .... .
4. The minimum cloud ceiling required for landing by an IMC-Rated Pilot descending through cloud for an approach and landing is ..... .

5. Should a pilot continue an approach for which the cloud ceiling is reported to be less than his calculated DH or MDH, or the visibility below the value required?

6. Is a visibility of 4000 given in a METAR sufficient for take-off by an IMC-Rated Pilot?

7. Is a visibility of 1500 given in a METAR sufficient for take-off by an IMC-Rated Pilot?

En Route

8. May an IMC-Rated Pilot fly in cloud?

9. Whilst cruising in IMC Conditions, what is the minimum suitable obstacle clearance?

Approach

10. A Precision Approach is one in which both tracking and accurate slope guidance is provided. (True/False)?

11. A Non-Precision Approach is one in which both tracking and accurate slope guidance is provided. (True/False)?

12. The minimum height calculated for a Precision Approach is known as the (Decision Height, DH/Minimum Descent Height, MDH).

13. The minimum height calculated for a Non-Precision Approach is known as the (Decision Height, DH/Minimum Descent Height, MDH).

14. The Missed Approach following a Precision Approach in which you do not become visual must be commenced:
(a) as soon as the DA(H) is reached.
(b) at the Missed Approach Point, MAPt, after tracking level to the aid.

15. The Missed Approach following a Non-Precision Approach in which you do not become visual must be commenced:
(a) as soon as the DA(H) is reached.
(b) at the MAPt, after tracking to the MAPt at or above the MDH.

16. Vertical distance shown on the Altimeter when QFE is set is known as (Height/Altitude).

17. Vertical distance shown on the Altimeter when QNH is set is known as (Height/Altitude).

18. On Final Approach, it is usual in the UK to have (QFE/QNH/1013 mb) set in the Altimeter subscale.

19. The Absolute Minimum Height for a Non-Precision Approach flown by an IMC-Rated Pilot is .... ft AAL.

20. The Absolute Minimum Height for a Precision Approach flown by an IMC-Rated Pilot is .... ft AAL.

21. Obstacle clearance information on Instrument Approach Charts is given in the form of O....... C......... H...... .

22. Most training aeroplanes have a nominal threshold speed, V_{AT}, of less than 91 kt and so, for the purposes of Obstacle Clearance Height, fall into Category (A/B/C/D/E).

23. Obstacle Clearance information, applicable to Category A aeroplanes, is specified in RAC 4-3. An IMC-Rated pilot must add .... ft to these, and then take the greater of this value and the Absolute Minima of ..... ft AAL for a Precision Approach or ..... ft AAL for a Non-Precision Approach, as appropriate.

24. If the published OCH for an ILS is 180 ft, then the System Minimum of .... ft (will/will not) take precedence. To this figure, an IMC-Rated Pilot (should/should not) add .... ft as an Altimeter Position Error Correction, plus a further .... ft to obtain a Decision Height of .... ft. This (is less than/equals/exceeds) the Absolute Minimum for an ILS of .... ft, which therefore makes the final Decision Height ..... ft.

25. If the published OCH for an ILS is 320 ft, then the System Minimum of .... ft (will/will not) take precedence. To this figure, an IMC-Rated Pilot (should/should not) add .... ft as an Altimeter Position Error Correction, plus a further .... ft to obtain a Minimum Descent Height of .... ft. This (is less than/equals/exceeds) the Absolute Minimum for an ILS of .... ft, which therefore makes the final Minimum Descent Height ..... ft.

26. If the published OCH for an NDB Approach is 600 ft, then the System Minimum of .... ft (will/will not) take precedence. To this figure, an IMC-Rated Pilot (should/should not) add .... ft as an Altimeter Position Error Correction, plus a further .... ft to obtain a Minimum Descent Height of .... ft. This (is less than/equals/exceeds) the Absolute Minimum for an NDB Approach of .... ft, which therefore makes the final Minimum Descent Height ..... ft.

27. If the published OCH for a VDF Approach is 420 ft, then the System Minimum of .... ft (will/will not) take precedence. To this figure, an IMC-Rated Pilot (should/should not) add .... ft as an Altimeter Position Error Correction, plus a further .... ft to obtain a Minimum Descent Height of .... ft. This (is less than/equals/exceeds) the Absolute Minimum for a VDF Approach of ..... ft, which therefore makes the final Minimum Descent Height ..... ft.

28. (i) What is the published OCH for a Rwy 02 VOR/DME Approach at Southampton/Eastleigh, and the Recommended Minima for an Instrument-Rated Pilot?
    (ii) What minima must an IMC-Rated Pilot use?
    (iii) Does the following weather report at Southampton/Eastleigh meet the recommended minima for approach and landing for an IMC-Rated Pilot?
          03015KT 1400 DZ BKN0600 08/08 Q1015
    (iv) What hazards to aviation (if any) would you expect from the weather described in the METAR?

29. What is the published OCH for a Rwy 09 ILS at Jersey, Channel Islands, and what are the recommended minima for an Instrument-Rated Pilot? What minima must an IMC-Rated Pilot use?

30. During an ILS Approach, ATC advises recommended minima of Decision Height 370 ft and RVR 800 metres. What minima should an IMC-Rated Pilot use?

31. During an ILS Approach, ATC advises recommended minima of Decision Height 250 ft and RVR 600 metres. What minima should an IMC-Rated Pilot use?

32. What are the recommended weather minima for an IMC-Rated Pilot to make a Rwy 13 NDB Approach at Plymouth? What are the recommended minima for a Rwy 13 NDB/DME Approach?

33. Is it advisable that a pilot be in practice and have flown an Instrument Approach within the previous few weeks before commencing an Instrument Approach in poor weather conditions?

34. If a pilot is out of practice, should he increase his personal minimum height for a particular Instrument Approach?

35. What instruments would you expect to be affected by the attitude change at the commencement of a Missed Approach, and for what reasons?

EXERCISES 20 – VISUAL MANOEUVRING

1. For Visual Manoeuvring (Circling) in the vicinity of an aerodrome, a minimum in-flight visibility of not less than ...... metres is recommended.

2. The Visual Manoeuvring (Circling) Area for Category A aeroplanes, that circle at less than 100 kt, is ..... nm radius from the runway thresholds.

3. The safety margin for Visual Manoeuvring in the Circling Area around an aerodrome is ...... ft above the highest obstacle. If the highest obstacle in the Circling Area is 370 ft, then the Visual Manoeuvring Height is ...... ft.

4. If there are no specific obstacles, then ..... ft is allowed for the growth of trees and foliage, etc., giving the lowest permissible Visual Manoeuvring OCH of .... ft.

5. What is the Visual Manoeuvring (Circling) OCH at Guernsey?

6. What is the Visual Manoeuvring (Circling) OCH at East Midlands?

7. What is the Visual Manoeuvring (Circling) OCH at Swansea?

8. An IMC-Rated Pilot can take off or land if the flight visibility below cloud is ..... metres or greater, and can fly on a Special VFR clearance in a Control Zone if the flight visibility is ..... km or greater.

EXERCISES on APPENDIX 1 – THE IMC RATING

1. The letters 'IMC' are an abbreviation for I....... M....... C....... .

2. The letters 'IFR' are an abbreviation for I........ F....... R........ .

3. An IMC Rating (is/is not) the same as an IFR Rating, which is also known as an Instrument Rating.

4. An Instrument Meteorological Conditions (IMC) Rating extends the privileges of a Private Pilot's Licence (Aeroplanes) Holder to allow flight as Pilot-in-Command, PIC – also known as Pilot-in-Charge – out of sight of the earth's surface. (True/False)?

5. An IMC Rating (extends/does not extend) the privileges of a PPL(A) Holder to allow flight as PIC in a Control Zone on a Special VFR Clearance with Flight Visibility less than 8 km but not less than 3 km.

6. An IMC Rating (extends/does not extend) the privileges of a PPL(A) Holder to allow flight as PIC when in IMC Outside Airspace Notified for ANO Schedule 8.

7. An IMC Rating (extends/does not extend) the privileges of a PPL(A) Holder to allow flight as PIC carrying passengers above 3000 ft AMSL in IMC or in a Flight Visibility less than 5 km at or below that height, when Outside ANO-Schedule-8 Notified Airspace.

8. An IMC Rating (extends/does not extend) the privileges of a PPL(A) Holder to allow flight as PIC during take-off or landing with a flight visibility below cloud of not less than 1800 m.

9. An IMC Rating (extends/does not extend) the privileges of a PPL(A) Holder to allow flight as PIC in controlled airspace under circumstances which require compliance with the Instrument Flight Rules.

10. An IMC Rating allows a pilot to fly in controlled airspace under IFR:
    - (a) never.
    - (b) in Entry/Exit Lanes.
    - (c) below 3000 ft AMSL.
    - (d) if he can see the ground.

11. An IMC Rating allows a pilot to fly in controlled airspace on an SVFR Clearance if the flight visibility is not less than:
    - (a) 10 nm.
    - (b) 8 km.
    - (c) 3 km.
    - (d) 1800 m.

12. Is the IMC Rating recognised in the UK?

13. Is the IMC Rating recognised in the Channel Islands?

14. Is the IMC Rating recognised in the Isle of Man?

15. Is the IMC Rating recognised in France?

16. Is the IMC Rating recognised in the USA?

17. Is the IMC Rating recognised anywhere outside the UK, Channel Islands and the Isle of Man?

18. An applicant for an IMC Rating must have .... hours of experience as an aeroplane pilot since the date of application for his PPL(A).

19. The IMC Rating Certificate of Test, C of T, is valid for a period of .... months from the date of the successful Flight Test.

20. Your initial Flight Test for an IMC Rating carried out on May 17th 1995 is successful, and the IMC Rating is issued to you on June 3rd. The last day for which the Rating is valid without a further Flight Test is .... ?

21. Your initial Flight Test for an IMC Rating carried out on December 23rd 1994 is successful, and the IMC Rating is issued to you on January 9th. The last day for which the Rating is valid without a further Flight Test is .... ?

22. The minimum Flight Visibility for take-off and landing for the Holder of an IMC Rating is .... m, below cloud.

ANSWERS

ANSWERS – ATTITUDE FLYING
(covering entire Section 1)
1. the flight instruments and what his eyes tell him
2. level, eyes
3. right-banked, the 'leans', use your eyes
4. should, eyes
5. up, backwards, use your eyes
6. down, forwards, use your eyes
7. vertigo
8. can
9. pitot and static pressures
10. static pressure
11. Regional QNH
12. 1013.2 mb
13. Aerodrome QNH
14. QFE
15. Aerodrome QNH, causing the Altimeter to read 'altitude' (UK AIP RAC 2-3)
16. suction
17. suction
18. (b)
19. (b)
20. (c)
21. (c)
22. remain unaffected
23. Airspeed Indicator only
24. dynamic, pitot, static
25. pitot
26. dynamic, zero
27. increases, too low
28. (c) – TAS 108 kt (see Vol. 3, Ch. 2)
29. TAS 115 kt
30. QNH 1012 mb, QFE 985 mb (see Vol. 3 Ch. 6)
31. 3010 ft AMSL; no – since 1000-foot clearance is required
32. sluggish, and lag behind
33. North and South
34. undershoot
35. overshoot
36. reversed
37. smaller near the Equator
38. East and West
39. AI, DI and Turn Co-ordinator (or Turn Indicator)
40. The gyroscope of the AI could run down, causing the AI to become sluggish and erratic.

ANSWERS 9 – RADAR
1. radar vectoring
2. (b) – Procedural Separation
3. Transponder
4. Surveillance Radar Approach
5. 300 ft/min
6. 450 ft/min
7. 1800 m
8. 600 ft AAL
9. 95 nm
10. 55 nm
11. 61 nm
12. UK AIP RAC 7-4

ANSWERS 10 – DME
1. Distance Measuring Equipment
2. (c) – slant distance
3. VHF-NAV
4. 10 nm in 5 min = GS 120 kt
5. 10 nm in 7 min = GS 86 kt
6. 14 nm
7. (a) – circular position line

ANSWERS 11a – NDB/ADF
1. Non-Directional Beacon
2. ground-based transmitter
3. Low Frequency or Medium Frequency bands (LF/MF)
4. Automatic Direction Finding
5. airborne receiver
6. its Morse Code IDENT
7. "dah-dit-dit-dit dit-dah-dah-dit dit-dah-dit-dit"
8. Select the ADF frequency, identify the NDB or Locator, and check that the needle is indeed 'ADFing'.

9. magnetic bearing to the ground station
10. magnetic bearing from the ground station
11. Relative Bearing Indicator
12. (i) QDM 280°M (ii) QDR 100°M
13. (i) QDM 240°M (ii) QDR 060°M
14. 25 nm
15. Locator
16. LOM (Locator Outer Marker)
17. may
18. may
19. +/–5° (UK AIP COM 0-4)
20. *Refer to a CAA 1/2 million aeronautical chart.*

ANSWERS 11b – RBI
1. QDM 075, QDR 255, QTE 251
2. QDM 330, QDR 150, QTE 146
3. right turn onto MH 130, RBI 270
4. right turn onto MH 100, RBI 300
5. right
6. left
7. right
8. 060°M
9. right
10. MH 345, RBI 355
11. MH 128, RBI 172
12. MH 360, RBI 090
13. MH 010, RBI 080
14. MH 030, RBI 090
15. 030°M, RBI 270
16. MH 037, RBI 263
17. RBI 084
18. RBI 264
19. RBI 275

ANSWERS 11c – RMI
1. QDM 075, QDR 255, QTE 251
2. QDM 330, QDR 150, QTE 146
3. right turn onto MH 130, RMI 040
4. right turn onto MH 100, RMI 040
5. right, RMI 075
6. left, RMI 320, RMI tail on 140
7. left, RMI 270, RMI tail on 090
8. 060°M
9. right
10. MH 345, RMI 340
11. MH 128, RMI 300, RMI tail 120
12. MH 360, RMI 090
13. MH 010, RMI 090
14. MH 030, RMI 120
15. 030°M, RMI 300
16. MH 037, RMI 300
17. RMI 149

ANSWERS 12 – VOR
1. VHF
2. DME
3. 67 nm
4. a radial is a magnetic bearing *FROM* a VOR ground station
5. QDR
6. MH 070
7. MH 230
8. Morse-code IDENT
9. +/–2° accuracy
10. VHF Omni-Directional Radio Range
11. VHF-NAV
12. Course Deviation Indicator
13. Omni Bearing Selector, Omni Bearing Indicator
14. 2°
15. 4°
16. 6°
17. 8°
18. 10° or more
19. 090 radial
20. 270 radial
21. 274 radial (i.e. 094-TO)
22. 092 radial
23. CFD, 116.5 MHz, *"dah-dit-dah-dit dit-dit-dah-dit dah-dit-dit"*
24. CFD 070 radial
25. NEW, 114.25 MHz, *"dah-dit dit dit-dah-dah"*
26. 258 NEW radial
27. 078 DCS radial
28. outbound from DCS on the 078 DCS radial, and inbound to NEW on the 258 NEW radial
29. (i) using the *DCS* VOR/DME combination to provide a radial and a distance; (ii) using *NEW* VOR/DME; (iii) using one of the VORs and an abeam position off the Carlisle NDB
30. 22 nm in 11 min = GS 120, 38 nm will take 19 min, ETA 1457
31. DOC 60 nm/50,000 ft; 100 nm in the sector 270°–360°T (UK AIP COM 2)
32. desired track is out to the right
33. desired track is out to the left
34. No, the VOR Cockpit Display is not heading sensitive.
35. (i) Aircraft B (ii) Aircraft B (iii) Aircraft D

ANSWERS 13 – ILS
1. Instrument Landing System, Precision Approach
2. Localizer, Glideslope, Marker Beacon(s)
3. VHF-NAV
4. no
5. yes, on different VHF-NAVs
6. 2.5°
7. 5°
8. 0.5°, 4 times
9. 25 nm, 17 nm
10. True
11. 300 ft/nm
12. 1500 ft AAL
13. 600 ft AAL
14. 300 ft/min
15. 600 ft/min
16. 500 ft/min
17. (a)
18. below
19. (a)
20. (a)
21. yes
22. no
23. No, since they radiate upwards.
24. low-pitched Morse signals *"-dah-dah-dah-dah-dah-"*, accompanied by a flashing blue marker light
25. +/–35° (UK AIP COM 0-5)
26. 10 nm (UK AIP COM 0-5), +/–8°
27. 3°, may
28. 1.35° to 5.25°

ANSWERS 14 – VDF
1. VHF Direction Finding
2. VHF D/F
3. VHF-COM
4. magnetic bearing to the station
5. magnetic bearing from station
6. +/–5°
7. should
8. left of track, turn right
9. right of track, turn left
10. right of track, turn left
11. left of track, turn right
12. In the VDF Approach, the pilot initiates his own heading corrections based on the QDMs given to him, and initiates his own descent; whereas, in a QGH Approach, ATC gives the pilot heading and descent instructions.

ANSWERS 15 – PREPARATION FOR FLIGHT
Meteorology
1. METAR; TAF
2. *Refer to Vol. 2, Ch. M11, or to the UK AIP MET Section.*
3. TEMPO
4. AIRMET
5. 3, plain, 4 times daily (i.e. every 6 hrs), UK and near Continent, 15,000 ft, 18,000 ft
6. every hour and half-hour (i.e. at H and H+30)
7. 2 hours from the time of observation
8. four
9. NO SIGnificant change during the two hours after the observation time
10. 2 hours
11. 4 hours
12. Aerodrome Forecast for Dundee, valid for the period between 1300 and 2200 UTC; Wind Velocity 180°T at 15 kt, Visibility 3000 metres, Cloud is overcast at 3000 ft AAL; becoming, between 1500–1800 UTC, Visibility 1000 metres. *No,* cannot operate on an IMC Rating throughout the TAF period, but can operate 1300–1500 UTC, after which the visibility is forecast to drop to 1000 m, which is below the IMC-Rating minimum of 1800 m required for take-off and landing at an aerodrome outside a Control Zone
13. Aerodrome Forecast for Lydd, valid from 1000–1800 UTC, W/V 280°T/20 kt, Visibility 6000 metres, Scattered Cloud (1–4 OKTAs) at base 1400 ft AAL; becoming, between 1200 and 1500 UTC, visibility 1200 m. *Cannot* operate on an IMC Rating after 1200 UTC due to visibility becoming less than the minimum for an IMC-Rating (1800 m) at Lydd (which is not in a Control Zone).

14. Aerodrome Forecast for Oxford, valid 1200–2000 UTC, W/V 350°T/mean speed 15 kt, with gusts to 25 kt, Visibility 1500 metres, Cloud: overcast at base 1000 ft AAL; becoming, between 1500 and 1800 UTC, Wind 280 °T/15 kt, Visibility 2500 m, Broken Cloud at base 1500 ft AAL. *Not* suitable for IMC-Rated flights until after 1800 UTC when the visibility improves from 1500 m to 2500 m after the change which is forecast to arrive between 1500–1800 UTC.

15. Aerodrome Forecast for Nottingham, valid 0800 to 1400 UTC, W/V 120°T/15 kt, Visibility 1800 m, Cloud: Overcast at base 800 ft AAL; becoming, between 1000–1200 UTC, Broken Cloud (5–7 OKTAs) base 1200 ft AAL. *Yes,* can operate on an IMC Rating throughout the TAF period as far as visibility is concerned, but low cloud base of 800 ft AAL at Nottingham (which has no instrument approach) until after 1200 UTC would require consideration of terrain clearance for manoeuvring in the circling area – *refer to AIP AGA for details of obstacles at Nottingham.*

16. SAUK indicates a METAR (Surface Actual) in the UK; with the observation taken at 0820 UTC at Newcastle; W/V 120°T/5 kt, Visibility 8 km, Haze, Scattered Cloud (1–4 OKTAs) at base 1400 ft AAL, Temperature +6°C, Dewpoint +5°C, QNH 1018 mb

17. Yes, the visibility at Halfpenny Green (which is outside a Control Zone) exceeds the minimum required of 1800 m, and the cloud base at 3500 ft AAL is well above any restrictions for an IMC-Rating. The gusty wind would be a consideration however, due to possible crosswind.

18. At Aberdeen, which is in a Control Zone, the weather between 1200 and 1400 UTC will be unsuitable for an IMC Rating for periods less than 60 minutes (TEMPO), as the visibility will drop to 2500 m, which is less than the 3 km (3000 m) required by an IMC-Rated Pilot for a Special VFR Clearance in a Control Zone; also, the cloud base will lower to 800 ft AAL, which would require attention to obstacle clearance in the circling area (600-ft clearance required); the gusty and strong winds and heavy rain during the brief periods are also best avoided by light aircraft for flight safety reasons.

19. Glasgow Weather Centre (041) 221 6116 (UK AIP MET 1)

Safety Altitudes
20. 1000 ft within 5 nm
21. 2610 ft on QNH
22. 5800 ft AMSL
23. 5200 ft AMSL
24. 4000 ft AMSL
25. FL55, FL75 *(see Vol. 2, Ch. L7)*
26. FL50 (Safety Altitude 2950 ft AMSL, and FL50 on 1013 mb is 3800 ft AMSL when QNH is 973 mb, which is satisfactory since it is above the Safety Altitude and clears the obstacles by more than 1000 ft – *see Vol. 3, Ch. 6*)
27. FL70 (Safety Altitude 3350 ft AMSL, and FL50 on 1013 mb is 3200 ft AMSL when QNH is 953 mb – not suitable; FL70, however, is 5200 ft AMSL, therefore satisfactory)

Computer Calculations
28. TAS 102 kt
29. TAS 100 kt
30. TAS 107 kt
31. TAS 100, Heading 360, GS 92
32. ETI 88 min; ETA 0245 UTC

Charts
33. 620 ft
34. 380 kHz, BRI – *"dah-dit-dit-dit dit-dah-dit dit-dit"* (from chart)

ANSWERS

35. 36 ft
36. 138°M, 49 nm; Safety Altitude
    3000 ft AMSL (based on spot
    height 1995 ft AMSL approx
    9 nm South of Bristol – to give
    1000 ft vertical clearance
    above the highest obstacle
    within 5 nm of track);
    ETI 25 minutes
37. 349.5 kHz, COM
    *"dah-dit-dah-dit
    dah-dah-dah dah-dah"*
38. Hang gliding (chart)
39. Cotswold ASR, Portland ASR
    (chart)
40. no (UK AIP RAC 3-1)
41. yes (UK AIP RAC 3-1)
42. 3000 ft AAL (UK AIP AGA 2-8
    and AIP RAC 2)
43. London Information on
    124.75 MHz (chart)
44. Yeovilton Area of Intense
    Aerial Activity – AIAA (chart)
45. MATZ (chart)
46. 127.35 MHz from Yeovilton
    (chart)
47. 40 nm (UK AIP RAC 3-8)
48. It transmits a two-letter Morse
    group for VL *"...– .–.."* in the
    colour red. (UK AIP AGA 4)
49. UK AIP RAC 3-8;
    when 15 nm or 5 minutes
    flying time from the MATZ
    boundary, whichever is
    greater, establish radio
    contact, with the call:
    *"Yeovilton Radar – this is
    (callsign) – request MATZ
    penetration."* When asked to,
    "Go ahead", continue with,
    *"callsign and type of aircraft –
    position – heading – altitude –
    intentions (i.e. destination)."*
50. Tower 133.85 MHz;
    Approach 120.60 MHz
    (UK AIP COM)
51. Bristol Airport PLC
    UK AIP AGA 2-8)
52. Rwy 09/27 is 2011 metres long
    (UK AIP AGA 2-8,
    Approach/Landing Charts)
53. UK AIP RAC 3-5
54. VOR/DME; 113.35 MHz, SAM
    (Southampton) *"dit-dit-dit
    dit-dah dah-dah"*

55. Bournemouth Control Zone
    (CTR), Class D airspace, from
    the surface to 2000 ft AMSL,
    Southampton Control Area
    (CTA), also Class D, from
    2000 ft AMSL to FL55 (chart)
56. 120.225 MHz (chart, UK AIP
    COM 2)
57. Call the Controlling Authority
    on the appropriate frequency
    and give details of:
    • position;
    • level; and
    • proposed track
    UK AIP RAC 3-5
58. UK AIP RAC 7, Instrument
    Approach Charts (Radar
    Vectoring Area)
59. P047 is a Prohibited Area
    within which the flight of
    aircraft is prohibited; it
    extends from the Surface to
    2200 ft AMSL for a radius of
    2 nm. (chart, UK AIP COM)
60. D020 is a Danger Area, from
    the Surface to 1500 ft AMSL,
    in which Naval Mortar Firing
    may occur; a Danger Area
    Crossing Service (DACS) is
    provided by Portland
    Approach on 124.15 MHz or
    via London Info on 124.75 MHz
    (chart).
61. 128.60 MHz, London VOLMET
    – South (UK AIP MET 3-1)
62. Range 20 nm; it is located on
    the aerodrome (AIP COM 2)

Fuel Calculations
63. 57 litres
64. 30 USG = 114 litres
65.

Stage	mins	USG
Route	100	15.8
Reserve	60	9.5
Total	160	25.3
Margin	143	22.7
Total carried	303	48.0

Fuel Required is 25.3 USG.
With 48 USG on Board at
start-up, there is 22.7 USG
and 143 minutes margin.

66.

Stage	mins	USG
Start, T/o & Climb		2.5
Route	73	8.5
Flight Fuel	73	11.0
Reserve	45	5.3
Fuel requ'd	118	16.3

Fuel required is 16.3 USG
= 62 litres, and this weighs
45 kg, which is 99 lb.

67.

Stage	mins	USG
Climb	–	2.0
Cruise	63	8.4
NDB Let-down	–	2.0
Climb	–	2.0
Diversion	17	2.3
Flight Fuel		16.7
Reserves		10.0
Fuel Required		26.7

With 30.0 USG on board at
take-off, 3.3 USG is available
for contingencies, which, at
8 USG/hr, is 24 minutes.

68. 46 US gallons

Weight-and-Balance
69. must not
70. a higher stalling speed, a
lower acceleration, a longer
take-off distance, a poorer
rate of climb, a lower
maximum operating altitude,
a longer landing distance
71. may
72. 6 lb
73. 420 lb
74. 406 lb

IFR
75. (a) – Rule 29: Minimum Height
Rule and Rule 30: Quadrantal
Rule *(see Vol. 2, Ch. L7)*
76. yes
77. optional (UK AIP RAC 3)
78. compulsory (UK AIP RAC 3)

En Route Calculations
79. 125 kt, 7 minutes
80. (i) 12° right using the 1:60 rule
(ii) 18° right

Flight Procedures
81. 40 nm of the aerodrome (UK
AIP RAC 7)
82. "Aircraft Callsign – Position
and Time over that position –
Altitude or Flight Level –
Estimate for Next Position and
Time over it"
83. 121.5 MHz; *MAYDAY* for an
Emergency, *PAN-PAN* for an
Urgency Message
84. 1500 ft, 2000 ft, glide clear,
higher, Rule 5
85. at or below, 1500 ft above the
nearest fixed object within
2000 ft of the aircraft or the
height needed to glide clear in
the event of engine failure,
whichever is the higher (Rule 5)
86. 1500–2000 ft
87. pilot
88. traffic information only
89. traffic information plus advice
on collision-avoidance action
90. active
91. should, ATC clearance, are
92. remain clear of the controlled
airspace and land as soon as
possible at a suitable aerodrome

Visual Illusions
93. can
94. steep, low
95. before
96. closer, undershoot

ANSWERS 16 – INSTRUMENT DEPARTURES
1. ceiling 600 ft, VIS 1800 m
2. Standard Instrument
Departure
3. Regional QNH
4. 1013.2 mb
5. *refer to Vol. 2, Ch. L4.*

ANSWERS 17 – HOLDING AND MANOEUVRING
1. (b) – racetrack
2. 4 minutes
3. 1 sec/kt
4. reducing the 60 sec by 15 sec,
and flying outbound for 45
seconds
5. 3 times the WCA

6. 15° right
7. *refer to the text*
8. Parallel Entry
9. Teardrop Entry
10. Direct Entry
11. *refer to the text*

ANSWERS 18 – INSTRUMENT APPROACHES

1. (b) – Aerodrome QNH
2. Minimum Sector Altitude, 300 m (1000 ft) vertical clearance within 25 nm, Sector Safe Altitude
3. °Magnetic
4. QFE Threshold, Altimeter indicates Height above the Runway Threshold
5. Aerodrome QFE, Altimeter indicates Height above Aerodrome Elevation
6. *refer to the text*
7. Arrival Segment
8. are, should
9. half-scale
10. +/–5°
11. Precision Approach
12. Precision Approach
13. Non-Precision Approach
14. (b)
15. (a) (option *(d)* is a recipe for disaster!)
16. (c)

ANSWERS 19 – INSTRUMENT MINIMA

Take-Off and Landing

1. a safe forced landing
2. 600 ft cloud ceiling, 1800 m visibility (AIP RAC 4-3)
3. 1800 m
4. at or above his calculated DH for a Precision Approach or his MDH for a Non-Precision Approach *(read the warning in AIP RAC 4-3)*
5. no (AIP RAC 4-3)
6. yes
7. no

En Route

8. yes
9. 1000 ft above the highest obstacle within 5 nm of track, or above the highest MEF for the proposed route

Approach

10. True
11. False
12. Decision Height, DH
13. Minimum Descent Height, MDH
14. (a)
15. (b)
16. Height
17. Altitude
18. QFE
19. 600 ft AAL (AIP RAC 4-3)
20. 500 ft AAL (AIP RAC 4-3)
21. Obstacle Clearance Height (OCH)
22. Category A
23. add 200 ft, Precision Approach 500 ft AAL, Non-Precision Approach 600 ft AAL
24. ILS System Minimum 200 ft, plus PEC 50 ft, plus 200 ft = DH 450 ft, which is less than ILS Absolute Minimum 500 ft; therefore Final DH = 500 ft
25. OCH 320 ft takes precedence over ILS System Minimum of 200 ft, plus PEC 50 ft, plus 200 ft = DH 570 ft, which exceeds the ILS Absolute Minimum of 500 ft; therefore Final DH = 570 ft
26. OCH 600 ft takes precedence over the NDB System Minimum of 300 ft (no PEC required as already included for a Non-Precision Approach), plus 200 ft for an IMC-Rated Pilot = MDH 800 ft, which is greater than the Absolute Minimum for a Non-Precision Approach of 600 ft; therefore Final MDH is 800 ft.
27. OCH 420 ft takes precedence over the VDF System Minimum of 300 ft (no PEC required as already included for a Non-Precision Approach), plus 200 ft for an IMC-Rated Pilot to give MDH 620 ft, which is greater than the Absolute Minimum for a Non-Precision Approach of 600 ft; therefore Final MDH is 620 ft.

28. (i) AIP RAC 4-3 gives OCH
500 ft for Rwy 02 VOR/DME *SAM*
(ii) Minima published for an
Instrument-Rated Pilot are
MDH 500 ft, RVR/MET VIS
1100 metres; consequently
minima for an IMC-Rated Pilot
are (500 + 200 =) MDH 700 ft
AAL, and Minimum Visibility
of 1800 m.
(iii) No, on two counts: cloud
base 600 ft AAL is below MDH
700 ft AAL, & visibility 1400 m
is less than the IMC-Rating
permitted visibility of 1800 m.
(iv) Hazards include low cloud
and poor visibility, and also
the possibility of fog/mist and
carburettor icing, because
OAT +8°C and dewpoint +8°C
indicates 100% relative
humidity, so very moist air,
and any further cooling in the
carburettor could cause icing,
especially when low engine
power is set, as on approach.
29. OCH 139, DH 250, RVR/VIS
800 m. For an IMC-Rated Pilot:
DH 500 (ILS Absolute
Minimum 500 exceeds 250 +
200 = 450), visibility 1800 m
(AIP RAC 4-3)
30. DH 570 (370 + 200 exceeds
Absolute Minimum 500 ft),
VIS 1800 m
31. DH 500 (Absolute Minimum
exceeds 250 + 200), VIS 1800 m
32. *Rwy 13 NDB:* MDH 1110 ft,
VIS 1800 m;
Rwy 13 NDB/DME: MDH 650 ft,
VIS 1800 m (AIP RAC 4-3)
33. yes
34. Yes, and it is recommended
that at least 100 ft be added to
the minimum height for the
approach.
35. The pressure instruments
(ASI, Altimeter and VSI) may
show temporary errors due to
fluctuations in the pressure
readings from the static vent
and the pitot tube with the
pitch attitude change.

ANSWERS 20 – VISUAL MANOEUVRING

1. 2000 m (AIP RAC 4-3)
2. 1.68 nm radius of the runway
   thresholds
3. 300 ft safety margin; Visual
   Manoeuvring OCH 670 ft AAL
4. 100 ft; lowest permissible
   Visual Manoeuvring OCH 400 ft
5. 450 ft AAL (AIP RAC 4-2)
6. 550 ft AAL (AIP RAC 4-2)
7. 520 ft AAL (AIP RAC 4-2)
8. 1800 m, 3 km

ANSWERS on APPENDIX 1 – THE IMC RATING

1. Instrument Meteorological
   Conditions
2. Instrument Flight Rules
3. is not
4. True
5. extends
6. extends
7. extends
8. extends
9. does not extend
10. (a) – never
11. (c) – 3 km
12. yes
13. yes
14. yes
15. no
16. no
17. no
18. 25 hours
19. 25 months
20. June 16th, 1997
21. January 22nd, 1997
22. 1800 m

INDEX

Refer also to **List of Abbreviations** at rear of Index

445

ABBREVIATIONS

AAL	– Above Aerodrome Level		FL	– Flight Level
ADF	– Automatic Direction Finder		g	– g-Force
AGA	– Aerodrome and Ground Aids *(Section of the AIP)*		GP	– Glidepath
			GS	– Glideslope
AGL	– Above Ground Level			– *also* Ground Speed
AH	– Artificial Horizon		HAT	– Height Above Threshold *(Jeppesen approach charts)*
AI	– Attitude Indicator			
AIP	– Aeronautical Information Publication		HDG	– Heading
			HF	– High Frequency
ALT	– Altitude		HI	– Heading Indicator
ALTN	– Alternate Aerodrome		hPa	– hectopascals
AMSL	– Above Mean Sea Level		HSI	– Horizontal Situation Indicator
ASI	– Air Speed Indicator		IAF	– Initial Approach Fix
ASR	– Approach Surveillance Radar – *also* Altimeter Setting Region		IAP	– Instrument Approach Procedure
ATC	– Air Traffic Control		IAS	– Indicated Airspeed
ATIS	– Automatic Terminal Information Service		ICAO	– International Civil Aviation Organisation
ATSU	– Air Traffic Service Unit		IF	– Intermediate Approach Fix
BFO	– Beat Frequency Oscillator		IFR	– Instrument Flight Rules
CAA	– Civil Aviation Authority		ILS	– Instrument Landing System
CAP	– Civil Air Publication		IMC	– Instrument Meteorological Conditions
CAS	– Calibrated Air Speed			
CDI	– Course Deviation Indicator		ISA	– International Standard Atmosphere
CTA	– Control Area			
CTR	– Control Zone		kHz	– kilohertz
DA	– Decision Altitude – *also* Density Altitude		L	– Locator beacon *(also* Lctr, *Jeppesen approach charts)*
DA(H)	– combination of DA & DH *(Jeppesen approach charts)*		LARS	– Lower Airspace Radar Service
			Lctr	– Locator beacon *(Jeppesen approach charts)*
DF	– Direction Finding (or Finder)			
DG	– Directional Gyro		LF	– Low Frequency
DH	– Decision Height – *also* Density Height		LITAS	– Low Intensity Two Colour Approach Slope System
DI	– Direction Indicator		LLZ	– Localizer *(also* LOC, *Jeppesen approach charts)*
DME	– Distance Measuring Equipment			
DOC	– Designated Operational Coverage		LOC	– Localizer *(Jeppesen approach charts)*
DR	– Deduced Reckoning		LOFT	– Line-Oriented Flight Training
EAT	– Expected Approach Time		LOM	– Locator/Outer Marker
EPR	– Engine Pressure Ratio		LOP	– Line of Position *(also* PL)
EGT	– Exhaust Gas Temperature		M	– degrees Magnetic
ELEV	– Elevation		MAP	– Aeronautical Maps and Charts *(Section of the AIP)*
FAF	– Final Approach Fix			
FAP	– Final Approach Point			– *also* Missed Approach Point *(Aerad & Jeppesen charts)*
FAT	– Final Approach Track			

MAPt	– Missed Approach Point *(also* MAP on *Aerad* and *Jeppesen approach charts)*
MATZ	– Military Air Traffic Zone
MB	– Magnetic Bearing
mb	– millibars
MDA	– Minimum Descent Altitude
MDA(H)	– combination of MDA & MDH *(Jeppesen approach charts)*
MDH	– Minimum Descent Height
MEF	– Maximum Elevation Figure
MF	– Medium Frequency
MH	– Magnetic Heating
MHA	– Minimum Holding Altitude
MHz	– Megahertz
MLS	– Microwave Landing System
MM	– Middle Marker
MSA	– Minimum Sector Altitude *(Jeppesen approach charts)* – *also* Minimum Safe Altitude
MSL	– Mean Sea Level
MTI	– Moving Target Indicator
NDB	– Non Directional Beacon
nm	– nautical miles
OBI	– Omni Bearing Indicator
OBS	– Omni Bearing Selector
OCA	– Obstacle Clearance Altitude
OCA(H)	– combination of OCA & OCH *(Jeppesen approach charts)*
OCH	– Obstacle Clearance Height
OM	– Outer Marker
OPS	– Operations
PANS-OPS	– Procedures for Air Navigation Services – Aircraft Operations
PAPI	– Precision Approach Path Indicator
PAR	– Precision Approach Radar
PEC	– Position Error Correction
PL	– Position Line (also LOP)
PPI	– Plan Position Indicator
QDM	– Magnetic Bearing to Station
QDR	– Magnetic Bearing from Station
QFE	– Altimeter Setting (for aerodrome level)
QGH Approach	– An ATC-assisted VDF-type Approach
QNE	– Pressure Height (1013.2 mb or hPa)
QNH	– Altimeter Setting (for height above mean sea level, i.e. altitude)
QTE	– True Bearing from the Station
RAC	– Rules of the Air and ATC *(Section of the AIP)*
RAS	– Radar Advisory Service – *also* Rectified Air Speed
RB	– Relative Bearing
RBI	– Relative Bearing Indicator
RDL	– Radial
RIS	– Radar Information Service
RMI	– Radio Magnetic Indicator
RNAV	– Area Navigation
RNC	– Radio Navigation Chart
RoD	– Rate of Descent
RTF	– Radio Telephony
RVR	– Runway Visual Range
RWY	– Runway
SAR	– Search and Rescue
SID	– Standard Instrument Departure
SMWP	– Specified Minimum Weather Provisions
SRA	– Surveillance Radar Approach
SSA	– Sector Safe Altitude *(Aerad approach charts)*
STAR	– Standard Terminal Arrival Route
T	– degrees True
TACAN	– Tactical Air Navigation radio navaid *(military)*
TAS	– True Air Speed
TCA	– Terminal Control Area (usually TMA)
TCH	– Threshold Crossing Height
TDZ	– Touch Down Zone
TDZE	– Touch Down Zone Elevation *(Jeppesen approach charts)*
THR	– Threshold
TMA	– Terminal Control Area
TTS	– Time To Station
UHF	– Ultra High Frequency
UTC	– Co-ordinated Universal Time
VASI or VASIS	– Visual Approach Slope Indicator System
V_{AT}	– Nominal Speed at Threshold
VDF	– VHF Direction Finding
V_{FE}	– Maximum Flaps Extended Speed
VFR	– Visual Flight Rules
VHF	– Very High Frequency
VIS	– Visibility
V_{LE}	– Maximum Landing Gear (Undercarriage) Extended Speed
VMC	– Visual Meteorological Conditions
VMH	– Visual Manoeuvring Height
V_{NE}	– Never Exceed Speed
VOR	– VHF Omni Range
VORTAC	– combination of VOR and TACAN
VRP	– Visual Reporting Point
VSI	– Vertical Speed Indicator
WCA	– Wind Correction Angle
W/V	– Wind Velocity